BIRDS OF CLEVELAND

Martin Blick

TEES VALLEY

ISBN 978-0-9563283-0-4

Published by Tees Valley Wildlife Trust

CONTENTS

FOREWORD

I am very pleased to write this forward to Martin Blick's excellent book "Birds of Cleveland". The book has had quite a long gestation, but it has been well worth the wait. I am overjoyed that Tees Valley Wildlife Trust has finally been able to publish this excellent volume which is the first modern comprehensive guide to the exciting variety of birds found in our area, despite its legacy of heavy industry and urban development. Indeed, industry has helped increase the range of habitats in the Tees Valley, although on the negative side, it has also resulted in the loss of much valued parts of Seal Sands and the estuary. Some 362 species of birds have been recorded, by a range of observers, including the dedicated members of the Teesmouth Bird Club to whom we are forever grateful. This is Tees Valley Wildlife Trust's first journey into scientific publishing and hopefully it will not be the last – my thanks to everyone involved.

David Counsell
Chair: Tees Valley Wildlife Trust

AUTHOR'S INTRODUCTION

Cleveland existed as a county from 1974 to 1996, although there are records for the area from the early 1800's and bird-watching began in earnest in the 1950's. The county was formed by joining two boroughs in the SE corner of Durham County and two boroughs in the NE corner of Yorkshire, this being roughly the lowlands around the mouth of the Tees.

The Teesmouth Bird Club was formed in 1960, principally to record the birds around the coastline from Hartlepool to Redcar, on the Tees marshes and around Teesside. From 1959 a monthly news sheet was produced detailing bird sightings in this area, but this was changed in 1967 to a quarterly publication. In 1974, the Teesmouth Bird Club adopted the same geographical boundary as Cleveland County and has since produced an annual county report.

The vast majority of the information in this book has been collated from the Teesmouth Bird Club reports, from the first monthly sheets to the latest annual report. As such it could not have been produced without the records supplied by the local bird-watchers over the years. Information has also been incorporated from several surveys, in particular, the Common Birds Census, the Wetland Birds Survey (formerly Birds of Estuaries Enquiry) at Teesmouth, Wildfowl Counts at Scaling Dam, Wynyard, Longnewton Reservoir, Lockwood Beck and Crookfoot Reservoir, the Heronries Census and the Beached Bird Survey. Historic records have been included from the existing avi-faunas of Yorkshire and County Durham.

Virtually all of the records of unusual birds have been considered by the Teesmouth Bird Club Records Committee and in the case of the rarer birds, by the British Birds Rarities Committee; no record is included that has been rejected or deemed unproven, by one or other of these bodies. Also, there are a few records that have been printed in one or more bird reports that proved under scrutiny to be less than convincing. Any such record has been omitted from this work.

Information on ringing and the resulting recoveries has been taken principally from the Teesmouth Bird Club Reports, but also from British Birds, the annual British Trust for Ornithology report and by direct contact with the Cleveland bird ringers, including Durham University teams and the Tees Ringing Group.

Many thousands of man-hours have been expended by Durham University at Teesmouth in trying to understand the estuary and its birds: not just by ringing birds, but also by observing the birds' habits when feeding and roosting; by looking closely at the nature and invertebrate fauna of Teesmouth's mudflats, and university workers have also monitored Teesmouth-ringed birds in other estuaries. Hopefully the resulting information will be conclusive enough to prevent the remainder of Seal Sands and other parts of Teesmouth from being damaged or destroyed. In today's climate, conservation is becoming a higher priority for people and industry. However, there are still lots of problems to overcome locally, as well as nationally, internationally and globally before the conservationist can rest easy; important habitats are still disappearing and the environment is sometimes not given the level of importance that it should be.

The book has three main parts, a site guide, a month by month section and a species list.

The species lists gives the known status of all 362 species recorded in a wild state in Cleveland up to the last day of 2007, although there are a few records of rare birds that have not been officially accepted or rejected by the relevant records committee up to the time of going to press. At the end of this section there are a further 40 or so species that are regarded as escapes from captivity. However, this section will almost certainly be incomplete since some observers do not report birds that are not considered to be genuine wild individuals. Also a few species, notably the rarer wildfowl, escape quite regularly and most individuals cannot be ascribed to either genuine vagrancy or local escapee.

A few additional accounts from neighbouring counties are given in the species descriptions if this affects the status of the birds in Cleveland.

The actual number of species recorded in Cleveland increases at a steady rate. Not only are there completely new birds to add to the list, averaging about one to two each year for the last five years (e.g. Lesser Yellowlegs, Cetti's Warbler, Long-billed Dowitcher) but also birds originally regarded as sub-species have been given full species status in recent years (e.g. Green-winged Teal, Hooded Crow, Yellow-legged Gull). Also birds formerly classified as escapes from captivity, have occasionally been upgraded to naturally occuring species (e.g. Ring-necked Parakeet, Snow Goose).

There is a considerable number of species potentially to be added to the Cleveland list in the future; over 200 species have occurred in Britain, but not Cleveland, some being much more likely than others. A few species have occurred in the county that have distinct races, e.g. Stonechat, Bean, Brent and White-fronted Geese, that could in the future be 'split' to create two separate species from one, and there are also some species currently regarded as escapes that could be upgraded, such as Ruddy Shelduck and White-headed Duck.

It should also be borne in mind that not all changes add to the official list; Eagle Owl was regarded as a true Cleveland bird for many years, before being consigned to the escape section, and Red-breasted Goose was also on the list, albeit briefly.

A month by month section gives a short summary of the bird-life for each month and an indication of when to see various species.

The Site guide outlines localities within Cleveland that are of particular ornithological interest. This is by no means a complete list of all potentially good sites since birds can and do turn up almost anywhere including suburban gardens, town centres and industrial complexes.

Several of the sites mentioned are private, access only being allowed by permit, but most have unlimited access by virtue of public footpaths and/or a benign landowner.

Sadly, rather too many of the sites covered are under threat of total or partial destruction, generally under the guise of 'development'. Not enough people yet appreciate nature and the long term effect on the environment against short term financial benefits.

Anyone not familiar with Cleveland might be surprised at the number of interesting areas and diversity of habitats in an area that is generally regarded by outsiders as highly industrialised. However, it is still quite easy to get away from the chimneys, cranes and warehouses and in many cases the birds themselves are able to co-exist in the shadow of industry.

The reader should be aware that the history of each species as detailed in this book will in almost every case be only part of the actual story. Many birds will have occurred in Cleveland without being seen by anybody, or will have been seen by persons unaware either of the bird recording system or of the interest an unusual bird creates. It is only in recent years that the media have become aware of birdwatchers and 'twitchers'.

As the author, I am acutely aware of the fact that this book does not give the whole picture and would genuinely like to receive any records and/or photographs of birds seen in the area designated as Cleveland, even from the distant past. Records within the past 12 months should be sent to the Cleveland Bird Recorder (see contacts). Any interesting observations, high counts, early or late migrants, from any year, decade or century can be sent to the author at the Tees Valley Wildlife Trust. Photographs would be especially welcome and would undoubtedly help to verify any records.

Finally, the author is happy to answer any queries and respond to comments regarding this publication which should be directed care of the Tees Valley Wildlife Trust.

Martin Blick

ACKNOWLEDGEMENTS

Tees Valley Wildlife Trust would like to thank most sincerely Northumbrian Water plc for its generous financial support, without which this publication would have been impossible.

Most of the knowledge we have today of Cleveland's bird-life is the direct result of hundreds of anonymous birdwatchers that have supplied many thousands of records over the last decades to the Teesmouth Bird Club. The annual Cleveland Bird Report is published by this charity and most of the information in this book is taken from these reports.

Thanks are also due to the following individuals whose assistance has been of value in the production of this work: - C.Bielby; D.J.Britton; W.I.Boustead; D.Clayton; Mrs A.L. Cooper; T. G.Dewdney; J.B.Dunnett; the late Prof. P. R.Evans; N.W.Harwood; G.Joynt; Miss L.Lampard; R.T.McAndrew; Miss L.Leadley; E.C.Parker; H.P.K. Robinson; D.W. Simpson; Dr D.Summers-Smith; A.J.Wallis; the late T.J.Williams and E.Wood.

Finally, my sincere thanks are due to I.Lawson, P.A.A. Baxter and W.E.Fletcher for the line drawings and to the late P.J.Stead and A.J.Wheeldon, without whose time and assistance this book would not have been completed.

Tees Valley Wildlife Trust Editorial Team

Steve Ashton
Mark Fishpool
Cliff Shepherd
Ken Smith
With assistance from Dr Peter Evans and Denis Summers-Smith
Thanks are also due the photographers who have contributed to the book including John Bridges, Brian Coates, Kenny Crooks, Paul Doherty, Peter Evans, Richard Hart, Geoff Iceton, Jim Pattinson, Wayne Richardson and Jeff Youngs.

A special thanks also goes to Ian Clennett from Norton James Design

INTRODUCTION TO CLEVELAND

For such a relatively small part of the United Kingdom, Cleveland must have one of the most diverse ranges of habitats. Many of us who live and work in the areas, which once made up the county of Cleveland, know that it has a lot to offer in terms of wildlife interest.

The area of Cleveland is now made up of the four local authorities of Hartlepool, Middlesbrough, Redcar and Cleveland and Stockton-on-Tees and has a wealth of species of flora and fauna. These habitats include the jewel in the crown; the Tees Estuary and Marshes. Other habitats of note are a superb piece of North Sea Coast, several lakes and reservoirs, rivers and marshes, open countryside, ancient and plantation woodland and part of the North York Moors National Park.

In the past, Cleveland came with a reputation of being an area with lots of heavy industry and chemical plants. Many of these still exist and, with the efforts of local organisations like the Industry and Nature Conservation Association (INCA), Tees Valley Wildlife Trust and others, nature and industry go hand in glove and many of the best places to see birds are in the heart of urban Teesside.

TOPOGRAPHY AND GEOLOGY

The topography of the area is dominated in the south by bold and lofty escarpments and precipitous coastal cliffs (hence the name Cleveland from Cliffland). This contrasts markedly with the low lying partially reclaimed coastal marshes and alluvial plains, characteristic of the tidal reaches of the Tees and the gentle undulating morainic landscape found in northern Cleveland.

The geological deposits of the county are also varied. Most of lowland Cleveland is formed from rocks of the Triassic age comprising mudstones and sandstones which sweep south in a broad arc from Seaton Carew to Darlington. To the north of this lies the southern tip of the Permian Magnesian limestone escarpment covering east Durham. In Cleveland this is largely overlain by thick glacial deposits.

The high ground in the south of the county is largely composed of rocks of the Jurassic age, which supports Cleveland's only example of moorland vegetation and associated birds. Other important geological deposits include glacial drift, recent alluvial sand and the Tertiary igneous intrusion of Whinstone rocks; known locally as the Cleveland Dyke.

Many of the harder rocks can be seen as outcrops which form features that can be important habitats or birding points e.g. Hartlepool Headland, the Cleveland escarpment, Eston Hills, Redcar Rocks and Guisborough Forest.

The changing geological strata from north to south and east to west gives rise to a wide range of natural habitats. The lime rich soils in the north contrast with the acid soils of the moors in the south. The glacial drift of the central region, the boulder clay exposures (especially near the coast) and alluvial soils brought down by the main waterways contribute to a diversity of plants as well as other animals.

CLEVELAND HABITATS

Woodland occupies 6% of the total land area in Cleveland. This includes a range from semi-natural broad leaved woodlands (with a canopy dominated by Ash and Wych Elm growing on base rich soils to those on more acidic soils dominated by Oak) to recent plantation woodland often containing conifers. This has an effect on the diversity and number of species of birds and other animals found in different woods.

Much of the grassland in Cleveland is known as "improved" pasture for grazing and although of very little botanical interest can be important for species such as Skylark. There are also patches of neutral, acid marshy and coastal grassland with a range of associated plants. About half the county is agricultural land and this traditionally was important for wildlife. However, over the past 50 years agricultural practices have reduced the value of such farmland for wildlife. The ploughing up and reseeding of traditional pastures and the use of herbicides, pesticides and fertilisers have destroyed many of Cleveland's herb rich meadows. This has resulted in the decline of birds such as Tree Sparrow and Barn Owl which rely on agricultural land.

Moorland occupies 1690 ha of the Cleveland landscape, much of it within the North York Moors National Park. This area has been managed by man either for sheep or grouse and as a result an important habitat has been created for birds including Hen Harrier.

Approximately 38 km of coastline form the eastern boundary of the county with the North Sea and, although parts have been disturbed by past industrial use, the majority still remains semi natural in character. Part of the coast has been designated as a Site of Special Scientific Interest (SSSI) and also forms part of the North Yorkshire Heritage Coast.

Other coastal features of importance are the areas around Teesmouth including the National Nature Reserve, Hart Warren, Seal Sands, Seaton Dunes and Common, South Gare and Coatham Sands as well as Cowpen Marsh SSSI. The improving environment has resulted in the return of breeding Harbour (Common) Seal to the estuary, considered to be the first example of its kind in Europe. During summer months Grey Seals from the Farne Islands and the Humber visit the sanctuary, but do not breed.

Cleveland has its fair share of wetlands including small areas of remnant saltmarsh, the Rivers Tees and Leven and a number of marshlands including Tees Valley Wildlife Trust reserves at Portrack Marsh and Coatham Marsh. Ponds and lakes are widely distributed throughout the county, but are mostly small. Many are found on the low lying ground near to the Tees, whilst other are associated with subsidence resulting from past brine extraction and ironstone mining. The most important ponds occur around the mouth of the Tees and are brackish in nature.

A major characteristic of urban areas is that change is constantly taking place. One industry is replaced by another and populations of species build up and then decline. As a result, land is constantly being recycled leading to changes in flora and fauna. These brownfield sites and other areas associated with people are also becoming increasingly important for wildlife. These include many of the green spaces owned by local authorities, which are managed with biodiversity in mind, especially those seeking Green Flag awards. Along with this, programmes on television are encouraging people to become interested in and manage their gardens for wildlife. The number of people feeding birds has increased. All these factors mean that gardens and urban green spaces are increasingly important for wildlife, especially since these are the areas with which people have immediate contact.

The RSPB and the Teesside Environmental Trust are working together to transform 1000 acres (380-ha) of former industrial land on the north side of the Tees into a world-class nature reserve. It will be a place where birds and people come together in a way that stimulates fun, enjoyment and learning for all. There will be new habitats for birds and exciting ways for visitors to watch them. Habitat creation work on site currently involves major earthmoving and re-landscaping of hundreds of thousands of tonnes of soil, clay and industrial waste. Part of what was once an industrial site has already been transformed into a wild flower meadow, derelict land has become a new wetland home for hundreds of birds and new reedbeds will attract new and exciting wildlife.

Cleveland offers the opportunity to experience a range of contrasting habitats all within close proximity of one another. Its strategic position on an important migration route for birds means that an impressive number of birds and species can often be seen, including the elusive rarity.

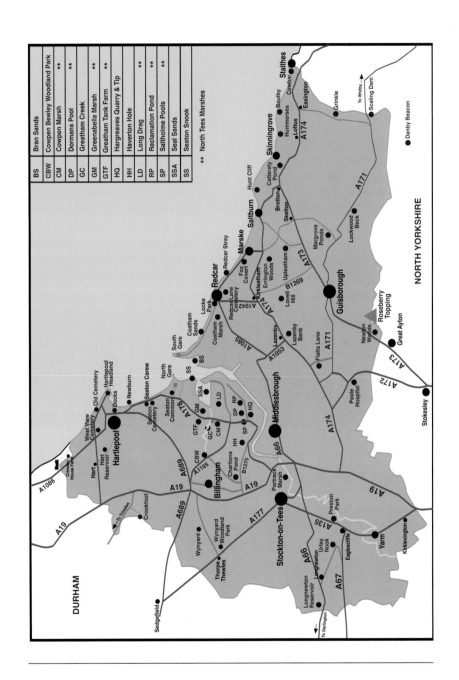

BS	Bran Sands
CBW	Cowpen Bewley Woodland Park
CM	Cowpen Marsh **
DP	Dormans Pool **
GC	Greatham Creek
GM	Greenabella Marsh **
GTF	Greatham Tank Farm **
HQ	Hargreaves Quarry & Tip
HH	Haverton Hole
LD	Long Drag **
RP	Reclamation Pond **
SP	Saltholme Pools **
SSA	Seal Sands
SS	Seaton Snook

** North Tees Marshes

DURHAM

NORTH YORKSHIRE

MONTHS OF THE YEAR

JANUARY

Although January is frequently the coldest month of the year, it is by no means the quietest bird-wise. Indeed, it is usually as a result of severe cold and sub-zero temperatures that large numbers of duck may be seen on Seal Sands or the Tees marshes, and relatively high numbers of sea-duck, divers and Iceland and Glaucous Gulls are seen along the coastline, as well as Snow Bunting, Lapland Bunting and Brambling in suitable habitat.

In the 1980s, one of the finest sights of the winter was the large gathering of diving duck at Seal Sands, principally Pochard, Goldeneye, Tufted Duck and Scaup. In recent years, significant numbers of Red-breasted Mergansers, Great Crested Grebes and Red-throated Divers have been seen on Seal Sands, particularly near Hartlepool Power Station. These in turn attract rarer birds such as Slavonian Grebe, Great Northern and Black-throated Divers.

Peak numbers of Shelduck, Mallard, Wigeon and Teal are sometimes recorded in January; most of these being on Seal Sands or the North Tees marshes, and it is frequently the best month for Bittern and Smew.

Waders seen around Seal Sands include small numbers of Black-tailed Godwit, several thousand Knot, and several hundred Curlew, Bar-tailed Godwit, Redshank, Dunlin and Oystercatcher.

This is probably the best month for seeing birds in Hartlepool Docks and Harbour. Occasionally all three regular divers are present as well as Shag, Great-crested and Red-necked Grebes, 20-30 Red-breasted Merganser and usually a Mediterranean or Glaucous Gull.

When weather conditions produce strong onshore winds, sea-watching can be productive. High numbers of auks, Shag, Red-throated Diver and Scaup can sometimes be seen as well as an occasional skua, Little Gull, Manx Shearwater and various ducks.

Providing the temperature stays above freezing point, quite reasonable numbers of Greylag Geese, ducks and Coot will frequent inland waters, such as Crookfoot Reservoir, Lockwood Beck and Scaling Dam, occasionally being joined by rarer ducks, grebes, divers and geese.

The moorland areas can appear quiet in the winter months, with only Red Grouse and

Meadow Pipit obvious. However, this can be a good time for raptors. A visit to Scaling Dam in January provides the best chance of seeing Hen Harrier, up to nine having been seen in January, as well as the possibility of Peregrine, Merlin and other birds of prey.

In the woodlands, tits and finches are moving around in flocks, often joined by species such as Nuthatch and Treecreeper. This is a good time of year to see some of the more elusive species, such as Hawfinch, and to study birds around woodland feeding stations. Species such as Willow Tit can be more obvious, for example at the Errington Wood feeding station.

Among the more interesting passerines to be seen in January is the regular flock of Snow Bunting at North or South Gare, and the less predictable Lapland Bunting. If the ground is covered by snow for more than a few days, quite large flocks of finches and buntings can be noted on the coast having moved from their inland haunts. Shore Lark can be seen in some years, usually in the Redcar-South Gare area, and several Stonechats usually frequent the North Tees marshes.

January is not a productive month for unusual species, although records have included the first European record of Double-crested Cormorant in 1989, the third Blue-winged Teal in 1999, numerous wintering Water Pipits since 1976, Short-toed Lark and Crane in 2003, up to 36 Hooded Crows in 1977 and the first winter records of Firecrest in 1984 and Avocet in 1989.

FEBRUARY

This is perhaps the quietest month of the year, numbers of the winter visitors being similar to those in January although there may be some fluctuation if there is any change in temperature.

February is probably the best month for seeing grebes and divers on the sea, a regular feature being the build-up of Great Crested Grebe in Hartlepool Bay. There are usually 1-2 Red-necked and Slavonian Grebes to be seen in the same area.

Should the wind become northerly and strong, large numbers of Little Auk may pass along the coast, although relatively little else is seen. In 1983, Little Auks were passing Hartlepool daily between 6th and 13th, at least 1,000 on 11th and at the same time about 350 were sitting on the sea in the bay.

Records of Bean Geese occur during this month more frequently than any other and February has also provided the highest count of Bewick's Swan.

Interesting February records include the 1st and 2nd records of White-billed Diver, in 1981 and 1996, the third Ross's Gull in 1983, the third record (and the first for over 100 years) of Ivory Gull in 1986, the first accepted record of Arctic Redpoll, also in 1986, and Ring-billed Gulls in 2001, 2002 and 2005.

MARCH

As days start to lengthen, the birdwatchers' thoughts turn to the first summer migrants, although there may still be frost and snow making its presence felt to the end of the month. Usually, it is the second half of March before the first true summer visitors are seen, although Ring Ouzel, Sand Martin and Wheatear often appear earlier.

Lesser Black-backed Gull and Chiffchaff both start to re-appear in good numbers, although there are usually a few wintering birds. In some years this is the best month to observe geese, including Brent Geese, as wintering birds move north. Also, both species of wild swan may pass through.

This is usually the month in which the last of some winter visitors, such as Snow Bunting, Smew, Waxwing, Hen Harrier and Great Northern Diver, are seen.

Some of Cleveland's waterbirds begin to appear on their breeding waters, species like Great Crested Grebe, Little Grebe, Mute Swan and Coot, although some of the birds involved may not have been moved very far during the winter. Only the Great Crested Grebes will have left altogether, the other three species moving perhaps to Seal Sands or the nearest area of unfrozen water if temperatures fall below freezing.

On reasonably warm sunny days, the beginning of the new breeding season can be sensed with birds like Skylark and Blackbird singing and Grey Partridge, Great Spotted Woodpecker, Fulmar, Ringed Plover and Coot proclaiming their territories.

Recently Crossbill have nested in Cleveland, and it is March when the red males are singing and displaying, this species being the earliest passerine in the area to breed. Other species whose nests have been found in this month include Mallard, Coot, Tawny Owl, Long-eared Owl and Blackbird, and both Heron and Rook are busy rebuilding the previous year's nests.

In most years it is the last week of the month before significant movement can be seen and summer visitors like Little Ringed Plover, Sandwich Tern, Yellow Wagtail, Willow Warbler, Swallow, House Martin, Sedge Warbler and White Wagtail have all been noted as early as the end of March. Other birds are sometimes involved in the movement at this time, for example Meadow Pipit, Goldcrest, Black Redstart, and occasionally Avocet.

Sea-watching in this month can be very unrewarding. Strong onshore winds in the months later in the year will generally create spectacular movements of seabirds, but similar conditions in March will usually produce nothing more than a few divers, ducks, Gannet and Fulmar. A few Hooded Crow have been seen moving at sea at the end of the month and species such as Kestrel, Rook and thrushes have been seen apparently arriving from the sea.

Again, this month is not noted for its rarities, but records of Ivory Gull and Gyr

Falcon, are remarkable, albeit both in 1837. Other records include the largest British flock of Parrot Crossbills in 1991, White Stork in 1995, at least four Arctic Redpolls in 1996 and Red Kites in 1995, 1996, 1998, 2002, 2006 and 2007.

APRIL

The majority of Cleveland's summer visitors are first seen in this month, although the beginning can be more like March. Meadow Pipit and Wheatear appear along the coast, with several thousand of the former and several hundred of the latter being involved during some weather conditions. These may be accompanied by Black Redstart, Robin, Goldcrest and various thrushes.

As the month progresses, numbers of summer visitors like Willow Warbler, Sedge Warbler, Whitethroat, Tree Pipit, Yellow Wagtail, House Martin and Swallow increase. Some of these are more likely to be first seen at inland sites and in years when conditions are not ideal for falls of migrants on the coast, they may not be present along the coast in spring. Willow Warblers and Cuckoos are probably the best example of this, usually being seen or heard first at the breeding site. The arrival of summer visitors livens up the woodlands, with a good range of warblers singing by the end of the month.

On the wader scene, Common Sandpiper, Whimbrel, Greenshank, Green Sandpiper and Little Ringed Plover generally appear during April, but the wintering waders such as Knot, Dunlin, Redshank, Grey Plover and Bar-tailed Godwit have almost all left Teesmouth by this time.

Numbers of most species of duck drop fairly quickly; very nearly all of the Wigeon, Teal, Goldeneye and Pochard having left by mid-April. Shelduck and Mallard will also be heading north, but at the same time, the local breeding birds will be prospecting for nest sites or incubating eggs.

Towards the end of the month, the later summer visitors are usually seen, including Cuckoo, Redstart, Lesser Whitethroat, Grasshopper Warbler, Spotted Flycatcher and Swift.

There is a lot of displaying and calling between pairs of Kittiwake, Herring Gull and Fulmar at the cliff-nesting sites and between pairs at the Black-headed Gull colonies, eggs probably being laid by the end of the month.

Interesting records include the earliest Wood Sandpiper, Temminck's Stint, Quail and Spotted Crake, all of which are generally recorded in May, as well as spectacular rarities such as Chough in 1957, the first Woodchat Shrike in 1971, the first Ross's Gull and second Mandarin in 1975, the second Ring-billed Gull in 1982, the only White-spotted Bluethroat, the third Short-toed Lark and a pair of Bearded Tits in 1983, the second Alpine Swift in 1985, the second and third Green-winged Teals in 1985 and 1986, the second Ring-necked Duck in 1988, Black Kites in 1988 and 1997, Red Kites in 1996 and 1999, Black Grouse in 1992, Savi's Warbler, Golden Oriole and a pair of American Wigeon in 1994, Nightingale in 1995, Black Stork, White Stork and Serin in 1996, Great White Egret in 1998, Rose-coloured Starling in 2003 and Red-rumped Swallow in 2003 and 2007.

MAY

One look at the list of rare birds seen in Cleveland in May is sufficient to whet the appetite of any birdwatcher. This is an excellent month for seeing many species of birds, not just rarities, but regular passage migrants.

Many of the summer visitors that were first noted in April will be in full song by early May, including all 10 breeding warblers. Some resident species could well be feeding young at the same time, particularly common birds like Blackbird, Song Thrush and Rook.

At Teesmouth, Redshank, Lapwing, Ringed Plover, Shelduck, Snipe, Little Grebe and Reed Bunting will all be incubating, while Yellow Wagtail, Common Tern and Little Tern will be nest building and displaying. There is also a noticeable build-up of Ringed Plover, Dunlin, Sanderling and Purple Sandpiper; this may only last for a few days or perhaps a week, but the annual peak count of the first two species is regularly recorded during this month. It is not unusual for one or two Little Stints, Temminck's Stints, Pectoral Sandpipers and Curlew Sandpipers to be seen at this time. Waders are also obvious on the moorlands in April and May, with breeding Curlew, Golden Plover, Lapwing and Snipe.

In some areas of Britain, there is an almost predictable passage of Dotterel in early May, yet there are few records for Cleveland in this month since the early part of the 20th century when the species was much commoner on passage. It is possible that there is a field or two somewhere in Cleveland that holds Dotterel regularly in May that has yet to be found.

If the wind becomes easterly or south easterly, the chance of a fall of migrants on the coast becomes high, especially if accompanied by rain or mist. Most migrant falls occur around the middle the month, although anything is possible throughout the month in these weather conditions. Birds that do occur are generally Scandinavian or north European species, presumably having left their wintering grounds and blown or drifted off-course. Species that can be expected include Bluethroat, Red-backed Shrike and Wryneck as well as some of the normal local summer visitors such as Spotted and Pied Flycatchers, most warblers, Redstart, Whinchat and hirundines.

Interesting May records include Marsh Sandpiper in 1963 and 2003, Red-throated

Pipit in 1963, 1976 and 1992, Savi's Warbler in 1982, 1989 and 1995, Great Reed Warbler in 1973, 2001 and 2002, Broad-billed Sandpiper in 1981, 1987 and 1994, Purple Heron and Siberian Stonechat in 1985, American Wigeon in 1986, 1988 and 2000, and Tawny Pipit in 1988, 1997 and 1999,

Add to this impressive list, several sighting of Golden Oriole, Avocet, Montagu's Harrier, Red-footed Falcon, Honey Buzzard, Spoonbill, Scarlet Rosefinch, Thrush Nightingale, Subalpine Warbler, Hoopoe, Corncrake, Kentish Plover, White-winged Black Tern, Green-winged Teal etc, and one can appreciate why birdwatchers look forward to May and the excitement it can bring.

JUNE

Almost all of the 120 or so species that breed in Cleveland are feeding young by early June, with the notable exception of Tufted Duck. At the same time, many young birds will be independent; species like Lapwing, Blackbird, Starling and Coot may well be incubating their second clutch.

Sea-watching begins to liven up with quite high numbers of Manx Shearwater and Puffin, the highest counts of this auk generally being in June during onshore winds. Occasionally Roseate Tern and skuas are noted and Black-throated Diver has been seen in summer plumage on more than one occasion off Hartlepool.

June is sometimes the quietest month around Teesmouth, with few waders to be seen, although small numbers of Dunlin, Sanderling, Knot and Curlew linger. In some years a few Ruff are observed with males in full breeding plumage occasionally being seen displaying to females.

Bearing in mind that relatively few birds are seen in June, it can be very entertaining, with Snow Goose, Lapland Bunting, Red-breasted Flycatcher, Icterine Warbler and Red-necked Phalarope all having occurred, as well as birds of prey such as Montagu's Harrier, Hobby, Red-footed Falcon and Honey Buzzard.

Interesting records include the only Lesser Grey Shrike in 1974, Bufflehead in 1994, Gull-billed Tern in 1991 and Lesser Scaup in 1999, most of Cleveland's Broad-billed Sandpipers, the first Booted Warbler in 1992, Rose-coloured Starling in 1973, 2002 and 2003, Wilson's Phalarope in 1965, 1966 and 1971, Great White Egret in 1974, 1999, 2000, 2001 and 2004, Purple Heron in 1975, Terek Sandpiper in 1979, Laughing Gull in 1981, Lesser Crested Tern in 1984 and 1995, American Wigeon in 1985, Buff-breasted Sandpiper in 1989, Franklin's Gull in 1991, Black Kite in 1993, American Golden Plover, Ross's Gull, Spotted Sandpiper and Great Reed Warbler in 1995, Alpine Swift in 2000 and 2002 and White Stork in 2005.

JULY

July can be one of the best months for watching along the coastline and Teesmouth. The return of many of the wader species begins in earnest and large numbers of terns and gulls roost and fish around the river mouth. A few waders can be found early in July, but it is usually about the middle of the month that there is a noticeable increase in the numbers of commoner species such as Redshank and Dunlin as well as Greenshank, Green Sandpiper and Whimbrel. Breeding-plumaged Knot, Bar-tailed Godwit, Grey Plover and Turnstone are frequently seen at this time, these adults generally preceding immature birds by several weeks. In July of most years a few Curlew Sandpiper and Black-tailed Godwit in breeding plumage are noted, as well as the occasional rarer wader.

A visit to North Gare Sands, Bran Sands or Coatham Sands on a late July evening will generally reveal some of the estuarine waders mentioned above as well as hundreds of Sandwich and Common Terns, together with smaller numbers of Arctic and Little Terns and possibly a few Roseate Tern. There may be a few Arctic Skua chasing the terns. Large numbers of gulls congregate around the river mouth at this time, 2000-3000 Black-headed Gulls being usual, with lesser numbers of Common, Herring and Great Black-backed Gulls. Occasional Glaucous, Little and Mediterranean Gulls have also been recorded in July, and Sabine's Gull and Long-tailed Skua have both been seen on more than one occasion.

Sea watching can be rewarding in July with large numbers of Manx Shearwaters, auks and Common Scoter passing along the coastline. A few other duck species are usually seen, such as Velvet Scoter, and on some days there is a noticeable southerly passage of waders.

Strong onshore winds are not as productive as in autumn, but Storm Petrel, Pomarine Skua and Great Shearwater have all been seen during onshore gales. In recent summers, Storm Petrels have been caught in reasonable numbers at night.

The interest around Teesmouth is not restricted solely to waders, however, the maximum number of summering Little Gull occur in this month. Ducklings of Shoveler, Gadwall, Pochard and Tufted Duck are reasonably easy to see, with over 100 Tufted Duck hatched in Cleveland in recent summers.

Young Black-headed Gulls appear along the coast from the beginning of the month, numbers steadily increasing as the birds leave their moorland colonies. It is usually late July or early August before young Herring and Common Gulls are seen at Teesmouth.

Inland, family parties of the tit species may be found in woodlands, gardens and hedgerows, and by late July, combine to form quite large flocks of mixed tits. A visit to an area of coniferous woodland at this time of year will generally produce large numbers of Chaffinches moving about in loose flocks, sometimes numbering more than 100 individuals.

July is not the best month for rarities. However, the only Great Spotted Cuckoo was seen in 1995 and King Eider in 1998, plus Ring-billed Gull in 1983 and 1995, Great White Egret in 1990 and 2003, and more than one Cory's Shearwater, Red-crested Pochard and White-rumped Sandpiper. In 1963 the first Little Ringed Plover attracted a lot of interest and a pair of Rollers in 1847 would almost certainly have nested if they had not been 'collected'.

AUGUST

The passage of many species can be seen (and heard) through Cleveland in August. Not only are waders, terns, skuas and gulls moving south, but small family parties of tits, chats, and finches can be seen in places where they are absent earlier in the year. Warblers and hirundines begin to move south, with warblers regularly being seen in gardens at this time. Many Swift, Sand Martin and Cuckoo leave for their winter quarters now.

Wader watching at Teesmouth can be exciting on some August days, as small numbers of species such as Ruff, Snipe, Greenshank and Golden Plover drop in, apparently from very high up, giving the observer the impression of witnessing migration as it is actually happening. The maximum numbers of Ruff, Whimbrel, Common and Wood Sandpipers and Spotted Redshank have been recorded in August and the estuarine waders such as Knot, Bar-tailed Godwit and Grey Plover are beginning to build up as young birds start to appear joining adults already present. Rarer waders like Temminck's Stint, Pectoral Sandpiper, Dotterel, Red-necked and Wilson's Phalaropes have all been recorded at Teesmouth in August. At the same time, waders that have bred on the moorlands are leaving for their winter haunts.

Numbers of gulls and terns are usually at their peak in August, although the actual total varies considerably from year to year. A sprat wreck in the river mouth or Tees Bay in August draws phenomenal numbers of gulls and terns, which in turn attract numbers of Arctic Skua. This is probably the best month to see Long-tailed Skua and Cory's Shearwater offshore, both species appearing regardless of the weather conditions.

Onshore gales produce spectacular passages of Manx Shearwater, Gannet and skuas; rarer birds like Great and Balearic Shearwaters, and Storm Petrel have been seen in these conditions. Ducks and divers also sometimes occur, although it is a month or so early for such birds to be seen in large numbers. A fall of passerine migrants is predictable given onshore winds, especially if combined with mist or rain. Good numbers of Willow Warbler occur in such conditions with lesser numbers of other warblers, Whinchat,

Spotted and Pied Flycatchers and Wheatear. Unusual birds like Ortolan Bunting, Red-backed Shrike, Icterine Warbler and Wryneck are regularly recorded in such conditions, favoured places being Hartlepool and South Gare.

Inland reservoirs frequently repay regular watching, with several sightings of Osprey and Black-necked Grebe in recent years, as well as Black Tern and the first signs of returning winter ducks such as Wigeon and Teal. If there is any mud exposed an assortment of passage waders may be visible.

August can be a good month to hear and see Tawny Owls in woodlands and parks, with adults feeding noisy fledglings.

August is a reasonable month for rarities, with the first record of Black Stork in 1862, Bonaparte's Gull in 1977, Long-toed Stint in 1982 and Pacific Golden Plover in 1995. The first and second records of Rose-coloured Starling occurred in the 19th century as well as the first Sharp-tailed Sandpiper in 1963 and Scarlet Rosefinch in 1977, the second Caspian Tern in 1972, Purple Heron in 1975, Great Snipe in 1976, American Golden Plover in 1984, American Wigeon in 1988, Arctic Warbler in 1991, Black Kite, Citrine Wagtail and Blue-winged Teal in 1994, Sharp-tailed Sandpiper, Baird's Sandpiper and Bee-eater in 1997, Caspian Tern in 2000, Lesser Yellowlegs in 2003, Spotted Sandpiper in 2004 and Roller in 2006. There are also several records of Crane, Greenish Warbler, White-rumped Sandpiper and White-winged Black Tern during the month.

SEPTEMBER

This is one of the best months for sea-watching, given suitable weather conditions. Ideally, the wind should be strong to gale-force, from a northerly quarter and accompanied by total cloud cover and rain. In these conditions Hartlepool Headland seems to be the best sea-watching position, but almost anywhere along the Cleveland coastline could be used. Such conditions may well excite the bird-watcher, but some of the birds observed during such weather must be struggling to survive.

Depending on when such weather occurs, hundreds and occasionally thousands of ducks are seen in a day, Wigeon, Teal and Common Scoter being the commonest. Hundreds of Arctic Skua, Manx Shearwater and Little Gull are frequently noted. Along with these birds, reasonable numbers of Red-throated Diver, Sooty Shearwater, Gannet, Great Skua and auks pass and unusual birds such as Leach's Petrel, Great Shearwater, Sabine's, Glaucous and Mediterranean Gulls, Pale-bellied Brent Goose and Black Tern are irregularly recorded. In recent years, quite large skeins of Barnacle Geese have been seen passing along the coast in late September or early October.

The passerines that occur during such weather conditions can vary from a few Willow Warbler and thrushes to hundreds of assorted warblers, thrushes, chats and other birds.

In a fall involving a lot of birds, commoner species, such as Willow Warbler, Wheatear and Meadow Pipit may be joined by a variety of rarer species.

As soon as the weather improves, most migrants move on. Large numbers of Wigeon and Teal sometimes rest around Seal Sands for a few days immediately after strong winds, but have mostly gone within a week or two.

The waders on the mudflats continue to increase in number as September progresses, whereas those found on the marshes are generally decreasing as birds move further south. Snipe is probably the only exception to this, often joined by one or two Jack Snipe in late September. It is also a reasonable month in which to see Pectoral Sandpiper, Spotted Crake and Buzzard at Teesmouth.

The approach of winter is suggested by the appearance of many of the usual winter visitors, including Redwing and Short-eared Owl. At the same time, summer has not entirely passed by, quite reasonable numbers of Swallow, Wheatear and terns still being around.

Inland birdwatching at woodland, farmland and upland sites, can be extremely unrewarding, most of the summer visitors having departed or ceased to call and the resident species, such as the finches and tits having formed flocks and dispersed in a fairly random fashion. Wood Pigeon and Collared Dove have been known to lay eggs as late as September, although the chances of the resulting young fledging must be reduced by the shortening daylight hours and decreasing temperatures.

September has an impressive list of rarities: including the only records of Little Bittern in 1852; Cirl Bunting in 1960; Black-billed Cuckoo in 1975; Short-billed Dowitcher in 1999 and Red-flanked Bluetail in 2001; also recorded this month, Little Shearwater in 1984; Red-rumped Swallow in 1995; Spotted Sandpiper in 1997; Citrine Wagtail in 1999; Lesser Yellowlegs in 2003; Night Heron in 1996; Paddyfield Warbler in 1969 and 1994; Little Bunting in 1983, 1989 and 2000; Booted Warbler in 1993 and 1999; Red-throated Pipit in 1998, two Blue-winged Teal in 1999 and Baird's Sandpiper in 2005.

OCTOBER

The early part of October can be like summer with various warblers, terns and other summer visitors still present. The first frosts of the winter are sometimes evident in October and almost all of the regular winter-visiting ducks, waders, thrushes and buntings are either passing through in good numbers or installed in their wintering quarters.

Severe cold or strong winds may well push the remaining summer visitors towards their wintering grounds, but these conditions can also produce excellent sea-watching and the occasional rare bird. Sea-watching can be as good as September, given similar strong winds. Very large numbers of ducks can be seen, especially Wigeon, Mallard, Common Scoter, as well as good numbers of Pomarine Skua, Little Auk and Kittiwake on occasion.

Many wintering thrushes arrive, sometimes thousands being recorded on a single day. Associated with the thrushes are winter visitors like Starling, Brambling, Chaffinch, Siskin, Woodcock, Long and Short-eared Owls.

Late migrants are not unusual in October, Yellow-browed Warbler, Firecrest and Red-breasted Flycatcher being seen regularly during the month with quite large numbers of Blackcap, Goldcrest and thrushes.

The Tees marshes have all but lost the terns, hirundines and waders that occur in summer and autumn, but ducks, gulls and some other waders are building up towards their winter peaks. The latest terns are almost always seen in this month and waders like Curlew Sandpiper, Greenshank and Little Stint are generally last recorded in mid to late October.

The first Goldeneye, Scaup, Whooper Swan and Dark-bellied Brent Geese usually occur at Teesmouth in October, as well as hundreds of Wigeon, and some Tufted Duck and Pochard. Large skeins of Pink-footed Geese regularly pass over Cleveland in October, more than 1,000 having been seen on some days.

Lapland and Snow Bunting, Shore Lark and Twite are usually first seen in October. Large numbers of Shore Lark occasionally appear during invasion years and this is one of the better months for seeing Rough-legged Buzzard and Bearded Tit.

The rarities in October have come from every conceivable direction and the following list of birds is arguably the most mouth-watering in this section. Rarities abound and include the only Houbara Bustard in 1892, Cliff Swallow in 1988, Red-eyed Vireo in 1991 and Great Knot in 1996, most Dusky, Radde's and Pallas's Warblers, and Richard's Pipits, Ring-necked Parakeet in 1990 and Pallid Swift in 1999. The list continues with White-tailed Eagle in 1836, 1915 and 1985, Little Bunting in 1902, 1972, 1988 and 1990, Red-footed Falcon in 1949 and 1969, Alpine Swift in 1976 and 1985, Paddyfield Warbler in 1984 and 1996, Ross's Gull in 1992, American Wigeon in 1997, Raven and Rustic Bunting in 1998, Great White Egret in 2002 and White-billed Diver in 2002 and 2007.

NOVEMBER

All the signs of winter are evident by the middle of November, with such avian pointers as flocks of Redwing, Fieldfare and Blackbird in fields and woods, and good numbers of Wigeon, Teal and Knot around Teesmouth.

A very few summer visitors are occasionally seen at the beginning of the month, as well as the occasional late passage migrant, such as Firecrest and Red-breasted Flycatcher. Two species that are mostly summer visitors are Blackcap and Chiffchaff, but can both be found regularly in November, sometimes as very late coastal migrants or at inland localities such as gardens, parks and woodlands. These inland birds probably remain throughout the winter and can be seen at woodland bird feeding stations alongside commoner species, including tits, finches and Great Spotted Woodpeckers.

At sea, passage of ducks and auks can be observed in suitable weather conditions, occasionally in very large numbers. November is probably the best period in which to see Little Auks passing along the coast, given strong northerly winds. Ducks seen in good numbers include Wigeon, Eider, Shelduck, Goldeneye and Common Scoter, usually with a good sprinkling of almost all the other duck species that occur. Passage of Great and Pomarine Skuas occasionally takes place in early November during strong onshore winds, though both are unpredictable. Some divers, grebes and geese pass along the coast at times.

At Teesmouth, the mudflats of Seal Sands can be teeming with birds, at times thousands of Knot and Dunlin, and hundreds of Curlew, Bar-tailed Godwit, Redshank, Oystercatcher, Wigeon and Teal being present. Flocks of diving duck sometimes appear on Seal Sands in November, mostly Goldeneye, Pochard and Tufted Duck, though this depends on the weather as much as the time of year. A few Brent Geese usually arrive in October or November, sometimes staying through the winter.

On the inland lakes and reservoirs, ducks and Coot are well on the way to their winter peaks, a few swans and geese sometimes appearing.

Relatively little in the way of rarities have been seen in November, though the first White-tailed Eagle was observed in 1823, Green-winged Teal in 1982, Parrot Crossbill in 1990, Pied Wheatear and Hume's Yellow-browed Warbler in 1994, Desert Wheatear in 2000 and 2005 and Cetti's Warbler in 2005. Other records include Tengmalm's Owl, Ivory Gull and Rose-coloured Starling in the 19th century, Glossy Ibis in 1900, Little Bunting in 1967, Surf Scoter in 1982 and 1995, several Richard's Pipit, Pallas's Warbler, Bearded Tit, Red Kite and Rough-legged Buzzard, Short-toed Lark in 1994, Arctic Redpoll in 1995, Woodlark in 1996, Pallid Swift and Ring-necked Duck in 2005 and Bonaparte's Gull in 2006.

DECEMBER

This can be the least exciting month of the year, although interesting birds can appear. Little movement is noted during the month, most species of wader and duck having reached their winter peaks, although a sudden cold spell further north can have an effect. The number of diving ducks is sometimes very low at coastal sites in a mild December, presumably because none of the inland waters have frozen over. Occasionally a Smew appears in mid to late December, although it is frequently January before any are seen. In recent years White-fronted Geese have arrived at Teesmouth in December. Thousands of Knot and hundreds of Redshank, Dunlin, Grey Plover, Curlew, Bar-tailed Godwit, Shelduck and Wigeon feed on Seal Sands. A few Brent Geese can usually also be found there.

Passerines noted in December include good numbers of Snow and sometimes Lapland Buntings, the highest winter count of both generally occurring during this month. Some Twite and Shore Lark are sometimes seen, but the latter bird has become very unpredictable in recent years. Water Pipit and Stonechat have increased recently, Scaling Dam and parts of Teesmouth being the usual localities for both species.

Sea passage is generally unexciting, with the occasional Manx Shearwater and Arctic, Pomarine and Great Skuas. Onshore gales also produce a trickle of auks, including a few Little Auk as well as relatively few ducks, divers and the occasional Glaucous and Iceland Gull. Both these species of white-winged gull can sometimes be seen around Hartlepool Headland and the fish quay and a few Red-breasted Merganser usually feed in the docks at this time. A diver or two can also often be found in these calmer waters, frequently staying into January.

Not a great deal of interest is generated rarity-wise in December, however the only Dusky Thrush appeared in 1959, the second Stone Curlew and Ferruginous Duck late in the 19th century, the first American Wigeon in 1973 and Ring-billed Gull in 1978, the third Serin in 1985, Red Kite in 1994 and two Arctic Redpolls in 1995 as well as several Bearded Tits and Bitterns.

Late Swallow, House Martin, Avocet, Whimbrel and Common Tern have all been noted in December, any such sighting being extremely unusual.

BIRD WATCHING LOCALITIES IN CLEVELAND

Cleveland offers special opportunities for watching a wide variety of birds. Despite its relatively small size, the area has many contrasting habitats ranging from the flat marshes bordering the Tees to moorlands, rugged coastline and coniferous forests. Even the former industrial land has its own specialist flora and fauna. All of these habitats attract many species of birds either to nest or pass through on annual migrations. Eighty four sites are listed below with some of the birds that can be seen at some time during the year.

It is, of course, possible for rarities to occur at any one of these sites, but rare birds more frequently visit some than others, because of their position and character. An asterisk (*) indicates the top six locations for rarities, with a comment on some of the unusual birds that have been seen in the past.

ALBERT PARK *NZ495192*

This public park in Middlesbrough is adjacent to the Dorman Museum (which contains Nelson's historic collection of stuffed birds) with a small boating lake and stream at the east end. The lake holds Canada Geese and tame Mallard, as well as Tufted Duck, Pochard and Goosander in winter. Rarer species such as Mandarin, Garganey, and Barnacle Goose have also been recorded. Common Terns sometimes fish here in summer and Grey Wagtails regularly feed in the concrete-sided stream. Most of the park is grass with large, mature trees, including hawthorns. The winter months can be entertaining with Great Spotted Woodpecker and Brambling recorded in most years and Waxwing in some. Nesting birds in the past have included Spotted Flycatcher and Mistle Thrush, whilst migrant warblers probably pass through regularly in spring and autumn. A short report of the birds seen in the 1880s and 1890s by T.A. Lofthouse includes Hoopoe, Corncrake, Wood Warbler and Pied Flycatcher, but the park was then on the outskirts of Middlesbrough and a much 'wilder' place.

BELASIS TECHNOLOGY PARK, BILLINGHAM
NZ476233

Created in 1990/91, superficially this small business park does not appear to offer much of wildlife interest, but within it a stream winds through pleasant green spaces between the buildings, with scattered stands of bushes and several reed-fringed ponds. Large numbers of Canada Geese are regularly seen, as well as Coot and Tufted Duck. A number of rarities have also been observed over the years.

BILLINGHAM BECK VALLEY NZ453223

An area of fields and freshwater marsh sandwiched between Norton and Billingham, with a beck flowing through which floods quite regularly in winter. Part of the valley is situated within Stockton Council's Country Park and this has been managed for the benefit of wildlife since the late 1980s. This is one of the best areas for wintering Kingfisher and has regular sightings of Bullfinch, Redpoll and Willow Tit. Breeding birds include Reed Warbler and Sedge Warbler.

BIRK BROW NZ657154

A fairly steep hillside adjacent to the A171 Middlesbrough to Whitby road, south-east of Guisborough, which has mature and younger conifers, together with some natural scrub and gorse. The area has breeding birds, including Goldcrest, Bullfinch and Long-tailed Tit. Species such as Crossbill, Long-eared Owl, Siskin, Lesser and Common Redpolls and Sparrowhawk have been seen amongst the trees and mixed flocks of tits regularly feed in the scrub areas. Singing Quail are heard occasionally in the adjacent fields. The largest flock of Parrot Crossbills ever recorded in Britain was seen here in March 1991.

BOULBY CLIFFS NZ752197

A stretch of approximately 3km of coastal cliffs near Boulby in East Cleveland, including a length of the Cleveland Way which passes along the top of the highest cliffs on the east coast in England. Most of the lower section of cliffs was dominated by the alum industry in the 19th century, the remains of which can still be seen today. The cliffs have about half of the breeding Kittiwakes, Cormorants, Fulmars and Rock Pipits and all of the Razorbills in Cleveland, together with a few Jackdaws, Feral Pigeons and House Martins. The location is an excellent place to witness seasonal migrations with the passage of Meadow and Tree Pipits, Swallow, House Martin, Goldfinch, Linnet and Pied and Yellow Wagtails being visible in spring and Starling, Chaffinch, Brambling and thrushes in autumn. There is relatively little vegetation on the cliffs, although passage migrants such as Black Redstart and Ring Ouzel are annual visitors, and Little Owl and Green Woodpecker are both quite easy to see. The fields on the top of the cliffs hold breeding Red-legged Partridge and winter visitors such as Snow and Lapland Bunting.

BOWESFIELD NZ442163

These three areas of marshy ground, ponds and fields are situated on the west bank of the River Tees midway between Stockton centre and Preston Park. Recently a road has been built across this area to link Stockton and Ingleby Barwick. The Tees Valley Wildlife Trust has developed a nature reserve here and there are various public footpaths giving access to the three areas. Quite large numbers of waders have been seen, including species such as Ruff, Black-tailed Godwit, Greenshank, and Wood and Curlew Sandpipers. At least one Sand Martin breeding colony is nearby and both Kingfisher and Reed Warbler are present in summer.

BRAN SANDS NZ554265

A medium-sized area of tidal mud and sandflats immediately to the west of South Gare. When the tide uncovers the shore, quite large numbers of waders such as Knot, Bar-tailed Godwit, Curlew and Redshank feed in the winter months and many gulls and terns rest here in autumn. Spring and autumn passages of waders can produce large numbers of Dunlin, which occasionally bring Curlew Sandpiper and Little Stint with them. Both the Great Knot in 1996 and the Short-billed Dowitcher in 1999 visited Bran Sands during their stay. When present, the gulls and terns are always worth checking as Glaucous and Mediterranean Gulls are regularly seen and birds like Iceland and Sabine's Gulls, Roseate Tern and skuas sometimes occur. Great Crested Grebes, Red-throated Divers and Cormorants frequently fish the area at high tide at appropriate times of the year.

BRINEFIELDS NZ512245

This is a fairly marshy area in private ownership with strictly no access east of the A178 Port Clarence to Seaton Carew Road. There are limited viewpoints but it can be seen from the footpath on the south side of Greatham Creek leading to the Seal Sands hides. It was once tidal mudflat but is now criss-crossed by slag tracks and roads with pumping equipment. The eastern edge has a long narrow pond with muddy edges, which proves very attractive to waders, especially in autumn. With its areas of slag and gravel, the site encourages breeding by Ringed Plovers and holds a fifth of the Cleveland population. Other breeding birds include Lapwing, Common Tern, Shelduck, Redshank and occasionally Little Ringed Plover. There is also a very small wood in the north-west corner, near the National Nature Reserve car park, which attracts passage migrants such as warblers and thrushes, and has a small Rookery. Large numbers of Dunlin and Ringed Plover frequently feed and rest on the Brinefields when the mudflats are covered by the tide. The more open grassy areas at the north end sometimes hold Golden Plover, Lapland Bunting and a few geese from time to time.

BROTTON - HUNLEY HALL GOLF CLUB
NZ693205

A large golf course between Brotton and the Cleveland Way along the top of the cliffs. It was created in the 1990s and has several public footpaths across and beside it giving good views. Several ponds have been created and some trees have been planted, although there is naturally a significant amount of disturbance by golfers. It is a good place to watch migrating birds; many that travel north-west over Boulby continue along this area, but tend to pass on a broader front.

CATTERSTY GILL NZ704204

A small valley which is a Tees Valley Wildlife Trust Nature Reserve, close to the Cleveland Way footpath, just north of Cattersty Pond with access by permissive path from the Cleveland Way. It has a good number of hawthorns in it, plus a few other trees, and attracts migrants in spring and autumn, but little at other times of the year. Cleveland's only Red-flanked Bluetail occurred here in September 2001.

CATTERSTY POND NZ704198

A small private pond situated between Hunley Hall golf course and Skinningrove steel works, surrounded by trees. The pond attracts over 100 Mallard at times, as well as Tufted Duck and Little Grebe. The bushes and trees around the pool do not cover a very large area so relatively little breeds there. There is no public access, but the pond can be viewed from surrounding footpaths and roads.

CHARLTON'S POND (BILLINGHAM POND)
NZ468232

An area of about 20 acres, with a large and small pond, fringed with reeds and some medium-sized trees, which is situated immediately north of the railway line and can be reached off Cowpen Lane. The site was originally a clay pit, but from 1912 it has been fished quite intensively. In the 1950s part of the pond was filled in, but the eastern end was fenced off and a 'bird sanctuary' created in 1968, this being the first official nature reserve in Cleveland. Some planting of trees has taken place in recent years. Mute Swans nest here. A small number of Mallard were introduced around 1967 and 100 to 200 Mallard now regularly winter on the pond. Small numbers of Tufted Duck and Pochard can also be seen at this time of year, with occasional sightings of other ducks, divers, Kingfisher and Water Rail. The rough ground and trees around the ponds support breeding Willow Warbler and Blackcap, with occasional views of Garden and Grasshopper Warbler. The first record for Europe of a Double-crested Cormorant attracted at least 1,500 birdwatchers to this spot in 1989.

COATHAM MARSH NZ586247 *

An area of marsh, part of which has been reclaimed and landscaped, sandwiched between the houses of Redcar and the industrial landscape of the iron and steel works. It is managed by Tees Valley Wildlife Trust as a nature reserve with access along a number of permissive paths. The area is worth a visit at any time of the year. Recent breeding birds including Sedge, Reed and Grasshopper Warblers, Mute Swan, Ruddy and Tufted Ducks, and Little Ringed Plover. Passage waders such as Spotted Redshank, Greenshank, Wood Sandpiper and Ruff are sometimes seen in spring and autumn. Teal, Wigeon, Gadwall, Shoveler, Pochard, Tufted Duck and Goldeneye regularly winter in reasonable numbers. Being close to the coast, Coatham Marsh tends to attract some passerines such as Willow Warbler, Blackcap and Redstart during passage times and Lapland Bunting and Goldfinch in winter. A duck decoy used to be operated on the marsh in the nineteenth century.

COATHAM SANDS NZ568267

The four kilometre stretch of beautiful beach running roughly east-west between Redcar and South Gare is a favourite wintering site for many of Cleveland's Sanderling and Snow Buntings, and occasionally has breeding Little Tern. A broad expanse of sand is exposed at low tide and this is used by some waders to feed, especially Sanderling with some Knot, Ringed Plover and Turnstone, and by large numbers of gulls as a night-time roost. At high tide only the higher reaches remain exposed. The area of sea just off the sands frequently holds Red-breasted Merganser, Eider and Red-throated Diver in winter and fishing terns in summer.

COATHAM WOOD *NZ399153*

This is a large area of "new" woodland between Urlay Nook and Longnewton, and adjacent to the Elementis site of Carter Moor. It comprises several fields that have been planted with native trees in the 1990s as part of the "Tees Forest" initiative. By the beginning of the 21st century all five species of regular-occurring owl had been recorded, and several owl boxes were installed in 2005. Other interesting species seen include Common Redpoll and Stonechat.

COWBAR NAB *NZ783191*

A small vertical-sided promontory in the extreme south-east corner of Cleveland, just across Easington Beck from Staithes (North Yorkshire). The long grass and sparse bushes on the top sometimes attract a few migrants. The sides, which are slowly eroding away, are used as nesting sites by about 250 pairs of Herring Gulls, and a few Kittiwakes and Fulmars. Sea-watching from this promontory has so far proved to be quite interesting, and probably nearly as productive as that at Hartlepool Headland, although there is no shelter from the elements. Large numbers of Manx Shearwater, Teal, Pomarine Skua, Gannet and auks have been seen together with rarer passage migrants.

COWPEN BEWLEY WOODLAND PARK
NZ484255

A group of ponds, marshes and woodland, beside the Stockton-Hartlepool railway line to the north of Cowpen Bewley village. The Park is managed by Stockton Borough Council and at times there are quite high numbers of dog-walkers in the area, but overall it remains an interesting place. In summer Tree Sparrow, Mute Swan, Little Grebe and Tufted Duck nest. Kingfisher, Tufted Duck and Pochard are seen regularly and Long and Short-eared Owls, and Green Sandpiper occasionally appear. The surrounding area is quite good for flocks of Tree Sparrow, Yellowhammer and winter thrushes, especially around the car park and adjacent feeding station.

COWPEN MARSH *NZ502250*

Now freshwater marsh, this used to be tidal mudflat before reclamation began. Most of the Marsh is managed for its conservation value, although a section of this is still shot over by Hartlepool and District Wildflowers Association (between 1st September and 31st January). Access to the site is restricted, but the National Nature Reserve car park is usually open off the A178 road from which part of the area can be viewed. The site consists of four wide reed-filled fleets which drain through the Brinefields to Greatham Creek when the water levels are high, but remain as ponds when low. In dry seasons, mud shows around the edges and is used by waders in spring and autumn. Breeding birds include Common Tern (on artificial islands), Tufted Duck, Ruddy Duck, Shoveler, Yellow Wagtail, Lapwing, Redshank and Swallow, with infrequent records of Garganey, Pintail, Black-tailed Godwit and Little Grebe. Spring and autumn passage can be interesting with most common waders seen, together with Spotted Redshank, Greenshank and Ruff and occasionally Temminck's and Little Stints and Curlew Sandpiper. Dabbling ducks use the area regularly, although geese and swans rarely stay long in winter. Three small hawthorn enclosures attract a few migrants such as Goldcrest, Pied Flycatcher and thrushes.

DORMANS POOL *NZ514232* *

Regarded by some as the most observed site for birds in Cleveland, the pool and surrounding marsh is privately owned, although the Teesmouth Bird Club operates a permit system for access to its car park and hide. Large numbers of duck spend the winter here, if the Pool remains unfrozen, and many waders feed at various times of the year. Breeding birds include Snipe, Redshank, Yellow Wagtail, Little Grebe, Tufted Duck, Pochard, Gadwall, Shoveler, Mute Swan and Reed and Sedge Warblers. The water level is quite critical especially for waders. In some years very little mud is exposed and few waders are seen; however, when more mud is visible hundreds of Dunlin, Lapwing and Golden Plover visit, along with many Redshank, Ringed Plover and Ruff. All of the regular passage waders such as Greenshank, Black-tailed Godwit, Little Stint and Curlew Sandpiper also appear. Rare waders like Temminck's Stint, Pectoral and White-rumped Sandpipers have been seen on several occasions. Greylag Geese sometimes number several hundred, although other geese and winter swans are usually only seen in very small numbers. Gulls frequently use the marsh as a night-time roost. Peregrine, Merlin, Sparrowhawk and Marsh Harrier hunt over the area at times.

EASINGTON BECK AND WOODS
NZ746140-777180

The beck forms the Cleveland boundary for very nearly all of its seven kilometres length flowing from near Scaling Dam to the sea between Cowbar and Staithes. Large sections of the beck are in woodland. It is ideal Dipper and Grey Wagtail habitat, being clean, sheltered and well away from human interference. At least five pairs of Dipper and four pairs of Grey Wagtail breed, as well as Moorhen and Mallard. Most of the woodland is deciduous, although not particularly mature, and breeding birds are those that one might expect, including Blackcap, Chiffchaff, Sparrowhawk, Jay, Great Spotted Woodpecker and Bullfinch. Green Woodpecker, Heron and Hawfinch have all been seen in the area, but probably do not nest on the Cleveland side every year. The woods are crossed by a number of public footpaths and Ridge Lane runs along the valley for most of its length from Staithes to Scaling.

ERRINGTON WOODS *NZ630204*

This is mainly coniferous woodland immediately to the south of New Marske. The whole area is well-used by the public, but remains interesting for wildlife with breeding Goldcrest, Woodcock, Long-tailed Tit, Marsh, Coal and Willow Tit and Jay. In some years Sparrowhawk and Great Spotted Woodpecker are present. Siskin has been heard singing in recent springs and Crossbills are seen sometimes, possibly breeding on occasion. Outside the breeding season, reasonable numbers of tits and Goldcrest can be found. There is a "winter" feeding station at the car park off Sandy Lane which attracts Willow Tit and Bullfinch

ESTON NAB AND MOOR *NZ567180*

The moorland on the Eston Hills is the only genuine example of this habitat away from the southern boundary of Cleveland. It is being slowly covered by birch and gorse, and two corners are very wet, but overall it is probably unique in Cleveland, despite parts of the area being damaged by fire in most summers. Reasonably large numbers of Willow Warblers, Meadow Pipits and Skylarks nest, as well as Tree Pipit, Curlew, Whinchat, Reed Bunting and Whitethroat. The eastern section, immediately to the south and east of the monument on the Nab, is partly covered by conifers of various ages and is fairly unexciting for bird watching. The usual conifer-nesting birds, such as Coal Tit, Redpoll, Jay, Sparrowhawk, Chaffinch and Goldcrest are present, and Crossbill, Green Woodpecker and Red-legged Partridge have been noted in the breeding season.

Other birds sometimes present include small numbers of Brambling, Siskin, Ring Ouzel and Long-eared Owl.

FLATTS LANE NZ553167

Several areas of woodland, scrub and gorse cover the former Ormesby Brick Works site at the western end of the Eston Hills. A visitor centre and car park is operated by Redcar and Cleveland Borough Council. Most woodland species of birds can be found in this area, including Great Spotted Woodpecker, Jay, Bullfinch, Long-tailed, Marsh and Willow Tits and Cuckoo. Eight out of Cleveland's ten breeding warblers are present during the summer, although Wood Warblers can be difficult to find. There are the usual resident woodland birds in the winter months, usually in small flocks, which are joined by some winter visitors such as Redwing, Fieldfare, Redpoll, Siskin and Brambling. Sparrowhawk regularly hunt through the area.

GREATHAM CREEK NZ485258-517256

A tidal river that rises in the Wynyard area and flows into Seaton Channel near Seal Sands. At low tide, around four to ten metres of mud is exposed on each side of the creek as far inland as the sewage works and this proves attractive to waders such as Redshank, Lapwing and Dunlin, especially in winter. Black-headed Gulls and Teal loaf on the mud at times and Wigeon sometimes feed in the area. At high tide, waders roost on the adjacent saltings, especially Redshank and Lapwing, and occasionally diving duck and Coot drift up and down the creek when the local freshwater is iced over. Up to ten Short-eared Owls and Rock Pipits usually spend the winter months in the area and an occasional Green Sandpiper is seen well upstream during this season. Cleveland's only Short-billed Dowitcher occurred here for several days in October 1999. There is access at various points from public and permissive footpaths.

GREENABELLA MARSH NZ515258

A large area of grassland adjacent to Seal Sands and Greatham Creek, with pools and marshy areas. Some disused brine wells exist on the southern part of the site. Most of the area is owned by Huntsman Tioxide, which has provided several small ponds for the benefit of wildlife. The slag areas previously created by ICI for its brine extraction have provided nest sites for Ringed Plover. The pool nearest to Greatham Creek bridge has been deepened in recent years, rendering it attractive to diving duck such as Goldeneye and Red-breasted Merganser. The long grass over most of the area encourages Short-eared Owls in winter, whilst Barn Owl, Hen and Marsh Harriers have hunted over it. This marsh is frequently the only area in Cleveland where Twite can be found, and Stonechat has become regular in recent winters.

For safety reasons access is controlled through Tioxide – please park in the visitor's car park and register your presence on site through reception or via telephone to security.

GUISBOROUGH FOREST NZ625145

The largest single expanse of coniferous woodland in Cleveland with a range of woodland species including Goldcrest, Chaffinch, Coal Tit, Long-eared Owl, Sparrowhawk and Woodcock, with perhaps Crossbill and Siskin. When the trees were first planted, Nightjar nested for several years and it is possible that they will return when some of the trees are cut down. Apart from the regimented rows of conifers that cover about 90% of the area, there are a few deciduous trees, mainly sycamore, and a rocky promontory called Highcliff Nab on which Fulmar have occasionally perched.

HARDWICK DENE NZ423204

A small beck valley close to the urban development at Hardwick in Stockton. Access is possible from several points via public footpaths, including from Darlington Back Lane and Cornforth Close. The Dene has scattered hawthorn and blackthorn and links to the local Nature Reserve Elm Tree Wood. It has a range of resident woodland species including Great Spotted Woodpecker, Goldfinch, Bullfinch and Sparrowhawk. Populations are increased by summer visitors including Willow Warbler and Blackcap.

HARTLEPOOL BAY NZ520320

This section of coastline between Hartlepool Docks and Seaton Carew can be very interesting in the winter months. There is an extensive section of rocks exposed at low tide, which regularly attracts large numbers of gulls. Species such as Glaucous, Mediterranean, Little and Lesser Black-backed Gulls are seen quite frequently and Sabine's, Iceland and Ross's Gulls have all been noted on more than one occasion in recent years. This area of sea is the best place in Cleveland to see Great Crested Grebe in the winter months and is a regular winter haunt of Red-breasted Merganser, Goldeneye and Red-throated Diver. Less common birds are frequently noted, such as Velvet Scoter, Long-tailed Duck, Black-throated and Great Northern Divers, Red-necked Grebe and Scaup. The beach is popular with Sanderling and Ringed Plover and the exposed rocks are frequented by Knot and Turnstone. The land immediately inland of the beach north of Seaton Carew used to be a municipal tip up to about 1986, but is now grassed over, with a few weedy areas, and attracts a flock of Snow Bunting in most winters.

HARTLEPOOL DOCKS & HARBOUR *NZ518338*

This area is especially interesting between November and March, but is also worth looking over at other times of the year. The harbour, with its associated fishing boats, attracts large numbers of Guillemots and Cormorants. The occasional duck and diver sit on the water in the harbour, but the majority of these birds feed and rest in the calmer waters of the docks. Red-breasted Merganser are a regular sight in the docks between December and March, with occasionally up to 35 to 40 present, and a diver or two is quite normal during the same period. This is most likely to be Red-throated Diver, although Black-throated Diver has been seen for several days or weeks. Unusual sea-birds such as Great Northern Diver, Red-necked Grebe, Little Auk and Leach's Petrel have all been recorded in the docks, generally during or after onshore gales. The West Harbour Dock has been renovated to include the provision of a purpose-built high tide island, which is used by roosting Turnstones, Oystercatchers, Cormorants and large gulls at various times of the year. Small numbers of Shag, Kittiwake and Purple Sandpiper can also appear.

HARTLEPOOL HEADLAND *NZ530338* *

This location is very well observed from April to November and has several small public gardens, bowling greens and areas of weed and mown grass. In suitable weather conditions (winds from the north or east combined with mist or rain) 'falls' of passerines are quite predictable, especially in May and between August and October. Predominant among these visitors are Willow Warbler, Wheatear, Redstart, Pied Flycatcher and thrushes. Sometimes they are accompanied by a sprinkling of unusual migrants, such as Firecrest; Yellow-browed, Icterine and Barred Warblers; Red-backed and Great Grey Shrikes, Wryneck; and Bluethroat. Many rarities have been found here. Looking near the lighthouse, if the wind is strong to gale force and from the north-west, north or north-east, can be very interesting to observe passing birds. The type of species seen depends on the time of year, the most exciting period being July to November. The best sea-watches have produced hundreds of divers, skuas and shearwaters and thousands of auks, ducks and terns, as well as a good selection of unusual birds like Sabine's Gull, Leach's and Storm Petrels, Long-tailed Skua, Black Guillemot, Little, Great and Cory's Shearwaters, Lesser Crested and Bridled Terns, Surf Scoter and phalaropes. The sea between the two breakwaters frequently offers some shelter in bad weather, and it is not unusual to find skuas, ducks and auks sitting on the surface when large numbers are passing out to sea. A flock of Eider, as well as a few Red-throated Diver and Shags regularly feed off the headland. The rocks when exposed at low tide are a winter haunt of Purple Sandpiper, Turnstone, Oystercatcher and Rock Pipit.

HAVERTON HOLE *NZ483233*

A series of pools with reeds and marshy areas to the north and east of Haverton Hill, which form part of the new RSPB Saltholme Nature Reserve. This has the largest colony of Reed Warblers in Cleveland. Good numbers of Coot, Moorhen, Sedge Warbler and Little Grebe nest here, as well as Mute Swan, Tufted Duck and occasionally Great Crested Grebe and Grasshopper Warbler. Two of the five pools were specifically created in the summer of 1988 for the benefit of wildlife and have attracted many Lapwing and some breeding Little Ringed Plover. In spring reasonably large numbers of hirundines gather over the water and Marsh Harrier is regularly recorded in May. Black Tern and Little Gull sometimes feed over the water in autumn and various duck such as Shoveler and Teal may be found. The reeds are used as a night-time roost by Yellow Wagtail and Reed Bunting, with the number of Yellow Wagtail sometimes reaching around 200-300. In winter, assuming the water is not frozen, around 100 Coot can sometimes be seen, as well as a lot of Snipe, a few Jack Snipe and some diving duck. Water Rail is present regularly and small groups of geese and wild swans sometimes feed in the adjacent fields. An area of hawthorn and scrub exists to the south of the main area, and Long-eared Owl occasionally roost here in the winter months. A pair of Marsh Harriers successfully bred on the site in 1996.

HAZEL GROVE *NZ656216*

This is a small wooded valley running down to the beach just to the north of the houses on the front at Saltburn. It holds migrants in spring and autumn but is rarely watched for birds. There are a few large pine trees in the centre, which probably explains one record of singing Siskin in April. Migrants such as Willow Warbler, Chiffchaff, Blackcap, Goldcrest, Redstart, Brambling, Yellow-browed Warbler and Pallas's Warbler have been seen. It is one of the few places where Marsh and Willow Tits can both be observed in Cleveland.

HEMLINGTON LAKE *NZ490147*

A large lake constructed within Hemlington and almost completely surrounded by houses. It is heavily fished and much disturbance is evidently a contributing factor to the lack of bird records. It attracts good numbers of small gulls and has some resident Mallard. Teal, Tufted Duck, Pochard, Goosander and Goldeneye have been regularly recorded mainly in winter.

HUNT CLIFF NZ691218

The western half of the cliffs between Saltburn and Skinningrove, which has the Cleveland Way footpath running along the top. In some years all of Cleveland's breeding Cormorant have nested on these cliffs (up to 64 pairs), as well as about half of the Kittiwakes, Fulmars and Rock Pipits. A large number of Herring Gull also nest. At each end of the cliffs are steep slopes with interesting vegetation and breeding Whitethroat. There are also scattered bushes, which hold a few migrants in spring and autumn. The fields on top of the cliffs occasionally support flocks of finches and buntings in autumn and winter. At high tide, the sea reaches the bottom of the cliffs, but at other times the rocks are exposed and these provide feeding platforms for Oystercatcher and Curlew, and resting areas for thousands of gulls. Goldeneye, Eider and Mallard frequently feed on the sea below the cliffs.

HUTTON HALL NZ598145

The parkland around Hutton Hall lies on the southern outskirts of Guisborough, close to Hutton village. The area is quite distinctive, consisting of open parkland with mature, mainly deciduous, trees. The area is well known in the winter as a site for Hawfinch, although numbers have declined in recent years. The mature trees attract Great Spotted Woodpecker and Nuthatch, whilst Green Woodpecker feed on the grassland. Lesser Spotted Woodpecker is recorded occasionally. Winter is a good time to view tit and finch flocks, the latter often including Redpoll, Siskin and Brambling. The estate is private, but is criss-crossed by minor roads and public footpaths that give good views of the whole area.

HUTTON LOWCROSS WOODS NZ595135

The Forest Enterprise woodland is about 70% coniferous, but does not have densely regimented trees. Hutton village is situated on the edge of the forest. There are several tracks and paths that meander through the forest, some leading to the moorland, Highcliff Nab and Roseberry Topping. The bird species are predictable with Chaffinch, Goldcrest and Coal Tit being the commonest breeding birds, and occasional sightings of Sparrowhawk, Woodcock, Jay, Redpoll, Nuthatch, Long-eared Owl, Hawfinch and Siskin. The last two species have been seen in recent winters with up to 100 Siskin in one flock. At times the area adjacent to Hutton Village holds most of Cleveland's breeding Wood Warblers.

HUMMERSEA *NZ718201*

Located immediately east of Skinningrove, the cliff top fields at Hummersea are a good place to view migrants in spring and autumn. The site is immediately west of the higher cliffs and more rugged countryside of Boulby and consists of fields, with hedgerows and good stands of scrub and gorse, particularly on the seaward side. There are mature trees around the houses in the hamlet of Hummersea that regularly attract rarer migrants particularly during autumn falls. The paddocks at the eastern end, adjacent to Boulby Cliff, are as good a place as anywhere in Cleveland for migrating Ring Ouzel. Hummersea is also a good place to see commoner farmland species, such as Yellowhammer and Skylark. Although there is an access road to Hummersea, the lane is narrow and parking is difficult without disrupting access to the cottages. Visitors should park in the seafront car park in Skinningrove and gain access to the site by walking eastwards along the Cleveland Way.

KILTON WOODS *NZ703175*

This is one of the largest stretches of natural woodland in Cleveland, extending from the lowest slopes of the moorland near Lockwood Beck along several narrow streams to a fairly broad valley between Loftus and Skinningrove. The upper section is quite dense and difficult to walk through, but from Liverton Mill downstream, there are a few narrow paths and at the Loftus end, the area is subject to some disturbance. All of the usual woodland birds can be found here including Great Spotted Woodpecker, Spotted Flycatcher, Chiffchaff, Blackcap, Garden Warbler, Marsh Tit and Tawny Owl. A few pairs of Grey Wagtails and Mallard breed along the streams and Dipper, Redstart, Green Woodpecker, and Sparrowhawk occasionally also breed. There are several public right of ways through the wood.

KIRKLEATHAM *NZ593217*

A small hamlet, with some architecturally interesting buildings and many mature trees. The latter have a good number of species, such as Long-tailed Tit, Great Spotted Woodpecker, Sparrowhawk, Tree Sparrow and Tawny Owl, all probably breeding in the area. Barn Owl has bred in the recent past and may still do so occasionally. The Hall in the village has been converted into a museum.

LEVEN VALLEY *NZ423127-450094*

A fairly narrow river meandering through farmland, woodland and areas of scrub and conifer from Crathorne to the River Tees, the whole area being about four kilometres to the south-east of Yarm. Access can be gained from several public rights of way along the valley and a walk along this valley on a sunny spring morning can be a delight. Resident woodland birds like Great Spotted Woodpecker, Bullfinch, Long-tailed Tit, Jay and Treecreeper can be relatively easy to find and more unusual birds such as Dipper, Kingfisher, Grey Wagtail, Green Woodpecker, and Red-legged Partridge probably breed in most years. In the winter months, Woodcock and Siskin can be almost guaranteed, the latter favouring the alders that line the river almost throughout its length. Interesting summer visitors include Cuckoo, Grasshopper Warbler, Chiffchaff and Blackcap. At the south end is Weary Bank Wood, which contains a heronry with over 20 pairs. Other species recorded here include Mandarin, Buzzard, Goosander and Lesser Spotted Woodpecker, the latter two species probably breeding occasionally.

LINTHORPE CEMETERY *NZ483187*

A larger than average cemetery by Cleveland standards situated beside the north end of Acklam Road in Middlesbrough. It has a substantial number of mature deciduous trees and a small number of pines. This is one of few areas of woodland surrounded by houses that has breeding Great Spotted Woodpecker, as well as Chiffchaff, Willow Warbler, Coal Tit and Treecreeper. Some migrants will use the area in spring and autumn, Pied Flycatcher and Garden Warbler having been recorded in August and Sparrowhawks hunt in the area throughout the year. Waxwings have been observed in more than one recent winter.

LOCKE PARK *NZ594248*

A fairly small park in Redcar with a boating lake and many trees and bushes. It is just across the road from Coatham Marsh and there is some movement of Mallards between the two, as well as the occasional Goosander, Scaup, Little Grebe and Wigeon, particularly in freezing conditions. Both Kingfisher and Grey Wagtail pass from one place to the other at times. The park is an attractive location for migrants from April to early June, and from mid-August to mid-November. A 'fall' of passerines on the coast will invariably produce some of these birds in the park and they tend to stay longer than at South Gare. Species such as Pied and Spotted Flycatchers, Willow Warbler, Chiffchaff, Blackcap, Whitethroat, Redstart, Brambling and the winter thrushes are annual visitors.

Breeding birds are not exceptional, although numbers of Goldfinches are present and Lesser Redpoll has nested. The park is used as a Blackbird roost in autumn and winter, and also occasionally by Collared Doves. Arguably Cleveland's most unexpected rarity – a Black-billed Cuckoo – was seen here in September 1975.

LOCKWOOD BECK *NZ668141*

A medium-sized reservoir situated alongside the A171 road to the east of Guisborough. Fishing is allowed around the entire shoreline and consequently the reservoir is not as interesting as Scaling Dam, though there is some movement of ducks between the two. Around 100 Mallard and ten to twenty Tufted Duck are usually seen during the winter months with occasional Pochard, Wigeon, Goldeneye, Goosander and the very occasional Smew, Whooper Swan and geese. A few Cormorant, Coot and Great Crested Grebe can generally be observed in spring and autumn. The trees around the reservoir attract assorted passerines at times, including Crossbill, Siskin, Lesser Redpoll, Tree Pipit and Goldcrest. Roding Woodcock have been seen in the area in spring. Greylag Geese have nested since about 1998 and Spotted Flycatcher can be seen in May and June. The stream along the western side of the reservoir frequently has Grey Wagtail, and Dipper can sometimes be observed both at the stream and along the edge of the reservoir. Red Grouse are present on the moorland immediately behind the reservoir, whilst Hen Harrier and Merlin have both been recorded quite regularly.

LONG DRAG *NZ516248*

A long, almost straight slag wall, which stretches from Dormans Pool to Greatham Creek and originally bordered the mudflats of Seal Sands, which can be reached from the Seal Sands Hide. The west side is the edge of the Brinefields and the land to the east was almost completely covered by dredged material from the river bed in the mid-1970s. Soon after this section of Seal Sands was reclaimed, the resulting land was used as a gull roost and Little Terns bred here in one year. The part closest to the Long Drag remains quite wet and attracts waders when mud is exposed, but the whole area is becoming established with reeds and long grass. This has encouraged Reed and Sedge Warblers to nest and has brought such unusual birds as Bittern, Bearded Tit, Spotted Crake, Marsh Harrier and Aquatic Warbler, but there is now very little mud for waders and relatively few gulls and terns can roost here. The section closest to Seal Sands was enclosed and rendered partially tidal in about 1998, this area attracting numbers of Curlew, Redshank and Shelduck when Seal Sands is covered. This area also has an impressive list of rarer species. The slag and grass surface of the Long Drag itself is sometimes attractive to migrants such as Wheatear, White Wagtail and Turtle Dove and the few bushes along the west side have held Willow Warbler, Stonechat, Chiffchaff and Goldcrest. In very cold weather Lapland, Snow and Corn Buntings, Shore Lark and Twite have all been seen on or beside the Long Drag.

LOVELL HILL NZ2597189

An area of marsh, ponds and small trees surrounded by fields, lying between Wilton Village and Guisborough. There is no public access, but the ponds can be viewed from Wilton Lane. It has a good selection of breeding birds, such as Grasshopper Warbler, Whitethroat, Lesser Whitethroat, Bullfinch, Long-tailed Tit, Cuckoo and Tufted Duck, and in some years Canada Goose, Teal and Water Rail have bred. Herons regularly visit the pond, nesting nearby, and up to six Cormorants have been seen in recent springs. This area would appear to be on a migration route since passage migrants are regularly observed in spring and autumn. Quite large numbers of passerines have been ringed here in recent years as can be seen by the recoveries mentioned for several species.

MARGROVE PONDS NZ653162

A small nature reserve containing several ponds, with a disused railway line that functions as a footpath, and some gorse, broom, willow and other small trees. It is situated in the valley between Charltons and Boosbeck, east of Guisborough. There are never many water birds in the area, though about 5-10 pairs of Moorhen, Coot, Mallard and Tufted Duck nest regularly, with Teal, Canada Goose, Little Grebe and Black-headed Gull breeding irregularly. Sedge Warbler and Reed Bunting nest in reasonable numbers. Winter visitors include the occasional Goldeneye, Shoveler, Jack Snipe, Whooper Swan and Water Rail and passage waders such as Greenshank and Green Sandpiper are seen frequently. The disused railway line and adjacent bushes hold breeding Whitethroat, Lesser Whitethroat, Grasshopper Warbler and Willow Tit.

MARSKE (REDCAR) FOX COVERT NZ631230

This mainly hawthorn-filled copse, with a small stream flowing through the bushes, is situated on the north-west edge of Marske, adjacent to the Redcar-Marske coast road. Nothing of interest breeds here, but during the spring and autumn passages, migrants are regularly seen in small numbers. It is a Collared Dove roost site. The copse is favoured by Goldcrest and thrushes in autumn and most of the usual passage migrants have been noted.

Birds of Cleveland

MARTON WEST BECK *NZ511150*

A narrow valley running approximately north to south through Coulby Newham, which is heavily disturbed at times, but still attracts interesting birds. The stream itself has been dammed in two places to form ponds, both of which look natural, and most of the adjoining hedgerows and trees have been left 'unimproved'. The birds seen on a regular basis include Kingfisher and Dipper, as well as Goldeneye, Sparrowhawk, Blackcap, Great Spotted Woodpecker and most usual winter woodland birds.

NEWHAM HALL *NZ518130*

This small area of parkland is situated on the edge of the former county of Cleveland to the south of Coulby Newham. It has a public footpath running through it, as well as a few small ponds and ornamental trees. The area looks like an ideal place for all three species of woodpecker to visit in winter, though only Great-spotted has been reported recently. Other birds seen include Quail, Red-legged Partridge, Wood Warbler, Blackcap and Sparrowhawk in summer, Common Sandpiper in autumn and reasonable numbers of thrushes, Bullfinch and Goldcrest in winter.

NEWTON WOOD *NZ575125*

A special area of ancient woodland belonging to the National Trust on the steep slope just below Roseberry Topping and reached by walking from Newton-under-Roseberry. It is predominantly mature oak, with a scattering of various other deciduous and a few coniferous trees. The regular woodland birds can be found breeding here including most of the tit family, Treecreeper, Green and Great Spotted Woodpeckers, Tawny Owl as well as Redstart, Tree Pipit, Wood Warbler and Pied Flycatcher, although the latter three species are not present every summer. Outside the breeding season, the area is fairly unexciting, Fieldfare, Redwing, Goldcrest and Nuthatch sometimes occurring during the winter months. For the butterfly enthusiasts, it is a good place for Purple Hairstreak in July and August.

NORTH GARE *NZ540284* *

The smaller of the two slag breakwaters that 'guard' the mouth of the Tees and certainly less interesting than South Gare. It is reached by walking south-east along the beach from Seaton Carew, or by driving to the car park off the A178 road. At low tide, quite large areas of slag and rocks are exposed which attract Turnstone, Purple Sandpiper and gulls, and at high tide, sea birds such as all 3 divers, Great Crested Grebe, Red-breasted Merganser, Common and Velvet Scoter, Eider and various other ducks can be seen, especially in winter. When there is a 'sprat wreck' in the river mouth, the North Gare can be an excellent vantage point from which to scrutinise the many thousands of birds that are occasionally attracted. Such gatherings have included Sabine's, Mediterranean, Glaucous and Iceland Gulls, Roseate and Black Tern and Long-tailed Skua. A few passerines occasionally feed around the Gare, in particular Snow Buntings in winter and migrants such as Black Redstart, Wheatear, Ring Ouzel and winter thrushes are quite regularly recorded. The sea buckthorn bushes between North Gare and Seaton Carew regularly hold migrants whenever such birds appear along the coastline, though rarely in the numbers that occur at Hartlepool and South Gare. All the usual migrant species have been recorded as well as the occasional rarity. The only Red-eyed Vireo to be seen in Cleveland was here in 1991.

NORTH GARE SANDS (SEATON SNOOK)
NZ540272

An area of sand that is covered at high-tide and is situated at the mouth of the river south of North Gare and east of Hartlepool Power Station. Access is via either of the two roads across Seaton Common from the A178. The sands are used as a gull, wader and tern roost at various times of the year and on occasions it holds many thousands of birds. When the high-tides are low, relatively little of the area is covered and it is almost always worth looking at the sands. At other high-tides, virtually nothing but a line of tipped slag remains above the water. Sometimes Little Terns nest here and a few pairs of Ringed Plover always attempt to breed above the normal high-tide line. This is probably the best place to see Roseate Tern (in July and August). A flock of Snow Buntings can regularly be found along the tide-line between November and February.

ORMESBY HALL NZ528168

An area of parkland with some well-established areas of trees owned by the National Trust. It is situated on the edge of Ormesby and the A174 Parkway runs along its southern side so there is a good deal of noise after about 8am each day. It is a very pleasant area to walk around but the number of bird species to be seen is quite limited. Breeding birds include Goldcrest, Tawny Owl, Great Spotted Woodpecker, Sparrowhawk and Mistle Thrush, whilst Hawfinch, Nuthatch and Wood Warbler have all been recorded in the past.

PARK WOOD *NZ595168*

An area of mixed woodland with various coniferous trees being randomly set in deciduous woodland, although the western end has fairly recently been planted with regimented rows of conifers. The wood is north of the A171 road within a mile of
Guisborough and is crossed by various public footpaths. There are sufficient mature
conifers for the wood to hold Crossbill, Siskin, Goldcrest and Coal Tit in winter, the last
two species later breeding. It also supports breeding Sparrowhawk, Tawny Owl, Great
Spotted Woodpecker, Jay and most of the common warblers. Park Wood is one of the
best areas to see Woodcock, especially in the winter months, and Green Woodpecker has
also been observed in some years.

PINCHINTHORPE RAILWAY LINE *NZ572153*

This section of the old railway track between Pinchinthorpe and Nunthorpe has been
developed as a walkway by the local authority, with access from the car park and visitor centre at the Pinchinthorpe end. It passes alongside farmland, stands of woodland
and areas of scrubby hedgerows. Some of the woods flood in wet weather and there is a
small pond at the east end where Jack Snipe has been seen. The walkway is a good location for Goldfinch, Whitethroat, Lesser Whitethroat, Great Spotted Woodpecker and
Sparrowhawk.

POOLE HOSPITAL *NZ534134*

A fairly small area of parkland, with a few ornamental trees and a pond, situated half
a mile to the south of Nunthorpe. The hospital no longer exists as such, but away
from the buildings the area is quite peaceful, despite the close proximity of houses and
the pond being fished on a regular basis. Regular breeding birds include Great Spotted
Woodpecker, Jay, Bullfinch, Willow Tit, Goldcrest, Tawny Owl and Coot. Other species
that breed occasionally include Lesser Spotted Woodpecker, Heron, Canada Goose,
Sparrowhawk, Herring Gull (on the buildings) and Chiffchaff. The area is quite interesting in winter with a regular flock of Lesser Redpoll and Siskin in the alders around the
pond and occasional records of Nuthatch, Kingfisher, Water Rail, Tufted Duck and
Hawfinch. At times quite large winter roosts of Greenfinch, Brambling and thrushes
have built up here, the ringing of which has provided numerous recoveries for these
species. Relatively few passage birds are seen in this area, although Yellow Wagtail,
hirundines and warblers have been noted in spring.

PORTRACK MARSH NZ465195

Situated between the north bank of the Tees and Portrack Industrial Estate, only a small percentage of the original marshes now remains, but it is still an interesting area. Tipping of refuse on to the area ceased in about 1993, a sewage treatment plant was built soon after and the nearby incinerator was shut down in 1998. A large pool was created in 1999 by Tees Valley Wildlife Trust and part of the area now forms one of its nature reserves. Parking and bus stops are available at the nearby Tees Barrage. Nearly all of the low-lying ground floods in winter and is attractive to ducks, with hundreds of Teal being seen in some years, as well as a few Gadwall, Wigeon, Tufted Duck, Pochard and Coot. Reasonable numbers of Snipe and a few Jack Snipe are winter visitors. Up to seven Short-eared Owls have been noted as well as the occasional Shoveler, Pintail and geese. Breeding birds include Coot, Mallard, Pheasant, Reed Bunting, Sedge and Reed Warblers and probably Snipe, Yellow Wagtail, Redshank and Red-legged Partridge. Migrant waders are quite regularly seen in spring and autumn, including Greenshank, Ruff, Green, Wood and Common Sandpipers. In winter it is possible to see up to 20 roosting herons.

PRESTON PARK NZ430158

A medium-sized public park on the west bank of the River Tees at the north end of Eaglescliffe with a museum and a small collection of pinioned ducks. There are relatively few mature trees in the area, although birds like Bullfinch, Nuthatch, Lesser Redpoll, Treecreeper, Goldcrest, Great Spotted Woodpecker and Blackcap occur regularly and some certainly breed. A walk along the river bank will reveal species such as Sand Martin (the biggest Cleveland colony in the 1990s), Grey Wagtail, Heron, Goosander and Common Sandpiper at relevant times of the year and in recent winters up to 63 Cormorant have roosted in the trees just downstream from the park.

RECLAMATION POND NZ520232

For many years this was the largest area of mud north of the river after Seal Sands, but since 1999 it has become the biggest freshwater pond in Stockton Borough. However, the long term future of this site is uncertain. The Reclamation Pond is 100 metres east of Dormans Pool. Access is via the same North Tees road as Dormans Pool and requires a permit from the Teesmouth Bird Club. When mud is visible, quite large numbers of waders congregate, particularly when the tide covers Seal Sands and especially in July to October. Relatively large numbers of Redshank, Dunlin, Lapwing, Grey

Plover and Shelduck can be seen sometimes, as well as reasonable numbers of passage waders like Greenshank, Ruff, Curlew Sandpiper and Little Stint. Since it has remained flooded, large numbers of Little and Great Crested Grebes, Gadwall, Shoveler, Smew, Ruddy Duck and Coot have been recorded. Occasionally this area is completely devoid of birds, whilst at other times it can be the most exciting part of Teesmouth.

REDCAR BEACH & ROCKS *NZ595260-NZ625250*

This stretch of beach from Redcar to Marske is considered by many to be the finest in Cleveland, but because of this, parts of it are subject to disturbance, especially in summer. The months between September and April are the best time to visit the area and sometimes large numbers of birds can be seen. When the beach and rocks are uncovered by the tide, many gulls rest here and there are quite regular sightings of Glaucous, Iceland, Mediterranean and Little Gulls. When undisturbed, parts of the beach are used as a wader roost, in particular by Sanderling, Knot, Oystercatcher and Ringed Plover. All four species feed in the area as well as Turnstone, Redshank and Purple Sandpiper when the tide is low or receding. Passerines regularly seen include Snow Bunting and Pied Wagtail in winter, with irregular sightings of Shore Lark, Twite and Rock Pipit. A small colony of Sand Martins has existed since about 1999. The sea off this stretch of beach can be very interesting during the winter months with annual sightings of all 3 divers, Eider, Long-tailed Duck, Common and Velvet Scoters, Red-breasted Merganser and the occasional Grey Phalarope, Scaup, Goosander and rarer grebes. Quite large numbers of skuas, auks and shearwaters pass along the coast at times, and can be seen here almost as well as from Hartlepool or South Gare.

REDCAR STRAY AND COASTAL FIELDS
NZ626234

Being adjacent to the sea, these fields between Redcar and Marske can be very interesting at certain times of the year. In the autumn and winter many Lapwing, Golden Plover, Skylark and gulls feed and rest here and at times high numbers of Lapland, Snow and Corn Buntings, Ruff and Linnets have been seen. Relatively little of interest breeds at this location, apart from a few pairs of Grey Partridge. At certain times of the year there are small areas of long grass and tall vegetation which prove attractive to passage migrants such as Willow Warbler, Redstart and Short-eared Owl. The high numbers of passerines frequently attract a Merlin or Sparrowhawk. This locality can be viewed from public rights of way.

RIVER TEES *NZ367104-NZ550280*

Stretching from just west of Yarm to the sea, this is the largest single area of water in Cleveland. A meandering section of the river between Newport and Stockton was replaced by a straight cut in the 19th century. Both the adjoining areas have been radically altered so that relatively little of the old course can be seen. Parts of the river have been dredged and widened at various times, with the construction of wharves, to give better access for shipping. Dredging still takes place on a regular basis between Teesport and the river mouth. Birds to be seen here vary considerably. The upper stretches of water in the Yarm-Eaglescliffe area attract birds like Goosander, Grey Wagtail, Kingfisher and Moorhen, while Sand Martins nest on the riverside in one or two places. In the Newport - Portrack area, mud is visible at low tide and this proves attractive to Redshank and Black-headed Gull. There is another stretch of mud adjacent to the former Hargreaves Quarry area, which sometimes holds hundreds of Shelduck, with a few Teal, Mallard, Redshank and Curlew. When large numbers of gulls are present in the estuary, many feed as far upstream as Haverton Hill. When the local freshwater is frozen over Coot have been known to feed close to the Transporter Bridge. Cormorant can be seen almost anywhere on the river, but mainly around the mouth and in the Preston Park-Yarm area. The Tees Barrage was erected across the river near Portrack Marsh in 1992/93 resulting in the river upstream becoming more like a lake. A semi-resident herd of Mute Swans has been around Thornaby Bridge since about 1995, with up to 75 being seen. Rarer species observed include Shag, Scaup, Osprey, Ring-billed Gull and Yellow-legged Gull. The summer is a good time to watch the Common Terns feeding on the river immediately below the Barrage.

ROPNER PARK *NZ433183*

A medium-sized park in south-west Stockton which has a pond and islands with a good number of mature trees. The pond is home to some farmyard-type ducks and Mallard. Species such as Heron, Red-breasted Merganser, Goosander, Little Grebe and Kingfisher are occasionally seen. The park is visited by regular woodland birds such as Great Spotted Woodpecker, Treecreeper, Chiffchaff, Bullfinch and Nuthatch.

ROSEBERRY TOPPING *NZ578126*

This landmark can be seen from many parts of Cleveland with spectacular views from the top; parts of the North York Moors, Pennines and Tyneside are visible on a clear day. The rock face itself holds a few pairs of Jackdaw and Fulmar and the surrounding bracken and rough ground are used by Meadow Pipits. In spring, passage migrants like Whinchat, Wheatear and Ring Ouzel are quite regularly seen and all three probably breed fairly close to the area.

ROSSMERE PARK NZ502299

A park beside Stockton Road in Hartlepool, which has a limited number of trees and a small lake with an island. In 1959 assorted pinioned ducks were introduced to this water, including Pintail, Tufted Duck and Red-crested Pochard and throughout the 1960s both Tufted Duck and Red-crested Pochard reared many broods of young, which were left to fly free and were regularly seen moving to Ward Jackson Park in Hartlepool. Virtually all of these ducks had disappeared by the early 1970s leaving several dozen Mallard, with occasional views of Scaup, Kingfisher and Blackcap and a regular winter roost of Little Egrets.

SALTBURN GILL NZ674206

A small wooded valley immediately to the east of Saltburn Woods, which is owned and managed by Tees Valley Wildlife Trust. A small stream runs through the valley to join the larger beck in Saltburn Woods just before the latter runs out on to the beach and into the sea. The stream is wide enough for breeding Grey Wagtail, but not Dipper, and the surrounding woodland supports breeding Sparrowhawk, Tawny Owl, Great Spotted Woodpecker, Marsh Tit, Chiffchaff, Lesser Whitethroat and Blackcap. Both Siskin and Lesser Redpoll have been seen and heard singing in spring in recent years. Birds in winter are as might be expected with flocks of assorted tits, Jay and Bullfinch. Both Goshawk and Buzzard have been reported here in recent years.

SALTBURN WOODS NZ664202

A very steep-sided valley on the eastern edge of Saltburn, which has a wide beck running through it and many mature deciduous trees. The seaward end has a miniature railway and ornamental gardens, but further inland the woodland is much more natural and better for birds. The stream itself is ideal for Dipper and Grey Wagtail, at least two pairs of each species breeding here and regularly being seen downstream almost to the high tide line. Most of the other regular woodland species breed here, including Jay, Great Spotted Woodpecker, Bullfinch, Tawny Owl, Nuthatch, Marsh Tit, Blackcap and Spotted Flycatcher. There is public access by a footpath on the southern side of the wood.

SALTERGILL WOODS NZ412103

Asmall secluded area of woodland with a stream running through it, near Kirklevington in the south-west corner of Cleveland. The former county boundary passes along the western edge of the woodland and the stream has been partly dammed to create a small lake adjacent to the Tall Trees Hotel at Yarm. Both Kingfisher and Grey Wagtail frequent the stream at times, but may not breed here every year. Wood Warbler was a regular breeding species, although usually only one pair. Woodland birds such as Chiffchaff, Jay, Bullfinch, Blackcap and Garden Warbler may all be found. Lesser Spotted Woodpecker and Hawfinch have both been known to attempt breeding in the past and may do so in the future.

SALTHOLME POOLS NZ506227

Recently acquired by Teesside Environmental Trust for the RSPB's Saltholme Nature Reserve, these pools and fields beside the A178 road north of Port Clarence are as well-watched as Dormans Pool and frequently just as exciting. There is deeper water here, consequently more diving duck use these pools and at times a large percentage of Teesmouth's wintering Wigeon and Teal feed around the water's edge. The area is as good as any at Teesmouth for wild swans and geese. In 2003-06 extensive marsh and pond creation work was carried out between Saltholme Pools and Haverton Hole. When all the proposed work is finished in 2008, it will have created a huge area of marsh and ponds. Water levels in the ponds and fields vary, creating muddy areas that are attractive to birds. The site is well-used by Redshank, Ruff, Curlew and Lapwing and, when mud is visible, by Dunlin, Ringed Plover, Turnstone and the normal passage waders such as Common, Green, Wood and Curlew Sandpipers, Little Stint, Little Ringed Plover, Spotted Redshank, Greenshank and Black-tailed Godwit. Since about 2002, a Peregrine has hunted this area throughout each winter, no doubt attracted by the huge numbers of potential prey species. The area has one of the best rarity lists, partly the result of intense watching throughout the year. Species seen include rarer ducks, grebes and waders. Access is limited at present but the RSPB expect to have the reserve and a visitor centre open in 2009.

SCALING DAM NZ742123

This is the largest reservoir in Cleveland, although only the western part is in the former county. The south-west corner is a nature reserve, but the remainder of the reservoir is quite heavily fished and can at times have large numbers of yachts on it. In the winter many Mallard, Wigeon and Coot feed here, with some diving duck and occasionally wild swans and geese. The hide overlooking the reserve used to be the best place in Cleveland in winter to see Hen Harrier. Other birds of prey, such as Merlin, Peregrine, and Short-eared Owl occasionally feed in the area. Osprey is an annual visitor principally in August. Breeding birds include Great Crested Grebe, Tufted Duck and Greylag Goose and at times, Little Grebe, Teal, Little Ringed Plover and Black-headed Gull. Depending on the water level, spring and autumn passages bring waders, such as Greenshank, Ruff, Little Stint and occasionally Little Gull and various terns.

SEAL SANDS NZ530260 *

The present area of mudflats situated between the Brinefields and Hartlepool Power Station represents only about 10% of the tidal mudflats that originally existed at Teesmouth. It is the only stretch of mudflats of any size between Lindisfarne and the Humber. Durham University has spent much time observing and ringing birds in this area, principally waders and Shelduck, and these studies have confirmed that Seal Sands is an essential feeding stage for many waders. This status has resulted in it being designated as part of the National Nature Reserve. The car park is situated off the A178 road and a footpath leads along Greatham Creek to the hides. Between July and April, thousands of waders can be seen feeding here, including species such as Redshank, Knot, Dunlin, Grey Plover, Curlew and Bar-tailed Godwit, with a variable percentage of them roosting in the same area at high tide. Dabbling ducks such as Shelduck, Wigeon, Teal and Mallard regularly use the area in the winter months and diving ducks such as Scaup, Tufted Duck, Goldeneye and Pochard sometimes winter in large numbers close to one of the Seal Sands hides. A few Brent Geese and Long-tailed Duck are usual, as well as a regular Peregrine and Merlin.

SEATON CAREW CHURCHYARD NZ525297

A small churchyard containing around 100-120 mature trees, situated about 200 metres inland of the road through Seaton Carew and close enough to the sea to attract some migrants in spring and autumn. It is too small to hold any significant breeding birds, but in the migration seasons is regularly visited by the commoner migrants, such as Redstart, Pied and Spotted Flycatchers, thrushes, Woodcock, Goldcrest, Sparrowhawk and various warblers.

SEATON COMMON *NZ528283*

An area of flat grazing land just inland of North Gare and the river mouth, and immediately to the south of Seaton Carew. The grass is generally kept very short and sections of it flood and become muddy at times which in turn attracts waders such as Curlew, Lapwing, Dunlin, Golden Plover, Turnstone, Snipe and Redshank. In the winter it is not unusual for numbers of Wigeon, Teal and Mallard to use the area and some geese, generally Brent, are seen in most winters. A few Lapland Bunting are quite frequently present on the Common in the winter months, although they can be difficult to see. Summer visitors such as Wheatear, Yellow Wagtail and pipits regularly feed on the open grassland when they are passing through in spring and autumn. Other birds recorded in recent years include Peregrine, Garganey, Whimbrel, Pale-bellied Brent Goose, Stonechat, Ring Ouzel, Shag, Hooded Crow, Water Pipit, Hen Harrier, Pectoral Sandpiper and Water Rail.

SEATON SANDS *NZ536289*

A pleasant stretch of beach between Seaton Carew and North Gare, which attracts quite large numbers of gulls and terns in autumn, and Sanderling in winter. On fine sunny days many people often visit this beach and limited bird life is evident. At very high tides, little beach is left exposed, but at low tides an enormous stretch of sand is visible as well as some rocks at the north end. Waders such as Sanderling, Ringed Plover and Turnstone feed on the beach and occasionally gulls and terns use the area as an evening roost, especially at low tide in autumn. A flock of Snow Buntings sometimes winters in the area, moving between this beach, North Gare and the golf course.

SKINNINGROVE *NZ713200*

A large, fairly steep-sided valley mid-way between Hunt Cliff and Boulby Cliffs with the stream from Kilton Woods running through to the sea. There are trees and assorted bushes, principally on the west side which undoubtedly attract migrants in both spring and autumn. The beach close to the village of Skinningrove is small but Cattersty Sands close by is used as a gull roost on occasions. Good numbers of Whitethroat nest in the valley sides and Grey Wagtail and Dipper may do so upstream of the village. Varying numbers of gulls feed offshore and unusual species such as Glaucous, Iceland, Mediterranean and Little Gulls have been recorded. The sea defences between the river mouth and jetty are often visited in autumn and winter by Stonechat and Black Redstart.

SOUTH GARE *NZ556277* *

Constructed in the 1880s to protect the mouth of the River Tees, this slag and concrete peninsula is worth looking around at any time of the year. Access is via the coast road to the west of Redcar, past the entrance to Coatham Marsh. Beside the lighthouse some shelter can be gained during sea watching, though it is generally not as productive as Hartlepool observatory. At low tide a large area of rock is exposed, principally to the east of the Gare and this is used as a feeding area by Turnstone, Oystercatcher and Purple Sandpiper, and as a resting area by Cormorant and gulls. The waters around the Gare are the only place in Cleveland where Eider can be almost guaranteed at any time of the year. They are also quite good for other sea duck, divers and occasional grebes generally during the months October to April. The areas of land beside the access road to the Gare can be very popular for migrants in spring and autumn. There are relatively few bushes and small trees, consequently those that do thrive act as magnets to the warblers and flycatchers. The open areas attract various species, including Wheatear, Whinchat and pipits. Sea watching can be very good at times, given suitable weather conditions. Compared to Hartlepool headland, South Gare usually records higher daily counts of skuas and ducks, but lower counts of shearwaters, petrels, and auks, when these species are 'on the move'. The reasons for such variation in numbers is not immediately apparent, though the fact that the observer at South Gare is exposed to the elements, slightly nearer to sea-level and not so far out to sea as the Hartlepool observer all contribute to the number of birds seen. Also, the skuas and ducks sometimes tend to congregate in the bay off Seaton Carew when heading north, having passed South Gare, and before reaching Hartlepool. The list of rare birds seen here is quite spectacular, including Britain's second Cliff Swallow.

STEWART PARK *NZ516162*

A large park situated alongside Marton Road in Middlesbrough. The Captain Cook Museum attracts the public, as do two small lakes with the assorted tame and pinioned wildfowl. These have included pairs of Black Swan, Barnacle Goose, Shelduck, Chinese Swan Goose, Tufted Duck, Pochard, Pintail, Mandarin, Wood Duck, Muscovy Duck and farmyard-type geese. At least one Mandarin, one Barnacle Goose and very nearly all of 100-150 Mallard are, or have been, free-flying at one time or another. There is also an enclosed series of aviaries which have held various ornamental species. The woodland is very attractive, with a wide variety of trees, including a superb example of Cedar of Lebanon and other assorted conifers. Typical woodland birds can be seen here, including Great Spotted Woodpecker, Jay, Spotted Flycatcher and Sparrowhawk. Species such as Hawfinch, Nuthatch, Siskin, Crossbill, Brambling and Blackcap have all been observed in recent winters. Spring and autumn passage migrants occasionally appear, including Wryneck and Bluethroat, and the former may have bred here in the distant past.

THE MOORLAND *NZ590127-NZ747113*

All of the genuine open heather moorland in Cleveland is in the narrow strip in the south-east corner of the former county. It stretches 17km from Roseberry Topping in the west to Scaling Dam in the east and incorporates Roseberry Common, Newton Moor, Guisborough Moor, Stanghow Moor, Sleddale, Moorsholm Moor, Gerrick Moor, Liverton Moor, Waupley Moor and Easington High Moor. This is all private land and most, if not all, is watched over by gamekeepers, but there are numerous footpaths and areas of open access. Red Grouse and Meadow Pipit breed over the whole area, plus smaller numbers of Curlew, Golden Plover, Cuckoo, Snipe and Whinchat and some of the rarest breeding birds in Cleveland such as Ring Ouzel, Merlin, Short-eared Owl and Wheatear. There was a Black-headed Gull colony in the extreme south-east corner on Easington High Moor and there is another on Stanghow Moor. Stonechat has nested on the eastern half of the moorlands since 2002. In the winter months Hen Harriers can usually be seen and Peregrine, Merlin and Short-eared Owl are fairly regular. There may be an area within the moorland (yet to be discovered) where Dotterel regularly rest for a day or two on spring passage.

WARREN WOOD *NZ740155*

Warren Wood forms an accessible part of the Grinkle Park estate, south of Loftus. The conifers here are in various stages of development from recently-planted to mature, and as such hold varied and distinctive bird populations. The recently planted areas held a pair of Nightjars in the 1980s and the mature trees have attracted Crossbills. Semi-mature areas hold breeding Whitethroat, Bullfinch, Willow Warbler and Woodcock, whilst both Tawny and Long-eared Owl may nest in some years. Red-legged Partridge and Quail have been recorded in the neighbouring fields in recent summers. Access can be gained along public roads and rights of way.

WEST VIEW CEMETERY *NZ496350*

A medium-sized cemetery at the north end of Hartlepool with a good number of fairly mature trees, situated about one kilometre from the sea. It attracts migrants in spring and autumn, all of the commoner birds such as Redstart, Blackcap, Redwing, Fieldfare, Goldcrest and Whinchat being seen here. Two other cemeteries close to the coast are also known to attract migrants (Seaton Carew and Redcar Lane); perhaps the other 15-20 cemeteries in Cleveland would repay regular watching.

WESTWORTH WOOD *NZ634137*

The majority of this woodland comprises open, well-spaced mature conifers. It has a very small reservoir at the south-east corner, as well as a few alder and hazel trees. The reservoir has held nothing more interesting than Common Sandpiper and Teal though it is almost never visited by birdwatchers. The woodland supports the usual species found in this type of habitat including large numbers of Chaffinch, Coal Tit and Goldcrest, plus Crossbill, Siskin, Lesser Redpoll, Sparrowhawk and Long-eared Owl in some years. Access is by walking along Butt Lane on the eastern edge of Guisborough and through the forest, although a map is essential to avoid getting lost in the woodland.

WILTON WOODS *NZ580190*

This is one of the largest areas of near-natural woodland in Cleveland and incorporates Lazenby Bank, Wilton Castle and village and Yearby Woods; a distance of about 4km. Access is quite easy, with footpaths through the woodland from Eston, Lazenby, Wilton Village and Yearby, but the area remains relatively peaceful and undisturbed. Breeding birds include all of the expected local woodland species, as well as Green Woodpecker and probably Redstart, Wood Warbler, and Hawfinch in some years.

WYNYARD *NZ420260*

This is a large estate, almost entirely in private ownership, to the north west of Wolviston which is about half agricultural and half woodland. There are no public footpaths in the area and access is by driving though the new Wynyard housing estate. A lot of the woodland is mature deciduous, but there are several quite large areas of regimented conifers, together with a lake and several small ponds. Construction of a sizeable housing estate, golf course and small industrial park has reduced the value of the area to birds. Just about every woodland species found in Cleveland has been seen at Wynyard, including Nuthatch, Buzzard, Green Woodpecker and Jay regularly and Lesser Spotted

Woodpecker, Hawfinch, Crossbill and Wood Warbler more occasionally. There has been a small heronry in the area since the 1970s, no more than about 20 pairs having been noted. The lake attracts breeding Great Crested Grebe, and almost all the usual species of duck have been seen here, as well as Goosander, Gadwall, Smew and Ruddy Duck.

WYNYARD WOODLAND PARK
(CASTLE EDEN WALKWAY) *NZ403242 – 404284*

This local authority country park is based on a four-kilometre section of disused railway line running approximately south to north between Thorpe Thewles and Wynyard Station (in Co Durham) with adjacent woodland and scrub. Footpaths have been improved and some conservation management undertaken for the benefit of the natural environment. Breeding birds include most of the typical woodland species such as Bullfinch, Great Spotted Woodpecker, all six species of tit, Jay, Cuckoo, Tree Pipit, Blackcap, Willow Warbler, Whitethroat and Sparrowhawk. Both Crossbill and Turtle Dove have nested, but may not do so annually. In winter the many hawthorns support winter thrushes as well as parties of tits, Tree Sparrows, Yellowhammer, Siskin, and Brambling. Red-legged Partridge are frequently seen and Quail occasionally call in nearby fields.

SPECIES LIST

MUTE SWAN *Cygnus olor*

This bird is widespread but not common, up to about 120-150 birds being present in Cleveland during the year, most of which can be found on the Tees Marshes and the River Tees at Stockton. About 20-25 pairs have nested since 2000, and about 50 cygnets being reared each year. Both the number of breeding pairs and number of cygnets reared has been slowly increasing since 1985.

Between 1978 and 1985, no cygnets were reared, although a few pairs laid eggs and hatched young, but the use of lead shot by fishermen probably killed many cygnets, as the birds ingested the shot from the bottom of their ponds. The banning of lead as weights in the 1980s has certainly been a factor in the recovery, at least locally, of this majestic bird. At the present time overhead power lines are probably the main cause of mortality.

Prior to 1978, a pair or two reared cygnets at Teesmouth, and Poole Hospital held a pair of Mute Swans at least into the 1950s, but they probably succumbed to intensive pressure from angling. In 1985, 1986 and 1987, two broods of cygnets were reared by pairs on Haverton Hole and Coatham Marsh. In 1988, nine pairs built nests in the area and four of these reared young. Since 1998 the number of breeding pairs has continued to increase. Interesting records include the Charlton's Pond pair that reared 10 cygnets in 1991 and a white cygnet, known as a 'Polish' Swan was reared on Ropner Park lake, Stockton in 2002.

There is generally an influx of birds to the marshes of Teesmouth in the summer months, the highest count being 98 in August 2003, including the resident breeding birds. Birds are occasionally seen passing along the coast and spending some time on the inland reservoirs, such as Scaling Dam, New Marske Reservoir and Crookfoot Reservoir.

With the Mute Swan being such a large and conspicuous bird, dead individuals are noticed and easy to find; consequently, there are a relatively high number of ringing recoveries. These include three ringed in Ward Jackson Park, Hartlepool, in 1961 and 1962 which moved north to Loch Leven in Kinross, Scotland, then to Druridge Bay in Northumberland and finally to Gateshead, Tyne and Wear. One bird survived until at least January 1974, thus being 13 years old. The two long-distance records concern a second year bird ringed at Boizenburg, Schwein, in eastern Germany in February 1977 and found dead at Teesmouth in January 1979 and a one year old female ringed at Loch of Strathbeg, Aberdeen, Scotland, on 30 July 1983 which hatched five young at Haverton Hole in 1985 and three young there in 1987.

In January 1986 about 200 Mute Swans were oiled at Berwick-on-Tweed, Northumberland, more than half of which died but the rest were ringed and released in March 1986. Of these birds, two were seen at Teesmouth in May 1987, one being seen in February - March 1988 and a third one in February 1988. One of the original two was at Charlton's Pond early in 1989 where it was found dead on 7 April.

Since 1989, there has been a group of ringers working on the Mute Swans in north east England which has resulted in about 80-90% of the birds in Cleveland bearing rings. This has shown that there is a regular movement of birds between Northumberland, Tyne & Wear and Cleveland, and to a lesser extent to southern Scotland and Yorkshire/Humberside. Other records of colour-ringed birds include three juveniles ringed in Cumbria in 1992 that were recorded at South Gare in February 1993, a juvenile ringed at Scarborough, North Yorkshire, in January 1993 that hit wires at South Gare in March 1993, an adult ringed at Billingham in November 1993 was found at Welney, Norfolk, in February 1994 and a cygnet ringed on Hemlington Lake in July 2002 was at Llandrindod, Wales, on 7 January 2004.

In late 1993, the newly-formed ponds at Belasis Technology Park, Billingham, attracted a sizeable gathering with 58 being the maximum. This site seemed to lose its appeal to swans in 1997, when large numbers appeared on the River Tees at Stockton, just downstream of Victoria Bridge almost certainly as a result of improved water quality following the construction of the Tees Barrage. The maximum count at Stockton is 75, and is greatly supported by bread provided by an interested public.

BEWICK'S SWAN (TUNDRA SWAN) *Cygnus columbianus*

This is the rarest of the three swans to occur in Cleveland, most records being in the months November to February. Prior to 1954, there were only two records. Since then records increased fairly rapidly, with the species being seen in every year from 1967 to 1998, with an average of 25 birds per year between 1974 and 1993. Between 1994 and 2003 it has averaged three birds per year, though none was seen in 1999 and 2001, and only one in 1996, 1997, 2000 and 2004.

This swan is strictly a winter visitor with earliest and latest dates of 11 October (2004) and 18 April (1954) respectively, although it is not seen at the beginning of every year. The largest herds seen have been 33 on Saltholme Pool from 25 March to 3 April 1960, 49 over Hartlepool Docks on 18 January 1972 and 54 on Scaling Dam on 26 February 1982.

Almost all of the sightings emanate from the marshes on the north side of the Tees with Saltholme Pools and Dormans Pool being favoured sites for Bewick's Swan. A small herd has been known to spend a few weeks around this area in November and December, but the record is held by a flock of five birds that arrived on 12 November 1974 and remained until 16 March 1975, a total of 125 days.

The inland waters such as Scaling Dam and Crookfoot Reservoir occasionally hold birds for a day or two but very rarely any longer. There are also a few records for Charlton's Pond, Hart Reservoir, Longnewton Reservoir and some other inland waters. Occasionally birds are also seen moving over the sea.

WHOOPER SWAN *Cygnus cygnus*

This, the larger of the two wintering swans, is more inclined to spend the winter in Cleveland, albeit in very small numbers. The first birds are usually seen in October and about 20-40 are often recorded in October and November with most birds passing straight through. However, a few usually spend several weeks or months in the area, the North Tees Marshes and associated fields being a favourite locality. There is sometimes an influx of birds in mid-March, and the last birds have usually left by mid-April, although an adult summered around Greatham Creek and Seal Sands in 1983, being present from 24 April to 21 August. The earliest and latest dates are 26 September (1995) and 25 May (1999) with the exception of the aforementioned summering bird and the highest count is an historic record of a herd of about 1,000 that flew over Teesmouth in the winter of 1880. In recent times, the highest count is 47 on Crookfoot Reservoir on 21 March 1961, although at least 100 passed through Cleveland in small groups in October and November 2003.

About 50% of the records are of birds seen on or over the Tees Marshes: other waters to hold birds include Scaling Dam, Lockwood Beck, Margrove Ponds, Crookfoot Reservoir, Lovell Hill, Longnewton Reservoir, Charlton's Pond and Cowpen Bewley Pond, although birds do occasionally feed in fields well away from water. Whooper Swans are rarely seen on the sea, but 10 were recorded off Redcar on 9 March 1980, six settled in Hartlepool Fish Quay on 1 January 1982 and 11 were off Hartlepool North Sands on 27 October 2004.

An indication of the origin of the birds seen in Cleveland is given by an adult on Saltholme Pools in late October 1991 that had been ringed as a cygnet in Iceland in July

1988. The same bird was also seen in Cork, Eire in February 1989, Cumbria in January 1990, Martin Mere, Lancashire, in the 1990/91 winter and was back in Iceland in April 1991.

A pinioned pair of adults was placed on Ropner Park Lake, Stockton in December 1990; they reared one young in 1991, but an adult died in the same year, and none were there in 1992.

A tame juvenile on Wilton Centre Lake in late December 1992 had been reared at Studley Park, North Yorkshire and was present at Teesmouth as an adult, until it was found dead in May 1998.

BEAN GOOSE *Anser fabalis*

Prior to 1978, this goose was the rarest of the seven regular species of geese that are seen in Britain, and had only been recorded in Cleveland in six of the previous 100 years. However, it is possible that it has occurred more often than these records suggest, since identification of grey geese can be quite difficult. There are two records for the 19th century, one shot out of 15 at Redcar in early 1879 and another shot at Marske on 17 November 1887. The next record is of 30 (one shot) by Greatham Creek in December 1954, followed by one at Saltburn on 1 January 1961 and a gaggle of seven around Cowpen Marsh on 8 February 1970 which decreased to five by the time they were last seen on 15 March 1970. A gaggle of 13 grey geese on Cowpen Marsh from 3 to 9 November 1976 proved on examination to be eight Greylags, two Pinkfeet and three Bean Geese, showing that care must be exercised in identification of groups of geese.

From 1978 onwards, this goose has become a reasonably regular visitor, being recorded in 20 out of the last 30 years, there being two on Seaton Common in February 1978 and an exceptional influx in January - February 1979, with 11 around Coatham from 2 to 5 January, 10 at Crookfoot Reservoir on 11 February, 22 near Skelton on 19-20 February and then 53 near New Marske on 24-25 February, this being the highest number of Bean Geese ever seen in Cleveland. Up to 41 were still present in the same fields on 4 March and five were on Seal Sands on 28 February.

Records since then are of one - two birds on Crookfoot Reservoir from 17 October to 4 November 1981, 11 near Hilton on 22 December 1981, 16-17 on Scaling Dam from 24 to 31 January 1982, 10 on Scaling Dam on 5 March 1982, but no more than eight birds since then, most records being from Crookfoot Reservoir, Scaling Dam and the North Tees Marshes.

Most birds occur between the last week of December and first week of March although the earliest and latest are 17 October (1981) and 17 April (1994), apart from one on the Reclamation Pond from 18 June to 2 July 1993.

Two races of Bean Goose occur in Britain, *A.f.serrirostris* (Tundra Bean Goose) and *A.f.fabalis* (Taiga Bean Goose), and, whilst it is not possible to determine the race on all records, both races seem to occur with roughly equal frequency in Cleveland.

PINK-FOOTED GOOSE *Anser brachyrhynchus*

Up to the early 1960s, this goose was a very regular passage bird over the Cleveland area in September-October, frequently numbering hundreds per year. Historically, grey geese were seen in their thousands over the Tees Marshes in the 1800s, the majority being Pink-footed Geese judging by the birds that were shot. Peak passage appears to have been in the last four months of the year, the return in the spring being far less noticeable.

Between the 1960s and 1986, Pink-footed Geese had become so unusual that rarely were skeins of more than 20 seen and in some years no more than 5-10 birds were recorded in total. After this time peak Pink-footed Goose numbers again increased:

Date	Over Location	Numbers
28 October 1976	Hartlepool	10
8 December 1979	Teesmouth	99
20 November 1986	Eston Moor	240
20 November 1986	Redcar	83
30 September 1987	Dormans Pool	80
23 October 1987	Billingham	110
27 October 1988	Hartlepool	120
15 October 1989	Nunthorpe	275
12 December 1992	Saltburn	340
14 November 1993	Hartlepool	542
30 November 1997	Cleveland	350-400
20 October 1998	Cleveland	1,600
Pink-footed Geese Peak Numbers		

At least 3,000-4,000 have flown south every autumn since 1999. An estimated 8,000 passed over Cleveland between mid-September and late November 2004. Passage generally extends from mid-September to mid-December and it is not unusual to hear skeins of Pink-footed Geese flying over at night in these periods. Also, a few skeins have recently been seen in the months January-March, presumably as the birds begin to return north. The large numbers noted each autumn since 1986 would seem to indicate a return to the abundance of the 1950s and 1960s. There are also a few records in April and one or two in the months May-August.

The majority of records come from the North Tees Marshes though both Wynyard and Crookfoot Reservoir regularly attract this species. Up to 119 Pink-footed Geese were at the latter water in February 2003. There are also frequent records of birds on Scaling Dam, and to a lesser extent on many of the fields around Cleveland.

About 12 pinioned birds have been kept on a pond by Guisborough Priory since the 1980s. A tame bird in Locke Park, Redcar, in May 1998 was ringed at Pensthorpe Waterfowl Park, Norfolk, in February 1997.

(GREATER) WHITE-FRONTED GOOSE
Anser albifrons

L ike Bean Goose, this is amongst the rarest of the seven regular species of geese occurring in Cleveland. It has never been numerous, being described as 'not uncommon in winter, but not in any large numbers' in the 19th century (Nelson 1907) and was first recorded in the 20th century in February 1954. Since then White-fronted Geese have been recorded in three of the years up to 1970 and virtually every year since 1971.

Nearly 60% of the records concern birds seen around Teesmouth, principally Dormans Pool, with several records of birds on Scaling Dam, Crookfoot Reservoir and Wynyard. Also a few birds have been noted in fields at Portrack, Marske and Saltburn in recent years.

Most of the records are of small numbers, between one to six birds being normal, but 31 were on Scaling Dam on 11 October 1959, 25 of which stayed for a week, 24 flew over Cowpen Marsh on 2 March 1978, 19 were on Cowpen Marsh on 29 January 1984, up to 55 were on Saltholme Pools in early December 1987, 69 were on Cowpen Marsh from 16 February to 3 March 1993 and an influx in January-February 1996 produced 26 at Scaling Dam, 26 at Kirkleatham, 42 at Crookfoot Reservoir and 38 at Redcar.

The majority of records concern the European race *A.a.albifrons*, but the Greenland race *A.a.flavirostris* is noted occasionally. Most of the records fall between mid-November and early March, January being the peak month; the earliest and latest dates are 11 October (1959) and 12 May (1982) apart from three July records of singles in 1974, 1979 and 1989.

GREYLAG GOOSE *Anser anser*

In the 19th century, this goose was a regular winter visitor in small numbers, although always being heavily outnumbered by Pink-footed Geese (Nelson 1907). Now, having bred in the area since about 1970, it is present throughout the year in good numbers, with approximately 70-80 breeding pairs, and generally outnumbers all the other geese species combined.

Wynyard used to hold the majority of the breeding birds with up to five-six pairs in most years to about 1990, but has now been overtaken by Scaling Dam with up to 35 pairs since 1985 and Saltholme Pools and Dormans Pool with about 15 pairs since 1993. In addition, single pairs have bred on Crookfoot Reservoir in some years from 1978, Cowpen Bewley Pond occasionally since 1987 and Lockwood Beck from 1992.

There is a wintering population that regularly commutes between Wynyard, Crookfoot Reservoir and Hurworth Burn in County Durham and can be found in almost any of the myriad of suitable fields around this area. As such they can be very difficult to find.

The number of birds at Scaling Dam has increased significantly since the late 1980s, 85 being seen in August 1989, up to 103 in 1994 and 1995, 168 in 1997, 212 in 1999, 335 in 2000, 397 in 2003, 560 in 2005 and 666 in 2007. Other inland waters occasionally hold this goose, including Lovell Hill, though almost any area of freshwater could hold a few and any field could support this goose if free from disturbance.

Very few birds were seen on the Tees Marshes up to late 1993, usually only single stragglers or very small groups, but up to 140 were present in the last three months of 1993, 158 in 1997, 705 in October 1999, 730 in October 2004 and 1,021 in September 2007.

Small skeins are occasionally noted as they pass along the coastline, especially during severe

Winter of...	Numbers
1972/73	77
1974/75	141
1977/78	172
1980/81	237
1982/83	280
1985/86	369
1986/87	458
1987/88	520
1994/95	530
1997/98	730
2000/01	600
2001/02	690

Greylag Goose Numbers - Wynyard - Crookfoot Reservoir - Hurworth Burn

weather conditions when they are often accompanied by large duck movements. These Greylags are thought more likely to be truly wild birds rather than the many semi-feral populations in northern England and southern Scotland.

Coastal movements include 35 passing Hartlepool with Brent Geese on 31 March 1958, 36 flying south over South Gare on 4 October 1966, 10 at Hartlepool and 64 passing South Gare on 21 October 1970. Very few have been seen over the sea in recent years, though skeins are now quite frequently noted over inland areas including Longnewton Reservoir and surrounding area. Any skein seen flying over these areas could be part of the Wynyard - Crookfoot Reservoir conglomeration.

Since 1995, neck-ringed birds have been noted in Cleveland. The first such bird was on the North Tees Marshes from December 1995 to February 1996, again from October 1996 to March 1997 and from October 1997 to March 1998. It had been ringed in a Swedish nest in June 1990, seen in Sweden in 1991, 1992 and 1993, Caithness in June 1994, North Yorkshire in November 1994 and August 1995, Orkney in March 1996 and Loch Leven in July and August 1997. Another bird, at Scaling Dam on 1 December 1999 was also ringed in a Swedish nest, in June 1995, and seen in Holland, Sweden, and Denmark from September 1995 to October 1999.

From December 2000 to March 2001, up to seven neck-ringed birds were in the Crookfoot Reservoir area: all had been ringed at Loch Eye, Ross-shire in October or November 2000 and were considered to be Icelandic birds. Two of these seven were last seen at Crookfoot on 16 March 2001 and were reported in Iceland on 29 April 2001, and another bird, ringed in Iceland in July 1997 was seen in Scotland in 1998, 1999, 2000 and 2001, and at Crookfoot in January 2003. At least six other birds from this population have been recorded at Crookfoot since 2001, and three of the 14 have been seen in Wynyard, yet none have been noted around Teesmouth or Scaling Dam. This suggests that the three Cleveland groups are more or less separate populations. Another Loch Eye ringed bird in October 1999, was seen in Northumberland from December 1999 to March 2000, Scotland in 2000, 2001 and 2002, and at Lovell Hill on 9 March 2004.

Birds showing the characteristics of Greylag Goose - Canada Goose hybrid have been seen on many occasions, with up to nine in recent years, and a Greylag - Pink-footed Goose hybrid was on Lockwood Beck in May 1998 and Coatham Marsh in October 1998.

SNOW GOOSE *Anser caerulescens*

This goose is another of the wildfowl species that is commonly kept in captivity, yet Canadian-ringed Snow Geese have been recorded in Britain, so some of the birds seen in Cleveland may be genuine vagrants.

A white-phase bird was on Lockwood Beck and Scaling Dam (with two Canada Geese) from 12 June 1961 to 9 January 1962. Both reservoirs froze over in late December 1961 and presumably this same bird flew south past North Gare on 27 December 1961 (together with the two Canada Geese). It, or another, arrived at Hartlepool from the north-east on 11 September 1961.

It was another 15 years before the species again occurred in Cleveland, when a blue-phase bird was seen from 12 June 1977, to early 1981, at Crookfoot Reservoir and Wynyard. The next record was also a blue-phase bird in Hargreaves Quarry from 24 to 30 May 1984, followed by 10 white-phase birds over Hartlepool and Dormans Pool on 21 September 1984, two white-phase birds at Scaling Dam on 26 April 1987 and single white-phase birds in the same location from 31 May to 10 June 1988, 1 March 1989 and 28 March to 7 April 1989. Also four birds (one white and three blue phase) were on Saltholme Pools on 22 June 1991.

More recently, two white-phase birds were seen over Longnewton Reservoir on 16 October 1996 and over the North Tees Marshes 10 days later, two white-phase birds were on Crookfoot Reservoir on 1 March 1998, a single white-phase bird was on the North Tees Marshes from 17 to 22 June 2003, and two white phase adults were at Margrove Ponds on 18 September 2007. These last two birds may have been hybrids between this species and Ross's Goose.

Of these records, 50% arrived in late May or June, 25% in September or October and 25% in March or April. Perhaps one would expect a more even spread of records through the months of the year if they had all escaped, or been released from, captivity. Snow Goose records for Cleveland are reviewed by Joynt (1999).

(GREATER) CANADA GOOSE *Branta canadensis*

This goose is a North American species introduced into Britain as an ornamental bird to grace the parks and estates of wealthy landowners sometime prior to 1785. Since then there have been numerous other introductions into many areas from which it has spread naturally to areas throughout England, and, to a lesser extent, Scotland, Wales and Ireland.

As a Cleveland bird, it had nested in Wynyard from at least 1973 and probably since 1967 when 14 were present in April. In 1973 there were 28 birds after the breeding season, 37 in 1976, 71 in 1980, 94 in 1984 and 103 in September 1984, but no goslings have been noted here since about 1992.

Other breeding records include an introduced pair on Rossmere Park Lake, Hartlepool in the late 1960s, which were never known to rear any young, although, goslings were seen here in 2003, single pairs on Crookfoot Reservoir in 1979 and 1983, and one to five pairs at Lovell Hill, Poole Hospital, Guisborough Priory, Margrove Pond,

South Gare and Skelton Castle from 1990 onwards. Also, one to two pairs have attempted to breed at Scaling Dam and the North Tees Marshes since about 2001. Thirteen pairs were known to have attempted to breed in Cleveland in 1991, at least 21 in 1994, at least 28 in 1997 and about 45-60 pairs since 2000.

The first record for the 20th century was in May 1957 when two were on the Reclamation Pond. Since then it has been recorded annually, the majority of records in the 1970s and 1980s occurring in May/June and September/October and particularly during the first two weeks of June. At that time relatively few birds were resident in Cleveland, and the Yorkshire population was known to migrate to the Beauly Firth in Scotland, many passing over Cleveland in early June, but then straggling back in August, September and October. From the 1990s there has been an established local movement between Lovell Hill and Guisborough at certain times of the year, and another between Albert and Stewart Parks in Middlesbrough.

The highest counts are up to 467 in the Lovell Hill-Wilton area in 1998, 508 on Bowesfield Nature Reserve in 2006 and 512 on North Tees marshes on 1 January 2007. By the year 2000, flocks of 100-200 could regularly be seen on many other waters including Skelton Castle, Wynyard, Belasis Technology Park, Haverton Hole, Scaling Dam, Margrove Ponds, Hemlington Lake, Locke Park, Steel House, Redcar boating lake and Wilton Centre lake. Whilst there is movement of birds between most of these waters, about 1,000 birds were in Cleveland by the 2003/04 winter, quite a high percentage of which utilise the bread-throwing public as their major food source.

There have been several reports of colour-ringed birds seen at Teesmouth, many of which have been found to originate in North Yorkshire, although two birds, with another 20, by the Long Drag in late August 1979 had been ringed near Cannock in Staffordshire.

A small race bird, probably *B.c.parvipes*, was on Scaling Dam on 30 October 2002, and it or another was on Coatham Marsh and Locke Park from 9 to 14 January 2003.

BARNACLE GOOSE *Branta leucopsis*

For the last 30 years, Barnacle Geese have been seen annually, although there are only two records for the first half of the 20th century. An increase in records became apparent during the early 1960s, probably as a result of better protection. The number of birds seen each year has been increasing during the 1970s and 1980s.

Date	Location	Highest counts
18 October 1961	Passing Hartlepool	28
2 October 1970	Over Teesmouth	35
3 October 1974	Over North Gare	100
1 October 1979	Flying south off Hartlepool	340
26 September 1985	Over Teesmouth	100
28 September 1986	By the Long Drag	110
1 October 1991	By the Long Drag	476
1 October 1991	At South Gare	200
3 October 1992	Over Teesmouth	480
4 October 1999	Flying west over Teesmouth	5,700
26 September 2002	Passing Hartlepool	490
28 September 2003	Passing Hartlepool and Teesmouth	1,200
7 October 2004	Passing Hartlepool	1,035
Barnacle Goose Numbers		

As can be seen from the above high counts, the last week of September and early October is the best time to see Barnacle Geese in Cleveland, although a few appear regularly in the months January-April and November-December. Apart from a record of one bird by Greatham Creek in May 1959, there were no records during the months of May-August prior to 1977. Since that year, one to six are quite regularly seen during the summer, usually with other geese, and frequently at Teesmouth. A few are sometimes noted on Crookfoot Reservoir, Scaling Dam, Wynyard, Seaton Common, Coatham Marsh and Lockwood Beck.

Colour-ringed birds have been noted since 1983; two of 13 birds on Seaton Common in January 1983 were ringed, the first as a juvenile at Caerlaverock in October 1976, being seen there for most of the following winter and in Norway in May 1978, 1980 and 1981. The other bird was ringed as an adult also at Caerlaverock in January 1980 and was observed there during the following winter and in Norway in May 1980, 1981 and 1982. The first bird was trapped with about 1600 Barnacle Geese on Spitzbergen in July 1977. At least 15 of 110 by the Long Drag on 28 September 1986 carried Spitzbergen colour rings and four of these were reported at Caerlaverock within a week of being seen at

Teesmouth. Another ringed as a pullus on Spitzbergen in July 1996 was in Cleveland from late February to early May 1997; one ringed as an adult on Spitzbergen in August 1995 was at Caerlaverock in the winters of 1995/96 and 1996/97 before being seen on Seaton Common on 16 October 1997 and another ringed as a pullus on Spitzbergen in the summer of 1997 remained around Cleveland from January to May 1998, becoming tame enough to come for bread with Canada Geese in Stewart and Albert Parks, Middlesbrough. If this last bird had not had a Spitzbergen ring on, it would have been assumed to be an escape from captivity, when coming for bread.

Pinioned or introduced free-flying birds have been seen in the 1980s at Stewart Park (two–three), Guisborough Priory (three–four) and Skelton Castle (one bird).

BRENT GOOSE *Branta bernicla*

Two races of this bird are seen in Cleveland; the dark-bellied race *B.b.bernicla* is a regular winter visitor and usually seen from mid-October to mid-March, while the pale-bellied race *B.b.hrota* is a regular passage migrant, principally in September and October. However, single birds of both races are occasionally seen in the summer months.

The Brent Goose was more abundant in the region during the 19th century, the species being described as "very common at Teesmouth" in the early 1800s and a wildfowler is reported to have shot 65 in the season of 1869. Other historical records include two at Teesmouth from August to October 1898, 17 at Teesmouth during the first week of June 1900 and nine near Wynyard on 3 June 1901. Additionally, a small party was present near Stockton in October 1932, one of which was shot. More recently, there have been four inland records: single dark-bellied birds on Crookfoot Reservoir from 9 to 23 December 1978; on 27 October 1985; on Scaling Dam on 2 December 1997 and Wynyard on 17 February 2006.

At Teesmouth, most birds stay on Seal Sands, occasionally being seen on the Brinefields, Seaton Common or at South Gare. Very occasionally they also frequent the adjacent marshes at Coatham, Cowpen, Greenabella and Dormans Pool.

There are also a few records of birds settled on the sea, off Redcar, Hartlepool and Seaton Carew, but most records from the coast concern birds in flight.

In most years, no more than about 20 birds are seen, although about 78 were reported for the whole of 1985 and parties of 63 passed Hartlepool on 31 March 1958, 55 were at South Gare on 27 March 1969, 60 were on Seal Sands on 22 October 1988, 70 passed Cowbar on 20 February 1996 and 249 flew south off Hartlepool on 5 December 2002. All these counts relate to birds of the dark-bellied race.

From about 1988 the pale-bellied race has become more numerous, and since 2000, birds of this race are the most likely to be seen in the winter months. Mixed flocks of both dark and pale-bellied races are not unusual.

The highest counts of pale-bellied Brent Goose are 230 on 13 September 1993 and 172 on 9 September 2001, all birds passing Hartlepool.

EGYPTIAN GOOSE *Alopochen aegyptiaca*

There are five records of birds of unknown origin, although all British birds are from introduced stock, principally to Norfolk. Singles were at Scaling Dam on 23 January 1990 and 14 January 2001, two were at South Gare on 4 July 1993, one was on Saltholme Pools on 22 and 23 June 2002, and from 1 to 16 October 2007.

A pair was introduced to Wilton Centre Lake in 1979, eggs being laid in 1980 and 1981 and several young were reared. The young were free-flying and dispersed after fledging. It is possible that the few records from other parts of the county were one or other of these birds. One of the original adults died in 1981, the remaining bird being present to about 1998.

(COMMON) SHELDUCK *Tadorna tadorna*

This duck is a common winter visitor to Teesmouth, with small numbers remaining during the summer to breed around the estuary. It is also a regular passage migrant along the coastline, especially in autumn, and an occasional visitor to inland waters.

A visit to Seal Sands between September and March will reveal several hundred, or perhaps 1,000 Shelduck on the mudflats, and approximately 4,440 were around Teesmouth on 16 January 1970 and about 3,570 on 21 November 1976. The January 1970 count of 4,440 was made when Seal Sands was about three times the size that it is at present.

In the 1980s regular counting showed that Teesmouth rated between 9th and 13th among the estuaries of Britain for wintering Shelduck, but by 2001 the estuary had dropped to 30th position.

There have always been about 5-15 breeding pairs around the Tees Marshes hatching up to 140 ducklings, which usually gather on Seal Sands or the Redcar Ore Terminal Pond. The first recorded Shelduck nest for Teesmouth was in 1883 (Nelson 1907). Crevices in the estuary's numerous slag walls probably hold the majority of the breeding pairs, particularly along the Long Drag and Greatham Creek. Up to three pairs have been known to breed on Crookfoot Reservoir since 1974, and single pairs have been seen with ducklings on Wynyard Lake, Hart Reservoir and Bowesfield Pond on occasions. There is also an historic record of a pair that attempted to nest in the sand dunes between Redcar and Marske in 1902. Artificial nest-holes have been created in two areas of the Tees Marshes.

In Britain as a whole, the majority of the adult Shelduck fly to north-west Germany after the breeding season to moult, so the majority of the birds present in July and August are juveniles together with a few adult minders. The three months July-September are generally when the lowest counts are made around Teesmouth; numbers then build up fairly quickly in October, November and December. At this time the highest numbers are seen passing along the coast, although no more than about 20-60 are usually seen on any one day. The return from Germany to Seal Sands (and other estuaries in eastern Britain) must take place at least partly during the hours of darkness. In some years very few are actually seen moving along the coast, the highest counts being 171 passing Hartlepool on 20 December 1964, 169 passing South Gare on 21 December 1969 and 100 passing South Gare in three hours on 16 November 1996.

Apart from Crookfoot Reservoir, where up to 30 are regularly recorded from March to July, very few Shelduck are seen on inland waters. It is not even recorded annually at Scaling Dam, Lockwood Beck or Longnewton Reservoir.

The colour-ringing and regular surveying of the Shelduck at Teesmouth has been conducted by Durham University during the late 1970s and early 1980s and has revealed that Teesmouth, especially Seal Sands is an important 'staging post' as well as a wintering ground. There may only be 1,000-2,000 Shelduck on Seal Sands on any one day between November and February, but about 3,000-4,000 individuals will probably have fed on Seal Sands during these months, some only staying a week or two before moving on.

Birds ringed as pulli during the summers (1976-1980) on the Firth of Forth and Hauxley in Northumberland have been seen at Teesmouth in the following winter, one as early as 2 September. Others include a bird ringed at Hambleton, Lancashire, in 1974 that was on Seal Sands on 1 November 1979, one from the Isle of Mull, Strathclyde, ringed in 1981 and seen on Seal Sands on 2 December 1983 and one ringed on Seal Sands that was recorded at Frinton-on-Sea, Essex, seven years later. Most of these juveniles move on after a few weeks or months, although one was known to be still present at Teesmouth the following May.

Birds ringed as full-grown juveniles on Seal Sands have been reported as follows: one on 23 August 1977 was not seen at Teesmouth again until April and May 1980, it was then found at Bolton-on-Swale, North Yorkshire, in early May 1981; one ringed on 1 November 1979 was found at Dornoch, Sutherland, in August 1984; one ringed on 20 November 1979 was recovered at East-Agder, Norway, on 3 April 1982; and one ringed in January was seen on the Firth of Forth three months later. Also a juvenile ringed on the Somme Estuary, France, on 16 December 1981 was present on Seal Sands on 3 June 1982, one ringed on Seal Sands on 9 September 1994 was reported taking bread in Locke Park, Redcar, from at least August to December 1997 and one ringed on Seal Sands in August 1997 was (illegally) shot at Hartlepool in November 1998.

Adults ringed at Teesmouth in November have been reported as follows: Washington, Tyne and Wear, in the same winter, in Co. Antrim, Co. Donegal, and Co. Down in Ireland in the following winter; four ringed in November 1977 lived at least 8 years, one being found dead at Blakeney Point, Norfolk, in January 1985, another at Longtown, Cumbria, in April 1985, another in Germany in October 1985 and the fourth at Alnmouth, Northumberland, in March 1989. Three others ringed in November 1977 were part of a small moulting flock at Grangetown on the Firth of Forth in summer 1979, but were back at Teesmouth in late autumn 1979 and subsequent autumns. Also one ringed on 4 November 1980 was found dead on Jersey in January 1983.

Adults ringed at Teesmouth in December have been seen at Widnes, Cheshire, in late autumn, Isle of Gigha, Strathclyde, in April and in Bangor, Gwynedd, in late March. Another bird, ringed in December 1983 was seen on Texel in January 1987. Of some adults ringed in January 1979, one was seen in the Netherlands in February 1980 and May 1981 and another at Port Glasgow, Strathclyde, on 4 July 1982. Others ringed in January have been noted on the Clyde Estuary in February and July and in Norfolk in February and April, one 11 years later. An adult ringed in February 1988 was in Schleswig-Holstein, Germany, on 1 October 1995 and one ringed on 3 June 1982 had apparently moved north to winter, being recorded at Budle Bay, Northumberland, on 28 January 1984.

Similar ringing studies have been carried out on the population at Aberlady Bay, Lothian, on the Firth of Forth, and a number of ringed birds have been observed at Teesmouth. Two adults which bred at Aberlady in the summer of 1980 were on Seal Sands on 1 November 1980. Other adults from Aberlady have been seen on Seal Sands as early as 6 October after having returned from their moulting grounds and others have been reported in two consecutive winters at Teesmouth: one ringed at Aberlady on 6 December 1972 was still on Seal Sands on 28 January 1980 and an adult from the Ythan, Aberdeenshire, breeding population, was on Seal Sands in late January 1979.

MANDARIN *Aix galericulata*

This colourful duck is native to Japan, China and adjacent parts of Russia; it was introduced to Britain as early as 1747, although it was not until the early part of the 20th century that the Mandarin became established in this country. The main population area is Surrey and Berkshire.

The first record was of two drakes at Locke Park, Redcar, from 30 May to 3 June 1967, followed by:

Date	Location	Number
24 April to 5 May 1975	Coatham Marsh	drake
4 November 1984	Coatham Marsh	drake
11 May 1986	River Leven, near Kirklevington	drake
3 May 1988	Coatham Marsh	drake
5 to 7 April 1989	Locke Park, Redcar	duck
2 to 19 November 1989	Scaling Dam	drake
24 to 28 April 1990	Haverton Hole	drake
10 April 1991	Coatham Marsh	pair
23 April 1993	Coatham Marsh	drake
20 September 1993	Wynyard	duck
17 January 1994	Coulby Newham	duck
22 April 1994	South Gare	two drakes
17 October 1994	South Gare	drake
December 1994 to January 1995	Coulby Newham	duck
16 April 1996	Pinchinthorpe	drake
Oct to Dec 1997	Cowbar	drake
April, May & September 1999	Cowbar	drake
11 June to 8 September 1999	Albert Park, Middlesbrough	drake
26 - 27 September 2002	Crookfoot Reservoir	three drakes
25 March 2003	Skelton Castle	drake
6 April 2004	Ward Jackson Park, Hartlepool	drake
8 to 15 April 2004	Stewart Park, Middlesbrough	drake
30 April to 2 June 2005	Lockwood Beck	drake
28 June 2005	Margrove Ponds	duck
28 August 2005	Scaling Dam	duck
Mandarin Records		

Between the 1984/85 winter and 1998, and possibly as far back as 1975, there has been a tame, full-winged drake at Stewart Park, with up to three other pinioned drakes, the origin of which is unknown. A tame, pinioned duck was also seen at Stewart Park in 2003, 2004 and 2007.

(EURASIAN) WIGEON *Anas penelope*

During the last half-century there has been a gradual increase in the number of Wigeon. This could be due to a variety of reasons including the general reduction in shooting pressure and habitat improvements. In the 19th century, very nearly all bird-recording was conducted with the help of a gun, and Nelson (1907) wrote that his earliest and latest records were 11 August (1883) and 15 May (1902) and that 23 had been shot on one occasion.

Wigeon can be found around Teesmouth in every month of the year, albeit in very small numbers in June and July, yet there has been no suggestion of breeding to date.

The most favoured area in Cleveland at the present time is Seal Sands and the North Tees Marshes. A total of 2,920 was recorded in January 1995, although the usual winter maximum is about 1,200-1,500. Between 50-200 are regularly seen in winter at Scaling Dam, Coatham Marsh, Bowesfield, Wynyard, Haverton Hole, Crookfoot Reservoir, Longnewton Reservoir, Portrack Marsh and Charlton's Pond, and small numbers can regularly be seen on virtually any other area of water and marsh in the winter months. Numbers vary considerably from winter to winter, probably in part depending on the growth of water-borne vegetation during the previous summer. Up to 445 were counted at Scaling Dam in December 1985 when there was a large growth of water-weed present in the reservoir.

Quite large numbers can be seen passing along the coastline during strong onshore winds, especially in the months September to November, several hundred frequently being recorded on such days from Hartlepool. During these conditions, large numbers can also be seen resting on the sea, the maximum being about 2,000 off South Gare on 3 November 1984. On the same day, at least 1,000 passed Hartlepool and about 500 were on the sea off Seaton Carew. The highest count of actual passage was 1,449 moving north off Hartlepool on 22 November 1969.

Pinioned birds are present in Preston Park and Guisborough Priory with up to five birds at each place in 1990, but at least eight at Guisborough Priory in 2004.

A partially-leucistic duck was on Seal Sands on 3 November 1976 and a similar duck was at Teesmouth in February and April 1987.

AMERICAN WIGEON *Anas americana*

There are ten records of this duck for Cleveland, some of which were probably genuine vagrants, since there are relatively few kept in captivity. They are: single drakes on Seal Sands on 4 December 1973, Dormans Pool on 2 June 1985 and almost certainly on Greatham Creek next day; a pair around the Cowpen Marsh - Long Drag area between 26 and 29 May 1986; a drake on Saltholme Pools between 5 and 7 May 1988; a drake on the North Tees Marshes from 29 August 1988 to at least 23 January 1989; an immature drake in the Greatham Creek area from 11 to 16 March 1990; a pair at Greatham Tank Farm on 30 April 1994; a drake on Seal Sands from 4 to 9 October 1997; a drake at South Gare on 19 April 1998; and a duck on Cowpen Marsh and Saltholme Pools on 6 - 7 May 2000.

GADWALL *Anas strepera*

This rather subtle-plumaged species of duck is present throughout the year, but there is also a small, but regular passage through Cleveland, primarily on the North Tees Marshes and usually during the months October-November and March-April.

Prior to 1950 there were less than ten records of this duck in Cleveland, but between 1951 and 1973 more were seen, reflecting in part a general increase in the number of Gadwall breeding in Britain. Almost all records were from the north side of Teesmouth, although up to three were noted at Scaling Dam in April-May 1960, September 1961 and June 1962. A few also passed Hartlepool in the months March, October and November in this period.

Gadwall numbers have continued to increase from 1974, there now being birds on the North Tees Marshes throughout the year, and regular records from Scaling Dam, Charlton's Pond, Cowpen Bewley Pond, Haverton Hole, Crookfoot Reservoir, Portrack Marsh, Hemlington Lake, Lovell Hill and other wetlands.

The highest number of Gadwall seen in Cleveland was at least 500 on the Tees Marshes during late October-early November 2005. Other high counts include 332 around the North Tees Marshes in November 2003 and 422 in October 2006, 52 on Charlton's Pond in October 2001 and 130 on Coatham Marsh in December 2004.

Despite this recent increase, very few Gadwall are seen passing at sea; no more than nine per day in recent years.

There are no ringing recoveries for this species. However, it should be noted that Gadwall have been introduced to many waters throughout Britain, including Cowpen Marsh in 1964.

Gadwall first bred in Yorkshire in 1954 and had increased to at least six pairs in 1980 (Mather 1986) and breeding was confirmed in Northumberland in 1965 with three pairs being present in 1983. Breeding probably occurred on a pond in Cleveland in 1993, and three broods of ducklings were seen at Teesmouth in July and August 1994. The number of breeding pairs has continued to increase with about 15-20 breeding pairs in Cleveland in the early 2000s.

(EURASIAN) TEAL *Anas crecca*

At times, Teal is the commonest duck around Teesmouth with over 1,000 being regularly recorded since 1978, usually in the months October-January, making Teesmouth an area of National Importance for wintering Teal. A total of 4,426 present around the estuary in mid-November 1984 is the highest count to date and is a great deal larger than the pre-1962 counts for Teesmouth.

In the past, and before the extensive reclamation of the Tees Estuary, it would appear that Teal were not particularly numerous. The highest number recorded prior to the 20th century is 23 shot in one day in September 1863 (Nelson 1907). There is no evidence of an increase during the first half of the 20th century, but 406 were counted in February 1967, 770 in December 1975, 1,523 in December 1978, 2,155 in December 1983 and 1,788 in November 1986. Since 1984, no more than 2,000 Teal have been counted, about 1,000-1,500 being a regular winter maximum. The one area recently favoured by large numbers of Teal is the un-reclaimed section of Bran Sands to the south-east of the Redcar Ore Terminal (this being regarded as part of Teesport).

Lesser numbers are regularly present on the reservoirs during the winter months, 100-250 occurring on Scaling Dam and 506 being seen there in December 2003. Up to 500 have been noted on Portrack Marsh in recent winters and virtually every other area of fresh water, including small ponds, occasionally hold Teal.

Breeding has been proven quite frequently since the 1960s on the freshwater marshes of Teesmouth, and ducklings have also been seen in at least ten years since 1959 on Scaling Dam, at least twice on Margrove Ponds since 1976, and at Haverton Hole in 2006.

Passage at sea is reasonably predictable between early August and mid-November under certain weather conditions, though usually less than 100 are recorded as a maximum daily count each year. The highest counts passing through have been: 281 at South Gare on 5 November 1967; 381 at Hartlepool on 22 November 1969; 377 at Hartlepool on 2 October 1981; at least 600 passing Cowbar on 24 August 1986; 553 at South Gare on 27 August 2000; 423 also South Gare on 2 September 2000; 385 at Hartlepool on 25 September 2001 and 720 also at Hartlepool on 25 August 2003. Also, about 1,000 were present on the sea off South Gare on 3 November 1984 (about ten days before the present record Teesmouth count of over 4,000).

There are two ringing recoveries, a drake ringed on Coatham Marsh on 29 October 1977 that was found dead at Carlisle, Cumbria, on 15 January 1982, and one ringed near Copenhagen, Denmark, on 10 March 1992 was found dead under the wires over the Reclamation Pond on 2 March 1998.

GREEN-WINGED TEAL *Anas carolinensis*

Originally Green-winged Teal was regarded as the American race of Eurasian Teal, but it was given full species status in 2000.

Single drakes have been seen on: Crookfoot Reservoir on 6 November 1982, 3 to 5 April 1996, 7 to 13 April 1997; the Brinefields on 31 March and 1 April 1985, and 19-20 May 2002; Greatham Tank Farm from 20 April to 1 May 1986; Scaling Dam on 19 May 1991 and 14 May 2004; Dormans Pool on 18 April 1993 and 13 to 19 April 1997; Coatham Marsh from 11 to 13 May 1995, 26 December 1997 and 19-20 June 2004; Greenabella Marsh from 15 to 20 May 1995; and one frequented the North Tees Marshes from 25 May to 23 June 2003, a second bird being present from 3 to 9 June 2003. These two drakes were seen together on Cowpen Marsh on 4 June 2003.

MALLARD *Anas platyrhynchos*

This is the common park lake duck. Indeed the parks of Cleveland probably hold more breeding Mallard than any other type of habitat. It also breeds at Teesmouth and at all of the local reservoirs, but these particular waters are much more important as wintering areas.

Mallard is also a passage migrant in reasonable numbers, many of the Scandinavian and north British birds moving south and west to their wintering grounds.

There is estimated to be about 500-600 pairs of Mallard breeding in Cleveland, probably 100 pairs being in the various parks such as Rossmere and Ward Jackson Parks in Hartlepool, Ropner Park in Stockton, Charlton's Pond in Billingham, Albert and Stewart Parks in Middlesbrough and Locke Park, Redcar.

The Tees Marshes between Seaton Carew, Haverton Hill and Redcar probably hold another 65-70 pairs and about 5-10 pairs nest at other waters such as Crookfoot Reservoir, Wynyard Lake, Poole Hospital, Billingham Bottoms, Scaling Dam, Margrove Pond and Grinkle Park.

About half of Cleveland is agricultural-type habitat and specific surveying of such habitat indicates that quite a reasonable number of pairs nest some distance from water. The ducklings usually appear between early May and mid-August, although they have been reported as early as the beginning of April and as late as the first week or two of October.

It is not known whether the Mallard that breed at Teesmouth and the reservoirs remain throughout the winter, but those that breed on the parks very likely remain on their lakes throughout the year taking advantage of bread and similar foodstuffs thrown to them by visitors.

The lowest numbers at Teesmouth are usually recorded in April, May and September with generally less than 100 being counted. There is a distinct increase in the number of adults present in June and July, probably a local movement to Teesmouth, using the area as a moulting site, with about 150-250 birds involved.

It is not until October that the wintering birds begin to arrive at Teesmouth and the various reservoirs with numbers usually reaching a peak in December or January. The highest counts at Teesmouth have been 1,750 in 1964 and 1968 and 1,150 in 1976 and 1980. At Scaling Dam up to 800 have been recorded in several winters and 1,484 in November 1979. At Longnewton Reservoir 820 were seen in September 1988, but 300-500 is the usual winter maximum, and at Lockwood Beck 510 were noted in November 1988 although 100-300 is more normal. The regular winter maximum at Crookfoot Reservoir is 200-300, however, 374 were present in February 1984. At Wynyard, 350-500 is usual, with a record 930 being present in December 1978. About 150-300 can also be seen at places such as Charlton's Pond, Albert Park, Hemlington Lake, Lovell Hill and New Marske Reservoir.

A small group of Mallard regularly feed on the sea off Cattersty Sands, Skinningrove, the only location in Cleveland where this duck can be regularly seen at sea. Up to 83 have been present in recent years.

In most winters about 2,100-2,600 Mallard are spread across Cleveland but approximately 3,200 were present in January 1980.

The peak duck passage along the coast is between late August and early December, but this species is almost always outnumbered by Wigeon, Teal, Goldeneye and Common Scoter. In most years no more than 20-50 per day are seen on the days of heavy duck passage, although 301 were recorded passing South Gare on 25 October 1966, and 268 passing South Gare on 20 October 1991.

Hand-reared Mallard have been introduced to several parks, mainly in the 1950s and 1960s, and these small isolated colonies seem well able to maintain or increase their numbers. In December 1990 a total of 30 waters were surveyed, including all of the park lakes, and this gave a minimum of 2,520 Mallard in Cleveland. Of this total 980 birds were regarded as tame and/or relying on food provided by people and 114 of the 2,520 showed non-Mallard type plumage variations, all but ten of which were on park lakes.

There are three ringing recoveries: one ringed in west Flanders, Belgium, on 9 June 1951 that was found dead at Teesmouth two months later, one ringed at Skelton on 15 August 1995 was killed at Pickering, North Yorkshire on 1 November 1995 and another ringed at Skelton on 2 April 1997 was killed at Redcar on 15 January 1999.

(NORTHERN) PINTAIL *Anas acuta*

This dabbling duck is a winter visitor to the North Tees Marshes, especially Dormans Pool, usually arriving in late August and September, and departing in March. The peak annual figure was between 12 and 30 from 1968 to 1998; with the exception of 60 on 7 March 1971 and 53 on 10 March 1968. From 1999 the annual maximum has steadily increased, there being 44 in 1999, 50 in 2000, 63 in 2001, 70 in 2002 and 73 on 17 February 2003, but no more than 59 since 2003.

This duck has probably never been very common, even prior to the extensive reclamations around the Tees Estuary. However, it may have been a more regular breeding species. The only recent breeding records concern single pairs that successfully reared young on Cowpen Marsh in 1954 and 1961, though in 1962 a nest on Cowpen Marsh was destroyed by a cow. It is possible that a pair has attempted to nest more recently than this, since one or two birds are quite frequently seen in suitable habitat during May, June and July. This is important because Pintail is a rare and sporadic breeder in the UK.

Most reservoirs and lakes, such as Crookfoot Reservoir, Wynyard, Lockwood Beck, Scaling Dam and Charlton's Pond, hold a bird or two occasionally, although 11 were on Scaling Dam on 22 October 1985 and 13 on Crookfoot Reservoir on 3 February 1968. Perhaps the most unusual site for a Pintail is the stream in the middle of Saltburn Woods. A duck, which was regarded as a wild, healthy individual, was present there on 8 December 1979.

A few Pintail pass along the coast during autumn passage, principally between late July and mid-November; the highest counts are 40 passing Cowbar on 27 September 1960, 32 passing South Gare on 5 November 1967, 26 passing Hartlepool on 3 November 1984, 52 passing South Gare on 22 September 1991 and 32 passing Hartlepool on 15 September 2000. Also 16 flew inland over Yarm on 18 September 1981.

Between 1959 and 1965, a pair or two bred at Rossmere Park, Hartlepool, although they were introduced and the original birds had their wings clipped. Also two pinioned drakes were in Stewart Park and at least six pinioned birds were at Guisborough Priory in the 1980s.

Hybrid drakes, showing Mallard and Pintail characteristics have been seen on Charlton's Pond from December 1980 to at least January 1987, and in January 1990, Albert Park Lake in November 1984, Crookfoot Reservoir in January 1998 and Skelton Castle in February 1999. Up to three hybrid ducks have been observed on a small pond at Upleatham from 1998 to 2002.

GARGANEY *Anas querquedula*

In some years this is the first summer visitor to be seen, with frequent records for March, the earliest being four on Greatham Tank Farm on 9 March (1980). Usually the first birds are seen between late March and early May, almost always on the marshes at Teesmouth and never numbering more than seven together.

There are June records in most years and this duck bred at Teesmouth in the 1880s and in at least nine years during the 20th century. This can be a rather secretive bird when nesting and as such easily overlooked in summer. However, single broods of ducklings have also been seen on the North Tees Marshes in 2002, and Upsall Carr in 2004 and 2005. This is a scarce breeding duck with between 50-150 pairs breeding in the UK.

In most years slightly more birds are seen in the autumn than spring although the drakes have lost their breeding plumage by August and can be fairly difficult to distinguish from Teal if not seen in flight. The highest count is of 23 recorded on Coatham Marsh on 25 August 1971 and 23 seen around the North Tees Marshes on 29 July 1975, the latter including four ducklings on Cowpen Marsh. Few are seen in September and October, and the latest date is 5 November (2007).

Approximately 70% of the birds seen in Cleveland are around the North Tees Marshes, most of the remainder being in the Coatham Marsh - South Gare area. There are also records from most other waters, including Scaling Dam, Crookfoot and Hart Reservoirs, Grinkle Park, Margrove Ponds, Lovell Hill, Bowesfield, Hemlington Lake, Albert Park and Yearby Pool.

About 20 records exist of birds passing at sea off Hartlepool and a drake flew north with Teal off Cowbar on 24 August 1986.

BLUE-WINGED TEAL *Anas discors*

There are five records of this North American species for Cleveland: single ducks on Coatham Marsh from 26 October to 14 November 1987; on the Reclamation Pond or Haverton Hole from 30 August to 29 September 1994; again on Haverton Hole from 1 to 11 January 1999; two eclipse drakes on Coatham Marsh on 9 September 1999; and an eclipse drake was at Haverton Hole from 31 August to 15 October 2007.

A drake Blue-winged Teal-Shoveler hybrid was at Haverton Hole from 11 November 2006 to 16 March 2007.

(NORTHERN) SHOVELER Anas clypeata

Shoveler can be found at Teesmouth throughout the year and occasionally on other ponds and reservoirs in Cleveland. It now breeds annually, with up to ten pairs in the Cowpen-Saltholme area. Breeding was proven in some years from 1974 and every year since 1990, although it has probably always been a nesting species in small numbers around Teesmouth since there are records of breeding prior to 1845 (Nelson 1907). Ducklings were also seen in 1910, eight pairs reported in 1916 and up to 12 pairs in the 1920s (Temperley 1951). Breeding was also proven at Crookfoot Reservoir in 1966 and 1969 and probably occurred in other years around that period.

The peak Teesmouth counts are usually in the months August-November and regularly reach 100-200 birds. This is probably a post-breeding dispersal from the breeding areas in north-east England and may be supplemented later in the year by north European birds, a few of which pass along the coast in autumn. The highest counts at Teesmouth are: 110 in August 1963; 139 in September 1988; 232 in October 1995; 260 in September 2000; and 308 in August 2005. There are relatively few Shoveler seen on the other waters in Cleveland, maxima being: Bowesfield 59 in October 2004 and 53 in August 2005; Cowpen Bewley Pond 43 in December 2003; Albert Park 22 in December 2000; Stewart Park 23 in January 2003; Scaling Dam 13 in November 1985; Wynyard 16 in August 1975; Longnewton Reservoir 15 in September 2004, and Lovell Hill nine in September 1988. A few are seen on other areas of water and marsh, including Portrack Marsh where breeding was suspected in 1983 but never proven.

RED-CRESTED POCHARD Netta rufina

Virtually every species of duck that could occur as a natural vagrant to Britain is kept in captivity in various wildfowl collections throughout the UK. The Red-crested Pochard is no exception and so all recent records cannot be regarded as definite wild birds, although those introduced to a park in Hartlepool during 1959 were never known to wander very far. A drake killed on Coatham Marsh on 20 January 1900 is arguably the only genuine record.

More recent records are singles on Scaling Dam from 14 November to 12 December 1971, 21 to 23 September 1975 (and Lockwood Beck on 12 October 1975), 23 July to 14 October 1978, 22 July to 16 September 1979 and 22 July 1980. Additionally, a drake was on Saltholme Pools on 14 - 15 November 1982, a duck was there on 6 October 1989, a duck was on Cowpen Bewley Pond on 25 - 26 October 1989 and single ducks were on Charlton's Pond from 2 November 1989 to 17 December 1991 and Albert Park lake from at least 15 November 1989 to 17 August 1990. These last two birds were almost certainly captive-bred birds since the Charlton's Pond bird had two primaries clipped on one wing and the Albert Park bird was tame enough to come for bread. A wandering duck was seen on five waters between 16 August and 18 September 1991, 11 November 1991 to 5 January 1992 and 14 October to 17 November 1992, a drake was on Saltholme Pools from 10 May to 26 August 1992 and 15 June to 6 July 1993, and four resided on Crookfoot Reservoir from 30 August to 13 September 1992, two still being there on 18 September 1992. One was also at this site from 20 August to 4 September 1994. The next were single ducks on Coatham Marsh on 29 January and 9-10 August 1998, and Scaling Dam from 12 September to 4 October 1998, then single drakes on Seal Sands on 26 March 2000, Cowpen Bewley Pond from 6 to 31 August 2001, Dormans Pool on 10 September 2001, around the North Tees Marshes from 17 April to 13 July 2003, Saltholme Pools on 1 October 2003, Coatham Marsh on 11 April 2004, then the North Tees Marshes from 12 April to at least 2 July 2004 and 7 May to 27 July 2005.

Approximately 70% of the birds have arrived in the 4-month period of late July to mid-November.

The birds introduced to Rossmere Park, Hartlepool in 1959 were allowed to remain full-winged, as were the resulting offspring and were known to fly around Hartlepool. They were sometimes seen at Ward Jackson Park in Hartlepool about two kilometres away and were known to breed there in at least one year during the 1960s, however, the whole population had disappeared by 1970. The introduction of three birds to Preston Park, Stockton, in about 1984, did not result in any young. These birds had their wings clipped, unlike the Washington Wildfowl and Wetland's Trust birds, some of which could visit Cleveland.

In 1991, the duck on Charlton's Pond was seen with nine ducklings on 10 June, seven of which successfully fledged, and all of these remained in Cleveland into 1992. By about mid-September 1991 it became apparent that these seven juveniles were in fact Mallard-Red-crested Pochard hybrids being two drakes and five ducks. All seven showed the Red-crested Pochard round-head shape and broad off-white wing-bar, but also a well-defined Mallard-like speculum. One male was on Saltholme Pools on 15 October 1991, on Wilton Centre lake from about 23 October 1991 to 26 March 1992 and on Scaling Dam on 9 March 1993, and at least four of the other six commuted between Charlton's Pond and Haverton Hole throughout 1992.

(COMMON) POCHARD *Aythya ferina*

This diving duck is a regular winter visitor in varying numbers to virtually all of the freshwater lakes and reservoirs in Cleveland, and several hundred used to congregate on Seal Sands in the 1970s and 1980s; it also bred in about 6-8 years in the early 20th century and in most years since 1986.

Prior to 1962, flocks of more than ten on Seal Sands were very rare, but from the 1960s the annual winter maximum steadily increased, always occurring in January or February, from 193 in the 1976-77 winter, 335 in the 1977-78 winter, 776 in 1978-9 winter to the largest number of 930 during the 1980-81 winter. Also, 850 were counted in the winter of 1981/82, but since 1985 no more than 115 have been observed. The figure of 930 was recorded on 30 January 1981 and is the largest count of Pochard ever made in Cleveland.

In the 1990s the areas of water around the North Tees Marshes became deeper, in particular Saltholme Pools, Dormans Pool and the Reclamation Pond, and therefore more attractive to Pochard. The highest marshland count was 242 in February 1996, 214 of which were on Saltholme Pools. It is now quite unusual to see Pochard on Seal Sands.

The number of Pochard using Scaling Dam has also declined quite considerably. The figures available include 96 in November 1961, 60 in July 1963, 95 in August 1967, 131 in July 1968, 160 in August 1969, 227 in November 1972, 160 in November 1975 and 241 on 17 October 1976. Since then, the annual maximum count has fluctuated between four and 88.

Some of the significant counts on other waters include: 35 in December 1961, 30 in December 1982 and 40 in February 1991 on Charlton's Pond; 44 in November 1962, 52 in November 1976, 96 in November 1980, 122 in December 1982 and 90 in November 1983 at Crookfoot Reservoir; and 72 in October 1969, 42 in October 1976 and 46 in October 1985 at Lockwood Beck.

Counting has not been conducted as regularly at places such as Lazenby Reservoir, Wynyard and Longnewton Reservoir, but they have held peaks of 50, 151 and 57 respectively, and it is not unusual to see Pochard on other waters including Skelton Castle, Hemlington Lake and Haverton Hole.

Passage at sea is recorded annually, the highest counts almost always being from Hartlepool in October or November. The highest figures are 81 in October 1963, 64 in November 1967, 46 in November 1972, 39 in October 1977, 44 in October 1982 and 97 on 3 November 1984.

Breeding was mentioned for Charlton's Pond in the years 1903, 1904 and 1919 and for some years after, occasionally involving more than more than one pair. Since 1986, breeding in the county has occurred in most years, with up to eight broods of ducklings being seen, primarily on Saltholme Pools, Haverton Hole and the Reclamation Pond.

Up to three pinioned birds were present on Stewart Park Lake during the 1980s.

An *Aythya* drake showing the characteristics of a Pochard/Ferruginous Duck hybrid was on Seal Sands in January and February 1979 and on 28 December 1981. Another *Aythya* drake with the characteristics of a Pochard/Tufted Duck hybrid was on Seal Sands on 28 December 1981 and 1 January 1982, and similar hybrid drakes have been seen around the North Tees Marshes every year since 1996.

RING-NECKED DUCK *Aythya collaris*

There are nine records of this North American duck for Cleveland. Single drakes have been recorded on: Crookfoot Reservoir on 5 May 1977; Charlton's Pond on 23 April 1988, moving to South Gare the next day; the sea at Hartlepool on 8 May 1993 then Crookfoot Reservoir on 9 - 10 May; the Reclamation Pond from at least 21 July to 25 August 2003; Stewart Park between 6 and 9 November 2006; Hemlington Lake on 14 December 2006; and occasionally between 10 and 26 January 2007. Two ducks were on Coatham Marsh between 16 November 2005 and 8 April 2006, one staying to 8 May 2006.

FERRUGINOUS DUCK *Aythya nyroca*

There are three historic records of this species all from the Redcar-Coatham Marsh area. The earliest is one taken in Coatham duck decoy on 17 January 1850. Another was shot 'locally' and displayed for sale in Redcar on 23 December 1876 and a third was shot with another seen on Coatham Marsh on 3 October 1878 (Nelson 1907).

TUFTED DUCK *Aythya fuligula*

There was a small but continuous increase in the number of Tufted Duck recorded in the area during the 20th century and especially in the last 20-30 years. In the 19th century, Tufted Duck was quite an unusual bird on the marshes and inland waters, and even up to the 1950s flocks seldom exceeded ten birds. In the 1960s, maxima of 41 were seen on Seal Sands, 38 on Crookfoot Reservoir and 30 on Scaling Dam, with numbers remaining steady for the first half of the 1970s. In 1975, 110 were on Scaling Dam in September, followed by 58 on Haverton Hole in March 1976, 86 and 54 at Teesmouth and Crookfoot Reservoir respectively in January 1977 and 167 at Teesmouth in January 1979, the largest number seen on any water in Cleveland at the time.

Since the 1980s, the maximum counts at Teesmouth have increased, and are now more likely to occur in the summer than the winter, 245 being seen in July 2003 and 276 in August 2006. At the reservoirs, numbers have been a little more consistent. The peak at Longnewton Reservoir is usually in September-October with about 40-70 being normal, although 119 were seen in October 1987 and 136 in October 1989. The peak at Scaling Dam often occurs in July-August or November-December and has remained about 50-100. Up to 55 have frequented Charlton's Pond, up to 51 have occurred on Cowpen Bewley Pond, Crookfoot Reservoir and Lockwood Beck, and up to 23 have been seen on Wynyard Lake and Margrove Ponds. A few, usually less than ten are frequently noted on most other waters such as Hart Reservoir, Wilton Centre Lake, Lazenby Reservoir and Poole Hospital Lake, although 65 were on Hart Reservoir in January 1997.

In recent winters a few birds have become tame enough to come for bread, primarily in parks, such as Stewart and Albert Park in Middlesbrough, Locke Park in Redcar and Cowpen Bewley Pond. During most winters about 120-160 are present in Cleveland, but at least 260 were present in January 1997, and over 200 have been counted in every summer since 1995, 376 being seen in August 1998.

The first known breeding was on Charlton's Pond in 1914, with one or two pairs being seen regularly until 1939. After this none were known to breed again in the county until 1960, when single broods of ducklings were seen on Crookfoot Reservoir and Scaling Dam. Up to three broods per year have since been observed at the first locality, and up to eight broods at the latter.

Breeding has been recorded at Lovell Hill in some years since 1970 and Margrove Ponds in most years since 1973. During the last 25 years, ducklings have been seen in some years around the North Tees Marshes, on Coatham Marsh, South Gare, Wilton Centre Lake, Wynyard Lake, Longnewton Reservoir and Haverton Hole.

Since the mid-1970s, the number of Tufted Duck broods for Cleveland as a whole can be summarised as: two broods in 1975 and 1976; five to seven during the years 1977-1983; 13 in 1984; 17 in 1985; 18-22 in the years 1986-1988; 23 broods containing 130 ducklings in 1991; 26 broods containing 155 ducklings in 1992; 28 broods containing about 170 ducklings in both 1993 and 1995; 33 broods containing about 200 ducklings in 1996 and 35 broods in 1999. However, the number of broods has declined in the first few years of the 21st Century, about 20-25 broods being reported annually.

Some pinioned birds were introduced to Rossmere Park Lake in 1959 and up to six broods were seen there during the 1960s, the last known breeding being in 1972.

Relatively few are seen along the coastline, with only one or two being noted in most winters sitting on the sea and a daily maximum of no more than about 10-30 is normal for both autumn and winter passage. The highest count was of 175 flying north past Hartlepool on 15 December 1963.

Drakes showing the characteristics of a hybrid between Tufted Duck and Scaup have been seen around Teesmouth in 1997 and 1998 and on Longnewton Reservoir in 2002 and 2003. At least one duck showing the characteristics of a hybrid between these two species was around Teesmouth in June, August and November 1997. Birds showing characteristics of Pochard/Tufted Duck hybrids are discussed under Pochard.

(GREATER) SCAUP *Aythya marila*

There has been a general decline in the population at Teesmouth. In the winter of 1788/89 approximately 1,000 were 'caught' off Hartlepool and were being sold for one shilling per dozen and Nelson (1907) states that up to 500 could occasionally be seen in the Redcar area.

Since then, the highest numbers have been 250 off Coatham and 170 on Seal Sands in January 1939, 250 in February 1954, 120 in February 1970 and 103 in January 1979 on Seal Sands. More recently, 143 were on the River Tees by the Redcar Ore Terminal in February 1996, with 186 in February 1997. In some winters no more than five to ten Scaup are recorded.

Higher numbers have been recorded flying along the coast, in particular from Hartlepool where at least 837 flew north on 18 November 1962, 208 passed on 18 January 1972 and 132 on 3 November 1984. Very few birds are now recorded actually on the sea, generally only single birds and then only for a day or two.

Scaup are sometimes noted on inland waters though in very small numbers and are most frequent during the spring and summer. All reservoirs such as Scaling Dam, Lockwood Beck, New Marske, Crookfoot, Hart and Longnewton Reservoirs have held Scaup as well as waters such as Charlton's Pond, Haverton Hole, Locke Park, Coatham Marsh and the North Tees Marshes. Most records are of one to four birds, although eight were present on Crookfoot Reservoir in November 1960 and 12 on Coatham Marsh in January 1985.

LESSER SCAUP *Aythya affinis*

Two records exist for this North American species: a drake alternated between Saltholme Pools and the Reclamation Pond from 6 June to at least 31 July 1999 - details of this record are given by Taylor (2000); and a duck was recorded on the Reclamation Pond and Dormans Pool between 7 and 15 January 2006.

(COMMON) EIDER *Somateria mollissima*

This sea duck is principally a regular winter visitor to the Cleveland coastline, although prior to the 1950s it was rather rare; and from the early 1980s a summer flock has also been present.

A report on the birds around Hartlepool, printed in 1815, stated that Eider were extremely rare with a bird being shot in 1789 (Sharp 1816), and Nelson (1907) records only six occurrences for the Tees Bay prior to 1907, the largest of which was a flock of 20 off South Gare on 2 February 1905. Since regular birdwatching began in the 1950s, more have been seen, partly due to more observers, but probably also as a result of the protection of the Farne Islands in Northumberland, the main breeding station to the north of Cleveland. Certainly a distinct increase in numbers also became evident in the mid-1950s in other parts of Britain (Taverner 1959).

The maximum winter counts of birds on the sea are 34 in Tees Bay in January 1958, 93 between Hartlepool and Redcar in January 1969, 54 off South Gare in January 1974, 110 off Redcar in March 1984, 208 off Hartlepool in March 1992 and 358 off Hartlepool in November - December 2005.

The highest numbers seen passing at sea have all been recorded from Hartlepool observatory, with 47 on 22 February 1969, 52 on 2 December 1978, 173 on 13 November 1983, 574 on 7 November 1995 and 1,460 on 12 November 1999, indicating a steady increase at least in the last 20 years of the 20th Century.

The Eider's favoured areas are virtually the whole of the Tees Bay between Hartlepool and South Gare and the stretch of coastline immediately to the south of South Gare as far as Marske. A few birds are occasionally seen inside Hartlepool Docks, on Seal Sands and on the sea to the south-east of Marske. Also, one was on Scaling Dam on 27 November 1960.

The appearance of a summering flock off South Gare in 1981 was unexpected, although there had been records of one or two birds in May, June and July before 1981. In 1981 there were up to 18 in the summer, up to 18 in 1982, up to 26 in 1983, up to 59 in 1984 and up to 39 in 1985. No more than two were present in the summers of 1986 and 1987, but up to 15 were noted in 1988, 30 in 1989, 55 in 1990, 63 in 1991, 69 in 1993, 84 in 1998 and 85 in 2000. Another summering flock appeared at Hartlepool in 1991, with up to 30 birds being seen, up to 52 being there in 1993, 49 in 1996 and 40 in 2004. It can be speculated that perhaps Eider will breed in Cleveland in the future.

There are two ringing recoveries for this species, both individuals being ringed on the Farne Islands in May 1965 and June 1980 and found dead at Hartlepool in May 1968 and April 1991 respectively.

KING EIDER *Somateria spectabilis*

A superb drake of this Arctic breeding species was at South Gare for about three hours and subsequently at Hartlepool for one and a half hours on 4 July 1998. Details are given by Blick (1999).

LONG-TAILED DUCK *Clangula hyemalis*

This duck is a winter visitor primarily occurring along the coastline, the vast majority of birds being noted between mid-October and early April. Birds are occasionally seen in May and September and very rarely in June-August.

Passage at sea is most obvious in October and November when onshore winds can produce quite high numbers, a total of 66 passing north off Hartlepool on 20, 21 and 22 October 1970 combined. The largest number seen on one day was 53 flying north on 9 November 2001, also off Hartlepool.

The highest count of birds on the sea during the last 30 years was 24 off Redcar on 6 February 1983, but in some winters only one or two birds are seen. It would seem that the status and numbers of this bird have not changed during the last century, it being recorded by Nelson (1907) as an irregular winter visitor with the highest number being at least 40 shot off Redcar between October 1887 and February 1888. About 40 were present in the Tees Bay on one occasion in mid-October 1887.

Between mid-October and April, a few birds are frequently present on Seal Sands and on the sea, almost anywhere between Hartlepool and Saltburn, usually with other species of duck.

Inland records are not unusual with at least one bird being noted about every two years. Some of these can stay for several weeks. Singles having been seen on Scaling Dam, Lockwood Beck, Crookfoot Reservoir, Charlton's Pond, New Marske Reservoir, Locke Park, Coatham Marsh, and the North Tees Marshes. Additionally, two have been seen on Scaling Dam, Longnewton Reservoir and Coatham Marsh on occasions, and one was found in a ditch between Yarm and Stockton in the autumn of 1824.

COMMON SCOTER *Melanitta nigra*

There has been a noticeable decline in the numbers of this sea duck spending the winter months off Cleveland's shoreline in recent decades, but there has not been a corresponding decline in those passing along the coastline.

During the 19th century it was described as a common winter visitor and up to 1963 it was normal for several hundred Common Scoter to spend the winter off Seaton Carew and between Redcar and Marske. Since then relatively few large flocks have been seen, with the exception of 220 off Redcar in November 1974, 630 in November 1982 and 420 in December 2004. Also, 514 were off Hartlepool in November 2005 and 365 were off Saltburn in November 1974, 310 in November 1997, 500 in November 2001 and 490 in November 2003. However, in some winters no more than 30-50 birds are seen on the sea.

The passage of Common Scoter along the coastline can be quite spectacular and starts as early as late June. The highest numbers are usually noted during the months July-November, all counts involving birds flying north off Hartlepool observatory: 850 on 10 August 1958; 1,009 over the two days 13-14 August 1966; 437 on 29 June 1968; 1,082 on 6 November 1982; 527 on 12-13 November 1983; 1,850 on 20 October 1991; 1,600 on 3 November 1998; 1,120 on 12 November 1999 and 665 on 9 November 2001. A few birds can also usually be seen passing along the coast in every other month of the year. An unusual pale coffee-coloured individual passed Hartlepool on 14 November 1964.

It is not unusual for a bird or two to be seen on Seal Sands or in Hartlepool Docks, probably sheltering from rough seas, but inland records are quite infrequent. Since systematic bird-recording began in this area in the 1950s, there has been an average of only two records of birds on freshwater every three years. Most concern single birds, but two or three have been seen a few times and 13 were on Scaling Dam on 16 April 1992. This reservoir has most of the inland records, the remainder being from Lockwood Beck, Crookfoot, Hart and Longnewton Reservoirs, Saltholme Pools, Coatham Marsh and Charlton's Pond.

SURF SCOTER *Melanitta perspicillata*

There are six records of this North American sea duck: a drake flying north past South Gare and Hartlepool on 17 September 1977 (and also observed passing Whitburn Observatory, Tyne & Wear); a duck which was present amongst 400-600 Common Scoter off Redcar from at least 10 to 30 November 1982; single drakes heading north past Hartlepool on 17 September 1990, 4 November 1995 and 23 September 2000, and a single duck off Hartlepool, on 11 November 2006.

VELVET SCOTER *Melanitta fusca*

This sea duck regularly winters off Cleveland, most sightings being in the Hartlepool and Redcar areas, although it used to be frequent off Seaton Carew until the Common Scoter flocks stopped resorting to that area.

November is the peak month for sightings, although it is quite regularly seen in the months July-February and occasionally during March-June. In recent years more birds have been noted as they pass along the coastline, rather than on the sea.

Velvet Scoter numbers appear to have changed little over the years, the highest number mentioned by Nelson (1907) is approximately 30 off Redcar during December 1895. More recently the highest counts have been: 24 off the Tees on 7 April 1956; 31 off Seaton Carew on 1 January 1961; 22 off Redcar on 6 November 1976; 24 passing

Hartlepool on 19 November 1991 and 6 October 2002; and 34 off Hartlepool on 23 November 2003; with probably the same 34 recorded at Saltburn on 27 December 2003.

There are still odd records on the sea off Seaton Carew, and occasionally Seal Sands. The only records on freshwater are a drake found dying on the ice at Locke Park on 7 March 1965, eight on Scaling Dam on 9 December 1960, one on Scaling Dam from 24 September to 24 December 1961 and one on Coatham Marsh from 3 to 14 April 1987.

BUFFLEHEAD *Bucephala albeola*

There is one record of this American duck, an immature male on Coatham Marsh from 1 to 7 June 1994. This is the ninth record for Britain, but the origin of this bird is open to speculation, in line with other transatlantic vagrant waterfowl.

(COMMON) GOLDENEYE *Bucephala clangula*

This is generally the commonest of the diving ducks on Seal Sands in the winter, but is almost invariably outnumbered by Tufted Duck and Pochard on the reservoirs. Although one or two are not unusual in September, birds usually start to appear in mid to late October, the numbers building up to a peak in December, January or February. They begin to move out in March and April with stragglers staying into May and occasionally birds are seen in the summer months.

The numbers of wintering birds at Teesmouth remained quite steady over at least 20 years up to 1977, then increased rapidly. The reasons for this increase are unclear but some possible factors are discussed by Smith (1984). The peak number recorded during the 1954/55 winter was 41, with 67 in 1963/64, 79 in 1976/77, 186 in 1977/78, 205 in 1978/79, 224 in 1979/80, 234 in 1980/81 and 470 in 1981/82 winter. At the time of this last count, Teesmouth held the 5th highest number of Goldeneye in Britain and was rated as a Nationally Important wintering ground for the species with the qualifying criteria of over 150 birds counted for five consecutive winters. Since January and February 1982 no more than 153 birds have been observed at Teesmouth; again the reasons for this decline are unclear. Also since 1995, most birds seen in winter have been on the area of water just south of Redcar Ore Terminal rather than on Seal Sands. In addition, up to 24 have been seen on the sea off Skinningrove in recent winters.

A few birds regularly occur on Saltholme Pools, Haverton Hole and Coatham Marsh and are included in the counts for Teesmouth. There are four inland waters that also hold wintering Goldeneye when they are not frozen over: Scaling Dam usually has 15-25 as a winter maximum, but 39 were seen in March 1972; Lockwood Beck, normally between six and ten birds, but 16 in March 1981; Crookfoot Reservoir, which in some winters has very few Goldeneye, held 43 in December 1977; and Longnewton Reservoir, which normally has 12-25 in winter, had a recorded maximum of 47 in January 2003.

Most other inland waters such as Hart Reservoir, Charlton's Pond, Hemlington Lake and New Marske Reservoir hold a few birds in some winters and one or two have been occasionally recorded on lakes such as Albert Park and Locke Park. Single birds have been seen on Billingham Bottoms and on the River Tees at Yarm and Stockton on more than one occasion.

Passage at sea can be witnessed at its best in October and November, especially if strong onshore winds prevail. Birds can also be seen over the sea in the months September-April and very occasionally in the summer. The highest counts are: 212 flying north at South Gare on 25 October 1966 followed by another 124 over the next two days; 425 flying north off Hartlepool over the 4 days 21-24 October 1970; at least 510 flying north off South Gare on 2 November 1986; about 1,200 flying north off South Gare on 20 October 1991; and 230 flying north at South Gare on 14 November 1999. When large numbers are passing, it is quite usual for flocks of Goldeneye to be seen on the sea, and to remain for a few days after the main passage. Up to 200 have been noted at such times and flocks can occur virtually anywhere along the coastline, with occasionally one or two birds resorting to Hartlepool Docks.

SMEW *Mergellus albellus*

This delightful sawbill is recorded in most winters principally during the months December-March, although the earliest and latest records are 4 October (1994) and 4 May (1946). In recent years this bird has been recorded more frequently in the area.

The favoured sites are Coatham Marsh, Scaling Dam, Lockwood Beck and Crookfoot Reservoir, and since 1998, Saltholme Pools and the Reclamation Pond. Birds have also been noted on other waters such as Wynyard Lake, Wilton Lake, Charlton's Pond, Hart Reservoir, Hartlepool Docks, on the sea between Hartlepool and Redcar and on the stream at Saltburn.

Historical records include two males shot at Teesmouth in December 1829 (Temperley 1951) and a male shot on a pond near Skelton in the winter of 1900 (Nelson 1907). Also, it is reported that the species was occasionally shot on the River Tees near Yarm (Nelson 1907).

There are a few records of birds passing along the coast in December-February, usually singles, but eight passed South Gare on 17 November 1966. The highest recent counts have been five on Coatham Marsh in February 1985, although at least eight and possibly 14 birds were noted in January-March 1985 spread around various locations in the county. Eight were present on Coatham Marsh on 7 February 1996, 10-12 on the Reclamation Pond in January-March 1999 and 13 on 14 March 1999. Five birds commuted between Saltholme Pools and the Reclamation Pond in the first three months of 2000, 2002 and 2003, and there were seven on the Reclamation Pond on 8 February 2001.

Based on records since 1960 the proportion of redheads to adult males is about 5:1.

RED-BREASTED MERGANSER *Mergus serrator*

The breeding range of this sawbill has slowly spread south from Scotland into England during the 20th century, although the expansion in the breeding range has not been as rapid as that of Goosander. Since suitable nesting habitat is lacking, the possibility of Red-breasted Merganser breeding in Cleveland must be considered to be low.

Nelson (1907) stated that it was a regular winter visitor, but records suggest that it was less common in the past than it is today. Historically the earliest and latest dates reported by Nelson were 22 September (1903) and 11 May (1898). Now it can be seen throughout the year around Hartlepool and South Gare, though with very few records for June-August.

Favoured areas are Hartlepool Harbour and Docks, North and South Gares and Redcar although it probably frequents every part of the county's coastline. A few usually occur on Seal Sands during the winter and in most years there are records of birds on freshwater.

A few birds are seen in September, but it is usually October before any numbers occur and the peak (of about 40-60) occurs between mid-November and mid-March. At least 66 were known to have been around Teesmouth in January 2001, 70 in November 2004 and 85 on Seal Sands on 22 February 2005.

Inland records are received for approximately two years out of every three, most being observed on Scaling Dam. One or two birds have occurred there on at least ten occasions, although five were present there in December 1975 and October 1982. Up to three birds have also been seen on Lockwood Beck, Crookfoot Reservoir, Charlton's Pond, Coatham Marsh, Hemlington Lake, Longnewton Reservoir and on several stretches of the River Tees. Up to eight were noted on Hart Reservoir in February and March 1979, coinciding with the highest count in Hartlepool Docks of 34 in January 1979. These inland records are spread evenly throughout the months October-April with very few records in June, July and September.

Movement along the coast can be quite noticeable in September-November, especially during strong onshore winds, 15-30 being regular daily counts in some autumns off Hartlepool; the highest count was 71 passing there on 21 October 1970.

Perhaps the last place one would expect to find a Red-breasted Merganser is on the roadside in a town. A drake was picked up in Stockton on 28 April 1961 and later released by the RSPCA.

A drake in the South Gare area from November 1989 to April 1990 carried an orange wing tag, and had been ringed on Holy Island, Northumberland on 19 August 1989. It had returned to the Holy Island area by 11 August 1990.

GOOSANDER *Mergus merganser*

There has been a slight but distinct, increase in the numbers of this duck being recorded in Cleveland over the last 20-30 years, no doubt due to the spread of breeding birds from Scotland into northern England. Goosanders were first known to breed in Scotland in 1871, birds presumably originating from Scandinavia. Despite much persecution by fishing interests the birds expanded into England where the first known breeding occurred in Northumberland in 1941 (Galloway and Meek 1979-83). By 1965 the bird was breeding in County Durham and by 1970 in Yorkshire (Mather 1986). Breeding was first proven in Cleveland in 1996, when ducklings were seen during May on the River Tees at Aislaby. Prior to 1996 there were one or two records of ducks seen on the highest reaches of the Tees in Cleveland in May and June, but these may have involved birds that were breeding further up the Tees in County Durham. Ducklings were present on the River Leven in June 1998 and a duck was seen to leave a hole in a tree in the same area in 2000, and ducks in suitable habitat, or ducklings have been seen in May/June in most years since then.

Although there are records for every month of the year, the majority are in November-March. There appears to be a slight movement of Goosander through Cleveland from November to January, and then a return of birds in March. Stragglers and perhaps local breeding birds are sometimes present in April, August and September, but very few are seen in May, June or July.

The Goosander's favourite areas are usually the five largest freshwater reservoirs, Scaling Dam, Crookfoot Reservoir, Lockwood Beck, Wynyard and Longnewton Reservoir. Birds are sometimes noted at most other smaller waters such as Charlton's

Pond, Hart Reservoir, Wilton Centre Lake, Hemlington Lake, Albert and Stewart Parks, and New Marske Reservoir.

It is not unusual for a bird or two to spend a few days on Seal Sands with wintering flocks of Goldeneye and Scaup, or to be seen on the Tees around the Preston Park-Yarm area, perhaps when ice covers other freshwater habitats.

The maximum numbers are seen in winter, probably related to the severity of the weather in Britain and Scandinavia. In some years no more than 15-20 are observed on the reservoirs, although the highest counts are 66 in Wynyard on 15 February 1999 and 67 on Longnewton Reservoir on 18 January 2001.

In most years a few are seen along the coastline, the highest counts being 15 passing Hartlepool on 8 December 1968 and 21 passing Cowbar on 24 August 1998.

An immature in Hartlepool Docks on 29 December 1977 carried a yellow wing-tag, indicating that it had been caught as a duckling on the North Tyne in July 1977.

RUDDY DUCK
Oxyura jamaicensis

This North American duck was first added to the official British List in 1971 having spread north and east from south-west England since the late 1950s; it first bred in Yorkshire in 1980 (Mather 1986), County Durham in 1986 and Cleveland in 1994.

The first Cleveland record was a duck on Scaling Dam from 24 October to 2 November 1982, an immature male was seen at three places in September 1983, followed by one in summer 1987, two in late September 1989, two in 1991 and seven in 1992.

Numbers increased rapidly from 1992: 11 birds in 1993; about 30 in 1994 including the first ducklings to be reared in Cleveland (four broods); and at least 40 in 1995, birds being present from March to November. In 1996 at least ten broods of ducklings were seen and birds were present from 29 February to 12 December. By 1998 Ruddy Ducks could be observed throughout the year. In 1999, 69 were counted on the North Tees Marshes in October, then 78 in October 2000 and 151 in September 2002. Numbers have dipped since 2003, presumably as the cull of this duck across Britain takes effect. Significant numbers were shot at Teesmouth in the summer of 2007.

The number of broods of ducklings has remained about 10-15 since 1998, favoured

---

breeding sites being Haverton Hole, Saltholme Pools, the Reclamation Pond and Margrove Ponds, and ducklings are known to hatch as late as September.

RED GROUSE (WILLOW PTARMIGAN)
Lagopus lagopus

Once thought to be the only bird unique to Britain, the Red Grouse is now considered to be a sub-species of the Willow Ptarmigan, which is found across northern Europe and America. It must be one of the most ignored species on the Cleveland list, presumably because it inhabits one of the least-watched habitats, namely, moorland and, with the exception of four records, has never been known to move from this habitat. A trip to the Cleveland section of the North York Moors National Park can nearly always be rewarded with good views of birds and the noisy go-back, go-back, go-back cry is one of the distinctive sounds of the area.

Despite appearances, the moorland is not a natural landscape and about 5,000 years ago was covered by forest. For centuries the moors have been grazed by sheep and today sheep farming and management for grouse shooting continue to maintain the landscape.

Between October and March small patches of heather are burned on an 8 to 15 year cycle to make a mosaic of heather of different heights. This provides habitat suitable for nesting and feeding for birds such as Red Grouse. Without controlled burning and grazing, much of this fragile environment would eventually return to woodland with heather being a minor part of the ground flora. However in the past, predatory animals and birds were eliminated from these areas by using any means possible to ensure Red Grouse survival in preference to other species.

Whilst the birds breed and feed on the moorland in summer, they sometimes move to adjacent upland fields to feed during severe cold in the winter. During the winter of 1878-1879, five were shot and another seen at Redcar. More recently, one was found dead by the roadside in Middlesbrough on 9 March 1994, one was seen at Dormans Pool on 14 December 1997 and one was in a Guisborough garden on 8 August 2002.

The present breeding population is estimated at 120-150 pairs.

BLACK GROUSE *Tetrao tetrix*

In the 19th century, there were several attempts to introduce this species to the moorland in Cleveland as well as to many other parts of the North York Moors.

It is known to have been 'put down' (introduced) in the 1840s along moor edges and in plantations around Girrick and in 1860 at Birk Brow. The records presumably resulting from these introductions include a breeding record at Waupley in 1860 and a male which spent some weeks in a rabbit warren on the cliffs near Loftus, probably Boulby, in the winter of 1864 (Nelson 1907). Apart from these efforts, there have been only four other records of Black Grouse in Cleveland: a male on Guisborough Moor in October 1903, two males beside Lockwood Beck in about 1954 and a pair beside Scaling Dam on 5 August 1962. The fourth record is of a female at South Gare on 18 April 1992.

Additionally, a bird described as a Black Grouse-Pheasant hybrid was shot on moorland near Loftus on 30 October 1894 (Nelson 1907).

RED-LEGGED PARTRIDGE *Alectoris rufa*

The introduction of this colourful bird to Britain was organised by sportsmen for shooting purposes, mainly in the 19th and early 20th centuries.

The first known record for Cleveland was in January 1899 when one was seen at Coatham, although the species was known to have been released not very far to the south of the county boundary in 1860 and 1890, in the Loftus-Moorsholm area in 1906 and near Wynyard before 1876 (Nelson 1907, Temperley 1951)

Records were rather few and far between up to about 1976, but since then it has been recorded annually and has increased fairly dramatically, the present population being estimated at about 90-120 pairs. Birds can now be found in most parts of the agricultural area in Cleveland. The increase is fairly well-documented, there being no known pairs in 1968, perhaps one in 1972, three-four in 1977-1980, about ten in 1982-1983, at least 20 pairs in 1986, probably 30-40 pairs in 1990 and about 60 pairs in 2000.

Apart from being in many fields, odd birds are occasionally seen amongst the slag tips at South Gare, one or two birds have been around Dormans Pool-Port Clarence Slag Tip since April 1977 (and seen with young in 1986), and single birds have been observed in suburban gardens at Acklam on 5 February 1981 and 22 March 1982.

Red-legged Partridge are still being artificially introduced to one or two areas, thus counts of 50 at Scaling Dam on 8 November 1986, could be just such introductions as opposed to a genuine natural gathering. There were also 153 at New Marske on 2 November 2006 and 210 at the same place on 8 October 2007.

The picture was further complicated by the introduction of Chukar and Chukar/Red-legged Partridge hybrids (known as Ogridge's Partridge), such individuals having been seen in Yorkshire and in Cleveland between 1981 and 1995.

GREY PARTRIDGE *Perdix perdix*

Cleveland has a substantial amount of agricultural land and much of this is suitable for Grey Partridge, though populations can also be found around some of the

---

industrial sites on Teesside. The breeding population is estimated at about 300-400 pairs. However, there has recently been quite a dramatic reduction in the British breeding population, probably due to intensive farming methods, which so far appears to have had little effect in Cleveland.

After the breeding season, the number of birds is at its highest and, assuming a reasonably successful season, there could be as many as 1,000 Grey Partridges in Cleveland at this time, the largest coveys being reported in the winter months. In most years these comprise of about 12-20 birds, but no doubt two or three coveys may combine, up to 30-50 birds being seen together quite frequently. In February 1986, during severe cold and snowy weather, at least 73 Grey Partridges formed a loose gathering in the fields between Redcar and Marske. On 29 October 1995, 72 were in the same fields.

Very occasionally, single birds are seen out of their normal habitat, there being records of birds in Middlesbrough centre, on Hartlepool Headland and on Seaton Carew beach.

(COMMON) QUAIL *Coturnix coturnix*

Due to its secretive nature, habit of calling at night and its liking for out-of-the-way fields, it is rarely seen, but is heard most years. Occasional birds are seen in spring and autumn, whilst on passage.

In the 19th century it was released in Wynyard prior to 1829 and recorded as breeding at Moorsholm in 1859, Greatham in 1868 and the Loftus area between 1875 and 1890. The agricultural methods then employed were probably more suited to the birds' breeding requirements, since there are no definite breeding records in the 20th century. However, Quail is extremely difficult to prove as a breeding bird.

This bird has been recorded every year since 1992, although it was almost certainly missed in earlier years. At least seven were noted in 1952, 12 in 1989 and 2000, and nine in 2001. The earliest and latest dates are 18 April (2002) and 2 September (1952), although most records are in May and June.

Favoured localities in recent years include Grinkle Park, Lingdale and Pinchinthorpe, although birds may call from any suitable field, especially on passage. There are at least two records of birds in gardens, and a few records of passage birds at Hartlepool and South Gare.

(COMMON) PHEASANT *Phasianus colchicus*

The Pheasant is one of only four species that have been deliberately introduced to Britain and breeds in Cleveland; the other three being Red-legged Partridge, Canada Goose and Little Owl. However, with the possible exception of a small number of Red-legged Partridges, the Pheasant is the only that is continuously being re-introduced. Several estates rear Pheasants as a commercial venture, releasing them into the wild to provide birds for shooting interests. Without this annual injection of birds into the system and the annual killing of Pheasants, it would be interesting to see how well the species would fare 'on its own'.

Pheasants breed in many areas of woodland, large and small, where it has not been deliberately introduced, so it can spread albeit rather slowly. The natural breeding population in Cleveland is very difficult to determine, but is probably in the region of 500-1,500 pairs.

It is not unusual for birds to be seen around the North Tees Marshes during the winter months and there are a few records from places like Hartlepool and South Gare. Nelson (1907) occasionally recorded Pheasants on the beach at Redcar.

RED-THROATED DIVER *Gavia stellata*

About 90% of the divers seen in Cleveland are identified as this species and as far as can be ascertained by past records, it has always been quite common along the coastline during the months September-April. It is also not unusual for a few birds to be seen during the summer months.

There are regular gatherings of this diver between Crimdon Dene and Hartlepool and between Redcar and Saltburn. It is also regularly recorded passing along the coast, especially during winter storms. Depending upon the weather conditions, high numbers of birds can be involved in these coastal movements. The majority of recording of sea-bird movement is conducted from Hartlepool Headland, although sea-watches are also carried out at both the North and South Gares.

The highest numbers are almost always in January, with peak counts including 65 on the sea off Hartlepool North Sands on 21 January 1978 and over 100 between Redcar and Saltburn on 22 January 1977. Daily totals of between 60 and 110 have also been recorded passing Hartlepool on 11 January 1964 and 1974, 1 February 1976, 15 and 27 January 1977, 24 December 1978 and 30 November 1997. Rather unexpectedly, the highest count occurred on 12 April 1970 during strong onshore winds when 180 flew north at Hartlepool. It is also worth noting that a total of 223 Red-throated Divers passed Hartlepool on the three days 14 to 16 January 1977.

Away from the open sea, Hartlepool Docks and the river mouth by Seal Sands are areas regularly visited by one or two birds in most winters, although up to 10 were present on Seal Sands in December 1995 and 24 in December 2004.

Since 1962, there has been an average of close to a bird per year on fresh water, the majority having occurred between December and mid-April, with a few in September-

November. Summer records are of a single bird on Coatham Marsh on 27 July 1985 and one, about one week dead, at Scaling Dam on 21 May 1967.

Birds have been recorded on more than one occasion on such inland waters as Hart Reservoir, Haverton Hole, Charlton's Pond, Scaling Dam, Lockwood Beck, Coatham Marsh and Crookfoot Reservoir, and could occur on almost any stretch on water. It has been noted that a large proportion of these inland birds are weak, oiled or both. The most unusual record for this species must be Albert Park in Middlesbrough where one was seen to land on 1 February 1963 but later died. Most inland records involve single birds, but two were present on Hart Reservoir from 3 to 7 March 1960 and on Scaling Dam on 13 February 1977.

BLACK-THROATED DIVER *Gavia arctica*

This diver is an annual visitor in very small numbers to Cleveland mainly during the winter months, but it is seen occasionally at other times of the year.

Specific identification of divers at long range can be difficult so this species may occur more frequently than the average record of nine to ten birds per year indicates.

It can be found almost anywhere offshore from November to April, and since 1980, one or two have been noted in Hartlepool Docks in most years, principally in December, January and February.

There are few records for the months May-October, but summer-plumaged birds have been seen passing along the coastline on more than one occasion in June, July and August. Rarely are more than two seen together, but four birds were off Saltburn on 13 April 1939; Redcar in February and March 1974 and flying past Hartlepool on 12 February 1977. The highest count is up to five off Redcar in January and February 1977.

There are 12 records of this diver on inland waters, three of them being in 1981. These records follow the pattern shown by Red-throated Diver, occurring almost entirely in the months of December-March. The earliest known inland record concerns one on Hart Reservoir on 27 January 1960 and singles have been seen on Coatham Marsh, Charlton's Pond, Wynyard Lake, Cattersty Pond, Crookfoot Reservoir (twice), Scaling Dam (four records), and a bird in summer plumage on Lockwood Beck Reservoir from 17 to 21 September 1988.

Between 1962 and 2006 there were 45 Red-throated Divers and 12 Black-throated Divers seen on inland waters and, between 1975 and 2004 about 30 Red-throated Divers and 16 Black-throated Divers recorded in Hartlepool Docks. It seems strange that when the two small divers can be viewed at reasonably close range on an enclosed area of water, the ratio of Red-throated to Black-throated is about 2:1 or 3:1. However, when they are seen at sea, the ratio soars to about 20:1, assuming correct identification. There is no evidence to suppose that Black-throated Divers seek sheltered water more readily than the slightly small Red-throated Diver, although the former does feed mainly on freshwater lochs during the breeding season whereas the latter generally feeds at sea.

GREAT NORTHERN DIVER *Gavia immer*

This is the largest of the three divers regularly encountered off the Cleveland coast, with an average of about ten birds per annum being recorded during the last 40 years. However, none were noted in 1963 and 1967, yet 16 passed Hartlepool in the last two months of 1968. Another six flew past Hartlepool on 14 November 1999 and 15 were counted between Redcar and Saltburn on 6 January 2007.

The majority of birds occur in the months October-April, with very few seen in the months May-September. Almost all are in complete immature or winter plumage, including some of the birds observed occasionally in May-June. There are very few records of birds in summer plumage, but these include the first inland record of a single bird on Crookfoot Reservoir on 5 November 1961. Rarely do birds venture further inland than the near coastal waters, although Great Northern Divers are occasionally seen on Seal Sands and in Hartlepool Docks, up to five being present at the former locality in February 1983.

The only other inland record concerns a single bird on Scaling Dam from 5 to 11 March 1994. The only bird to be found dead in the recent past was picked up in Hartlepool Docks on 2 January 1977, having been present since mid-December 1976. On dissection, it was found to be an adult female just beginning to moult into summer plumage, but no cause of death could be found.

No particular part of the coastline appears to be favoured by this diver, but the stretch between South Gare and Marske usually holds up to four birds in most winters. Passage birds are usually seen off Hartlepool Headland, no doubt because the majority of sea-watching is done from this point.

WHITE-BILLED DIVER
(YELLOW-BILLED DIVER) *Gavia adamsii*

There are five records of this spectacular Arctic species, all involving single birds. The first was in Hartlepool fish quay when large numbers of observers were able to study the bird at close range during its stay from 14 to 22 February 1981; the other records are from Cowbar on 14 February 1996, and of birds passing Hartlepool on 14 September 2002, 18 October 2002 and 13 October 2007.

LITTLE GREBE *Tachybaptus ruficollis*

This is the more common of the two grebes that breed in Cleveland, although there are probably no more than 50 breeding pairs each year.

The majority of Little Grebes breed on the North Tees Marshes, in particular, Haverton Hole, Cowpen Marsh, Saltholme Pools, Dormans Pool and the Reclamation Pond. The other localities to hold regular breeding pairs are Coatham Marsh, Cowpen Bewley Pond, Scaling Dam, South Gare, Margrove Ponds and Charlton's Pond. Also, single pairs have been seen in recent summers at Guisborough Priory, Hemlington Lake, Wilton Centre Lake, Coatham Stob Pools at Elton, Skelton Castle, Portrack Marsh, Lovell Hill, Cattersty Pond and Stewart Park. Eggs are regularly laid in March, small young often being seen in late March and early April.

From August to the end of the year, there is a general dispersal of birds from the breeding sites to other waters. This is assumed to take place at night since birds have rarely been seen in flight, but dead birds have been found after colliding with overhead wires.

Small gatherings are regularly recorded on reservoirs after the breeding season, in particular, Scaling Dam, Crookfoot, Hart and New Marske Reservoirs with between six and fifteen birds being quite usual, although 19 were on Crookfoot Reservoir on 7 August 1976, and 21 on Scaling Dam in September 1991 and October 2003.

Significant numbers have been seen on the North Tees marshes in August and September, generally no more than 100 although 152 were counted on 13 September 2000, including 98 on the Reclamation Pond.

As the weather deteriorates in November and December, most Little Grebes leave the area, presumably moving south, but a few birds remain. The occasional bird spends a few days or weeks on park lakes, such as Albert Park or Ropner Park, and should the fresh water freeze over, they resort to Hartlepool Docks, Seal Sands and occasionally inland reaches of the River Tees around Eaglescliffe and Yarm. This species' favourite part of Hartlepool Docks, the timber pools, were reclaimed during the 1960s, though up to five have been seen in the docks in recent years.

It is unusual to see this species on the open sea, but singles have been observed on several occasions between September and December and there are records of seven off Redcar on 8 November 1905 and a flock of six sheltering behind the Hartlepool breakwater during a strong northerly gale on 1 October 1979.

In late February and March the number of birds begins to increase, drawing attention to their presence by their distinctive trilling call.

GREAT CRESTED GREBE *Podiceps cristatus*

During the latter half of the 19th Century, Great Crested Grebes were killed throughout Britain for their feathers, resulting in near-extinction for the bird nationally and a temporary absence in this area for over 100 years.

This water bird can now be found in Cleveland throughout the year, breeding on several waters, and wintering on the sea in two or three areas along the coast.

The first known breeding attempt in the 20th Century came from Charlton's Pond in 1944, although the eggs were taken. It was then another 24 years before young birds were successfully reared, by a single pair on Scaling Dam in 1968. Pairs have attempted to breed at Scaling Dam every year since. One pair has nested on Wynyard Lake every year since 1973 and recently a second pair has attempted to breed there. One pair reared young on Crookfoot Reservoir in about 1976 and attempted to breed in several other years, but this water body is a poor breeding site since it has virtually no marginal vegetation. One pair has nested annually on Charlton's Pond since 1980, and has been known to rear two broods in one summer. Single pairs have also frequented Lockwood Beck since about 1983. Pairs have reared young on Haverton Hole, Saltholme Pools, Dormans Pool and the Reclamation Pond in some years since 1986, and a pair has reared young at Cowpen Bewley Pond in several years since about 1982.

By 2001-03, between two and five pairs were nesting on Haverton Hole, Saltholme Pools, Dormans Pool, the Reclamation Pond and Scaling Dam, and about 25 pairs have bred in Cleveland each year since about 2000. In spring it is quite usual to see non-breeding birds on the inland waters with approximately 30-35 pairs usually being counted in April-May. There is frequent evidence of territorial disputes between pairs suggesting a shortage of suitable nesting sites. A small amount of planting of suitable vegetation on some waters, combined with some measure of protection for nesting birds would probably increase the breeding population.

At times there are autumn gatherings of this grebe, similar to those of Little Grebe, with Crookfoot Reservoir (up to 14 birds) and Scaling Dam (up to 20 birds) being favoured locations in the 1980s. The Reclamation Pond has held the highest numbers since about 2000, with up to 42 in August 2005.

Quite recently Great Crested Grebe has also become a regular winter visitor on the coastal waters, especially in the months January to March, the largest gathering of 69 birds being noted in Hartlepool Bay on 15 February 1997 and 14 February 1998. Also, 10 to 15 birds can sometimes be observed off Hartlepool North Sands and a few birds pass along the coastline in autumn.

RED-NECKED GREBE *Podiceps grisegena*

This bird is an annual visitor, mainly in the winter, but with records from August to March. There are more records for January and February than any other month and most of the birds seen in August and September are recorded passing along the coast.

Few birds have been noted in the months April-July, but these include individuals in beautiful breeding plumage on Cowpen Marsh on 6 May 1962, off Redcar on 8 June 1992, South Gare on 29 May 1992 and 20 June 1998. A bird also summered on Scaling Dam in 1993 and 1994. It, or another, was there in March-April 1995 and February-March 1997, but unfortunately never attracted a mate.

In most years eight to ten birds are recorded, although at least 19 were seen in February 1979 and 16-18 in each of the years 1996, 1997 and 1998, but only four in 2004.

It is interesting to speculate how many birds were actually involved in 1891, when Nelson (1907) wrote 'there were at least 35 off Redcar on 19 January 1891 and many more in the following month'.

Virtually all of the coastal records concern birds between the Hartlepool Headland and Marske, including Hartlepool Docks, Seaton Carew, Seal Sands, North and South Gares and Redcar. As with a number of other species, this probably reflects the distribution of birdwatchers as much as the grebes.

Inland the bird is not recorded every year. Since 1973 most inland birds are reported from Scaling Dam, and occasionally from the Tees Marshes, Lockwood Beck, Crookfoot Reservoir, Hart Reservoir, Longnewton Reservoir, Hemlington Lake and Wilton Centre Lake. As with virtually all water birds which live in coastal areas, a small percentage become oiled, with two of the 19 birds recorded in February 1979 dying as a result.

SLAVONIAN GREBE *Podiceps auritus*

Care must be exercised when identifying small grebes, especially in transitional plumages. Slavonian Grebes are more likely to occur than Black-necked Grebes on the sea in this area and are mostly recorded in the months October to April, with the occasional May and August record.

Between 1940 and 1973 there was an average of just over one bird every two years, although in 1907, Nelson wrote that this species was an annual visitor along the coast-line. Between 1973 and 1994 there was an average of three birds every year, although none was recorded in 1980 and in the last ten years there has been an average of seven - eight per year, but at least ten in 1996, 2002 and 2006.

The stretch of coastline between South Gare and Saltburn seems to be the favourite location, nearly 50% of the records since 1940 being from this area of sea. A few birds have been seen around Hartlepool Headland and Docks, and in the North Gare - Seal Sands area. Compared to Black-necked Grebe there are relatively few records of Slavonian Grebe on freshwater, although at least 10 Slavonian Grebes have occurred on Scaling Dam and occasionally birds are seen on other inland waters, including Lockwood Beck, Crookfoot Reservoir, Hart Reservoir, Portrack Marsh, Haverton Hole, Coatham Marsh, Saltholme Pools, the Reclamation Pond, Hemlington Lake and even the small pond by Teesside Crown Court in central Middlesbrough.

On freshwater most birds stay no more than a few days, but one remained on Coatham Marsh from 2 March to 2 May 1988 and one or two commuted between Seal Sands and the Reclamation Pond from 24 October 2003 to 2 May 2004. All three birds had acquired complete summer plumage by the end of April. There are several other records of summer-plumaged birds in April, and a single on Scaling Dam on 27 May 1992.

Three birds have been noted together on several occasions and a group of four were off South Gare on 8 December 2001, and up to six commuted between Seal Sands and the Reclamation Pond in February - April 2006.

What must rate as one of the most interesting recoveries concerns an oiled bird near Saltburn in April 1963, which had been ringed as a full-grown bird on Lake Molotooskoye, about 250 miles north-north-east of Moscow, Russia, in July 1962. This suggests that at least some of the birds seen in Cleveland are Scandinavian or Russian in origin, rather than Scottish.

BLACK-NECKED GREBE *Podiceps nigricollis*

This bird is a rare, but annual, visitor to Cleveland, appearing almost invariably on freshwater rather than the sea. The birds seen in the 1940s-60s, occurred mostly in the latter half of the year and averaged just over two birds every three years, whereas the birds in the 1970s and 1980s were more widely spread throughout the year, with a slight bias towards August and October. During this period occurrences averaged just over one per year.

Birds seen since 1990 have principally occurred in the months April and May and have averaged five birds per year, though none was seen in 1996. At least ten occurred in 2002 including the highest recent count of four on Saltholme Pools from 22 to 24 April 2002, and 12 in 2004. There is also a record of 11 off South Gare on 30 October 1976; these birds were seen to fly out to sea.

Since 1970, the favoured localities have been Scaling Dam, Crookfoot Reservoir, Saltholme Pools and Haverton Hole, although there has never been any proof of breeding despite the appearance of birds in summer plumage in recent years, and nest-building being noted on more than one occasion.

There has been a distinct tendency for birds seen since the 1970s to stay for several days, whereas, prior to 1970, only 7 out of 22 birds were known to stay for more than one day. A bird on Longnewton Reservoir in 1984 was present from 3 November to 18 December, a pair on Scaling Dam in 1995 stayed from 17 April to 21 May, one in Hartlepool Docks was seen from 4 December 1999 to 18 February 2000 and another commuted between Saltholme Pools and the Reclamation Pond from 10 May to 18 July 2001.

(NORTHERN) FULMAR *Fulmarus glacialis*

Prior to the 1920s, this bird was an irregular visitor in fairly small numbers along the Cleveland coast, but since about 1922 it has bred on the cliffs between Saltburn and Cowbar.

The two main breeding areas are the highest cliffs between Saltburn and Skinningrove (Hunt Cliff) and between Skinningrove and Cowbar (Boulby). Chislett (1952) mentions breeding on cliffs from Bridlington to Hunt Cliff and many were said to be present in 1949. These cliffs are now regularly surveyed giving counts as shown in the table.

It should, however, be noted that Fulmars are fairly difficult to survey accurately, so these figures should be considered as best estimates. Since 1961, a few birds have been seen on Roseberry Topping and Highcliff Nab in the summer, but young birds are rarely, if ever, recorded on these easily accessible por-

Year	Number of pairs
1969	266
1977	185
1986	340
1990	160
1991	160
1995	290
1997	310
2000	230
2003	260
2006	240
Nesting Fulmar records	

tions of cliff. No more than three or four pairs have been noted at either place in the last few years.

The Fulmar is a regular passage bird at sea, the highest numbers being seen in the months February-September and especially July-September. A few can be seen in the months October-January, although the vast majority winter to the south of Cleveland. A few birds return to their breeding cliffs as early as late November.

The highest number ever recorded for Cleveland occurred on 27 August 1962, when an estimated 21,000 passed Hartlepool. Nothing like it has been recorded since, but

1,000-2,000 passed Hartlepool on 24 April 1971 and 11 September 1976, and about 1,000 per hour passed Cowbar on the morning of 8 August 1994.

In most years, one or two birds of the blue phase are seen during times of passage, these birds are generally regarded as coming from the northern part of the species' range, but seven were seen in late August 1962, nine passed Hartlepool on 29 August 1998 and 41 passed Cowbar on 3 November 1998. Also, single pure white birds passed Hartlepool on 3 September 1965 and 6 September 1982.

A few birds fly over inland sites every year, usually over the Tees Marshes and mostly between April and August. Singles have also been seen over places as far inland as Scaling Dam, Longnewton Reservoir, Yarm and Wynyard. One circled a block of flats in Billingham on 12 June 1966 and another circled the Teesside Polytechnic building in Middlesbrough on 12 June 1980.

There are four recoveries of birds, all having been ringed in Scotland. The first three were ringed as nestlings: ringed Eday, Orkney on 26 July 1977, dead Seaton Carew on 15 April 1979; ringed Inchkeith, Fife in summer 1974, dead Saltburn 4 April 1987; and ringed Skirza, Wick, Highland on 3 August 1985, dead Redcar 8 June 1992 and ringed Newburgh, Grampian on 11 May 1978, dead Saltburn 27 April 1985.

GREAT SHEARWATER *Puffinus gravis*

This shearwater is a rare bird off Cleveland, 21 birds having been seen, but only six within the last 20 years.

The first definite record concerns two birds off Teesmouth on 18 July 1931. More recently, three singles were seen in 1959, on 29 August and 10 October off Hartlepool and 20 September off South Gare. Next was a single bird on 26 August 1969 off Hartlepool, followed by one on 19 October 1970 off South Gare. In 1976, a total of seven birds passed Hartlepool, the most seen in any year and included the most on any day with three on 29 August. Also two passed on 8 July and singles on 28 August and 12 September. Since this record year, singles have been seen off Hartlepool on 5 September 1984, 22 August 1998, 2 September 2000, 29 August 2003, 7 August 2005, 9 September 2005 and 10 September 2007.

The earliest and latest records are on 8 July (1976) and 19 October (1970), although late August and early September appears to be the favoured period.

CORY'S SHEARWATER *Calonectris diomedea*

There are nearly 30 accepted records for this species, all in the months July-September, and there are several other records of large shearwaters that, by the descriptions, could have been either Cory's or Great Shearwaters.

See table below for accepted records.

Date	Location - off	Details
14 September 1972	Hartlepool	Single bird
6 July 1985	Skinningrove	Single bird - seen from a boat
31 July 1985	Hartlepool	Single bird
31 July 1987	Hartlepool	Three
16 August 1987	Hartlepool	Single bird
18 August 1990	Hartlepool	Single bird
2 September 1990	South Gare	Single bird
8 September 1990	Cowbar	Single bird
15 August 1993	Cowbar	Single bird
18 August 1993	Hartlepool	Single bird
12 September 1993	Hartlepool	Single bird
12 September 1993	South Gare	Single bird
10 July 1995	Hartlepool	Single bird
9 and 29 July 1995	Cowbar	Single bird
5,7and 27 August 1995	Hartlepool	Single bird
26 August 1995	Hartlepool	Two
4 August 1996	Hartlepool	Single bird
21 August1999	Cowbar	Single bird
2 and 3 September 2000	Hartlepool	Single bird
2 September 2000	Cowbar	Single bird
7 July 2001	Hartlepool	Single bird
14 July 2001	Hartlepool	Two
19 and 31August 2001	Hartlepool	Single bird
25 August 2002	Hartlepool	Two
Cory's Shearwater records		

SOOTY SHEARWATER *Puffinus griseus*

The first British specimen of this species was obtained in the Tees Bay in August 1828 by Mr G.Marwood and it was exhibited at a meeting of the Zoological Society in July 1832 by Arthur Strickland (Strickland 1832). At the time it was considered to be a dark form of the Great Shearwater.

A visit to Hartlepool during strong north-easterly winds in August or September will almost certainly yield Sooty Shearwater as well as other birds like skuas, terns and duck. The highest counts are 206 on 11 September 1976, 509 on 17 September 2001 and 1,954 on 22 September 2002. All were flying north off Hartlepool, although in most years the highest daily count is no more than 30, and occasionally less than 10 are seen in any one year. The peak months, as mentioned above, are August and September, but there are frequently a few birds in July and occasionally in October and November. The earliest and latest dates are 20 April (1965) and 28 December (1978).

Very few birds are seen away from Hartlepool, but one bathed off Seaton Snook on 18 August 1955 and another followed a fishing boat into Hartlepool Harbour on 26 July 1995. Sea watching off South Gare has revealed a few Sooty Shearwaters, but never anything like the numbers that pass Hartlepool, and in addition a few have been seen off Cowbar where regular sea watching may indicate numbers equal to Hartlepool.

There are no inland records, nor have any dead individuals been recorded.

MANX SHEARWATER *Puffinus puffinus*

Despite the fact that this seabird does not breed any nearer than the Shetlands or the Scillies, it is a regular summer and autumn visitor offshore, with sometimes several hundred passing in a single day. An indication of the origin of these birds is given by a dead bird found at Redcar in June 1971 that had been ringed as a pullus on the Welsh island of Skokholm on 23 August 1968, and another found inland at Elton in June 1997 that had been ringed as a full-grown bird on the Welsh island of Bardsey in August 1994.

The main passage occurs between mid-June and mid-September with stragglers frequently passing in April, May, October and November and very occasionally December - March. Mid-winter records only occur during strong onshore winds, the earliest known being 18 January 1888 off Redcar (Nelson 1907). Over the years the highest counts have been steadily increasing, 419 on 30 August 1959, 500 on 24 July 1969, 541 on 1 August 1978, 1,075 on 4 August 1984, 1,150 on 31 July 1985, 1,005 on 16 July 1996 and 1,644 on 29 August 2003, all counts being made from Hartlepool Headland. It is not unusual for small flocks to linger, and presumably feed, offshore in summer; however, an estimated 1,500-2,200 off Hartlepool between 24 August and 1 September 2003 was unprecedented.

Manx Shearwaters are also seen from other points along the coastline, but usually involve fewer birds, although a total of 780 passed Cowbar on 26 July 1985 over a period of two and a half hours.

As one would expect, there are a few records of birds being blown inland during storms, singles being picked up at Kirklevington on 5 September 1967, Billingham on 4 September 1974 and flying over Yarm on 11 September 1976, this last bird being seen during a north-easterly gale. Also there is an old record of 'one at Middlesbrough, September 1905' (Chislett 1952). A bird on the Reclamation Pond on 24 and 25 July 1988 was taken into care but later died.

BALEARIC SHEARWATER *Puffinus mauretanicus*

This bird was previously known as Mediterranean Shearwater *Puffinus p. yelkouan*, a subspecies of Manx Shearwater, however, since 1991, it has been given full species status.

The first record was one shot off Redcar in the autumn of 1877. There were no further reports until 4 October 1959 when three were seen off North Gare. From the 1960s to the 1980s it averaged about one bird every 2 years, but since the early 1990s Balearic Shearwater has been an annual late summer passage migrant. Most birds are recorded passing Hartlepool, though a few have been seen off South Gare, Marske and Cowbar. Balearic Shearwaters in Cleveland have been reviewed by Joynt (1998).

The earliest and latest dates are 14 July (1989) and 19 October (2003), but most birds pass in late August and September. The majority of the records are of single birds, although two have been seen on several occasions, three passed Hartlepool on 22 August 1993 and five were noted on 25 August 2003 and 22 September 2003.

MACARONESIAN SHEARWATER *Puffinus baroli*

This was previously regarded as a race of Little Shearwater *Puffinus assimilis*. There are three records of this bird. Two flew north with two Manx Shearwaters off Hartlepool on 24 September 1984 and singles flew north off Hartlepool on 7 September 1990 and 15 July 2000.

WILSON'S PETREL
(WILSON'S STORM-PETREL) *Oceanites oceanicus*

One flew north past Hartlepool Headland on 7 September 2006, the only record for Cleveland (Taylor 2007).

STORM PETREL
(EUROPEAN STORM-PETREL) *Hydrobates pelagicus*

The nearest known nesting colonies of this petrel are on Scottish islands and it is far more numerous than Leach's Petrel on its breeding grounds, yet the latter is just as frequently seen off the Cleveland coast.

In the last 40 years it has been seen during the day (as opposed to trapped at night) on about 20 occasions, mostly involving single birds off Hartlepool, however, a total of nine passed between 30 July and 1 August 1978, with six of them occurring on 31 July 1978. Seven were seen off Hartlepool on 3 June 2001, five on 9 September 2001 and 12 next day. There were eight on 19 September 2004 and 16 on 24 September 2004. Historic records include reports of 'large numbers' five miles off Teesmouth in June 1908.

There is a single inland record of a bird at Charlton's Pond on 29 October 1962. The earliest and latest dates for this species are 3 June (2001) and 25 November (2007).

Since 1989, night-time trapping along the coastline, principally at Hartlepool, has resulted in up to 78 birds per year being caught and ringed, usually in July and August. This would seem to indicate that Storm Petrels are regularly offshore at night in these months. One bird was caught at South Gare on 12 August 1979 and re-trapped on Yell, Shetland on 4 August 1980, the first of about 30 ringing recoveries from approximately 250 trapped so far in Cleveland. These records show that this seabird can fly to Fife Ness and Collieston, Scotland in about 24 hours and can reach Norway within three days.

Others have been know to fly from Flamborough Head and Filey Brigg in Yorkshire, Isle of May, North Ronaldsay in Orkney within a few days, and Calf of Man, Sanda Island in Strathclyde and Wooltach Point in Dyfed within 2-3 weeks.

Birds have also been re-trapped in all of these locations a year or two after ringing, as well as Seahouses in Northumberland, Brough of Birsay in Orkney, Strumble Head in Dyfed, and Trotternish on Isle of Skye. One bird found dead at Saltburn on 6 June 1992 had been ringed at Collieston, Grampian, on 7 August 1989.

LEACH'S PETREL (LEACH'S STORM-PETREL)
Oceanodroma leucorhoa

For such a small seabird, this species is remarkably resilient to severe weather conditions and it is usually seen in Cleveland during strong north-west to north-east winds, though one was seen during a westerly gale. In the last 40 years, Leach's Petrels have been observed in 18 years, although it probably passes our coastline more frequently than this suggests.

In most of the years only single birds have been recorded, mainly off Hartlepool, but also off South Gare and once on Seal Sands. This last bird was recorded during a westerly gale on 13 September 1980 and was seen to arrive over land before settling to feed near Hartlepool Power Station. It remained in the area for several hours. Notable years for this species are: 1965 when nine and possibly up to 12, birds were seen at Hartlepool Observatory, Hartlepool Docks and South Gare

between 20 and 27 November; 1974 when three passed Hartlepool on 29 October, followed by another 13 the next day; 1989, when seven passed Hartlepool on 8 September, 29 next day and three on 10 September; and 1993 when 25 passed Hartlepool on 13 September followed by three next day.

There are four records of birds picked up inland: September 1932 near Middlesbrough; October and November 1952 in Yarm and September 1972 inland of Seaton Carew. With the exception of the above records for 1932 and 1952, the only reports prior to 1960 are singles at Marske in October 1910, on Cowpen Marsh in September 1914 and at South Gare in October 1955.

The earliest and latest dates are 2 September (1989) and 28 December (1978), both at Hartlepool, although there was one at South Gare on 23 February 2005.

(NORTHERN) GANNET Morus bassanus

The nearest Gannet colony to Cleveland is on Bempton Cliffs, North Yorkshire, but five of the six recoveries concern birds ringed on Bass Rock, Lothian, Scotland, the closest colony to the north of Cleveland and one of the biggest in Britain, with over 40,000 pairs.

Very few birds are seen off the coastline in January and February, more being observed in March-May and quite large numbers are occasionally recorded between June and October. Sightings in November and December tend to depend on the occurrence of onshore winds, as does the highest count in each year. Notable counts since 1950 include: 500 flying south off Cowbar on 29 September 1960; 640 flying north at Hartlepool on 2 September 1965; about 200 fishing between South Gare and Redcar on 5 August 1967; 701 flying north at Hartlepool on 2 August 1972; 72 following a fishing boat into Hartlepool Harbour on 29 December 1979; about 200 fishing off South Gare on 3 and 4 September 1983; 140 per hour passing north at South Gare on the morning of 24 March 1986; 300 per hour passing Hartlepool on 5 August 1993; 684 passing

Hartlepool in 1 hour on 1 October 1995; 700 per hour passing Cowbar on 4 October 1999; 470 per hour passing Hartlepool on 2 September 2000 and 550 per hour passing Hartlepool on 27 April 2004.

Date	Location	Notes
January 1823	Stockton	shot
27 May 1955	cricket field in Stockton	picked up
26 October 1962	field at Guisborough	
12 September 1966	Longnewton	under wires
9 September 1969	Billingham	flying over
17 October 1970	Saltholme Pools	flying inland
2 May 1978	Middlesbrough	picked up
18 March 1979	Greatham Creek	found asleep on the roadside
8 April 1986	Cowpen Marsh	picked up exhausted
January 1989	Longnewton Reservoir	oiled adult was found dead
13 September 1993	Lazenby	flying over
29 September 1995	Stockton and Norton	flying over
6 October 1998	Redcar Lane Cemetery	picked up
22 December 2003	Middlesbrough	picked up
Inland Records of Single Gannets		

At least three of the birds found on the ground were released back to the sea after periods of recovery.

The five Bass Rock recoveries mentioned above were all ringed as pulli during the summers of 1936, 1937, 1949, 1950 and 1963. They were found dead at Seaton Carew on 24 September 1936, Saltburn on 11 August 1940, Hartlepool on 9 September 1953, North Gare Sands on 10 June 1953 and Coatham Sands on 24 May 1987 respectively. This last bird had lived for 24 years, a respectable though not very unusual age for a large seabird. The sixth recovery was of a pullus ringed at Skarvklakken, Andoya, in northern Norway on 3 August 1972 and found dead at Hartlepool on 17 October 1972, this being the first Norwegian-ringed Gannet recovered in Britain.

(GREAT) CORMORANT *Phalacrocorax carbo*

This rather prehistoric-looking bird can be found around the mouth of the Tees throughout the year, at Hartlepool mostly in the winter and breeding on the cliffs to the south of Saltburn from April to August. Also, a few birds can be seen on inland waters at any time of the year. It is likely that the status of the Cormorant in this area has remained unchanged for decades, if not centuries, although the number of birds seen around the mouth of the Tees has increased in recent years.

In the past Cormorants in Cleveland were actively persecuted, presumably by fishermen. The colony on Boulby Cliffs was completely driven away by the lowering of a lighted tar barrel over the cliff edge in 1867 (Nelson 1907), but some birds did return, and a few pairs were seen there in most years between 1889 and 1901, and in 1943. In the late 1940s and 1950s, 30-40 pairs were breeding at the Boulby colony and the Hunt Cliff colony was thriving with about 20 pairs, although 36 nests were counted in 1948.

The Boulby colony had disappeared by 1970 but two pairs were again present in 1990, nine pairs in 1991, 12 in 1992, 19 in 1995 and 25-43 pairs between 1996 and 2004. The Hunt Cliff colony slowly increased to a peak of 64 pairs in 1990 but dropped to 48 pairs in 1992, 45 in 1996 and 26-35 pairs between 1997 and 2004. The ledges of the nesting colonies are also utilised as roost sites, 147 being counted on Hunt Cliff in July 1985.

Cormorants are present around the mouth of the Tees throughout the year, usually standing with wings outstretched on the rocks and sand spits at low tide, and various jetties at high tide. The monthly high tide counts carried out as part of the Wetlands Bird Survey, formerly the Birds of Estuaries Enquiry, show that peak numbers usually occur in August or September . Since regular counting began, the highest counts have been 136 in September 1969, 185 in February 1977, 336 in September 1989, 480 in September 1990, 731 in August 1995 and 772 in August 2003. Over the ten years 1995- 2004 the average maximum has been 516, which is well above the National Significance Threshold of 230.

Quite high numbers of Cormorants (and Shags) are sometimes recorded moving along the coast, usually under the influence of high winds. The highest numbers are 230, most if not all being Cormorants flying south between Crimdon Dene and Hartlepool on 1 March 1962, 164 flying south at South Gare on 26 November 1977 and 130 flying south at Hartlepool on 9 February 1978.

As well as sheltering in the mouth of the Tees, Cormorants also use the docks and harbour area of Hartlepool often during severe weather conditions, 77 being counted there in January 1986.

There are several ringing recoveries which indicate the origin of some, if not most, of the wintering and summering birds. At least five birds were ringed as pulli on the Farne Islands, Northumberland, three of which were reported at Hartlepool or Redcar in April or May of the following year. It is interesting to note that the earliest of the recoveries involves a bird ringed in 1913. Colour-ringing in the 1990s has shown that birds ringed in the nest at Rutland Water, Besthorpe in Nottinghamshire, Abberton Reservoir in Essex, Haweswater in Cumbria, and Craigleith, North Berwick, have reached Teesmouth by July or August, approximately two months after fledging. One ringed in the nest at

Rutland Water in June 1998 was at Longnewton Reservoir in April 2000 and another ringed in the nest at Abberton Reservoir in Essex in May 1998 was on Seal Sands in 1999, Spain in 2001 and was back at Teesmouth in August 2002. Also, a bird ringed as a nestling at Mochrum, near Newton Stewart in Dumfries and Galloway on 26 July 1969 was on Seal Sands on 17 October 1982.

Cormorants frequently fish at inland lakes and reservoirs, a few birds regularly being seen on Scaling Dam, Lockwood Beck, Lazenby Reservoir, Crookfoot Reservoir, Hemlington Lake and Charlton's Pond. The bird is unpopular with anglers, and this disapproval was illustrated in the winter of 1971/72 when up to 11 birds resorted to Charlton's Pond to feed. At least two were killed despite the pond having been a nature reserve since 1968 and more were to be destroyed in the following winter, but few have been seen there since 1972. The highest inland counts are 76 on Haverton Hole at dawn on 21 August 1998 and 111 at Crookfoot Reservoir on 17 August 2003.

Cormorants regularly feed on the higher reaches of the Tees as far upstream as the Yarm area. Up to 65 roost in the trees by Preston-on-Tees, downstream from Yarm, in the winter months, this gathering having been noted regularly since 1984.

Birds also fly frequently over the Tees at Middlesbrough and Thornaby commuting between this section of the river and the estuary.

DOUBLE-CRESTED CORMORANT
Phalacrocorax auritus

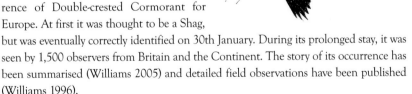

An immature was present on Charlton's Pond from at least 11 January to 27 April 1989, though it rarely roosted here and occasionally went missing for a day or two. It may have been present since 8 December 1988 and was seen at Haverton Hole on several occasions. It again visited the pond on 16 June 1989.

This is a North American species and the Cleveland bird is the first recorded occurrence of Double-crested Cormorant for Europe. At first it was thought to be a Shag, but was eventually correctly identified on 30th January. During its prolonged stay, it was seen by 1,500 observers from Britain and the Continent. The story of its occurrence has been summarised (Williams 2005) and detailed field observations have been published (Williams 1996).

(EUROPEAN) SHAG *Phalacrocorax aristotelis*

This smaller relative of the Cormorant is principally a winter visitor to the Cleveland coast with most records falling in the months of September – April. However, it is also quite frequently seen in May and August and occasionally in June and July. The status and numbers probably have not changed very much in the 20th century, although it was regarded as quite rare in the Redcar area in the 1880s.

All of the high counts have involved birds flying south at Hartlepool with 102 on 21 November 1965 (about 250 Cormorants and Shags combined passed South Gare on the same day), 177 on 1 February 1976, 206 on 26 November 1977, 203 on 9 September 1989, 267 on 20 October 1991 and 187 on 10 November 2001.

The largest numbers of birds seen on the sea, or at roost, include 37 at South Gare in December 1954, 71 in Hartlepool Harbour on 23 February 1977 and 163 at South Gare on 19 January 1991.

The Shag is quite a rare visitor to inland waters, most such records probably involving ailing or dying birds. Singles have been seen at Charlton's Pond (oiled January 1969), Reclamation Pond (dying on 30 April 1975), Scaling Dam (18 March 1984), and Saltholme Pools (picked up on 1 October 1989). One spent virtually all of April 1960 on the lake in Stewart Park, Middlesbrough, apparently surviving quite well. Two birds were seen on Lockwood Beck on 9 January 1977 and Scaling Dam on 1 January 1985.

There are at least 16 records of birds ringed as pulli on Bass Rock, the Farne Islands or Isle of May that have been found dead between Hartlepool and Skinningrove, mostly in the months November-February. All but four of these were no more than nine months old. The oldest was ringed on The Lamb, North Berwick, in June 1971 and found at Saltburn in February 1993. There are also sightings of at least four colour-ringed birds from the Isle of May that have been seen at South Gare in March, April or May after ringing.

(GREAT) BITTERN *Botaurus stellaris*

Based on records over the last 50 years, the Bittern is a rare but regular visitor, averaging one bird every year, although there was only one in the six years 1973-78. There were seven in the period 1979-84 and five in 1993, 1999 and 2000. Bittern are secretive in nature and well camouflaged, so it could well be that it is a more frequent visitor than the records suggest. There are as many records in the last ten years as the previous forty.

Prior to about 1800 it probably bred in the then untouched and very extensive areas of marsh around Teesmouth, but the national trend towards the drainage and destruction of wetlands in the 19th century was almost certainly responsible for the complete extinction of the bird as a breeding species in this area and the drastic decline in the entire British population. However the creation of marsh/reedbed habitats between Haverton Hole and Saltholme Pools in 2002-05 is intended to create habitat specifically for Bittern.

Although rare, it has been recorded in Cleveland in every month of the year, with most records during the months December-February. However, one at Lovell Hill in May 1979 was heard booming on 4th but unfortunately found dead on 18th.

As one would expect, the majority of records emanate from the marshes around Teesmouth, in particular, Dormans Pool, Haverton Hole and Coatham Marsh. However, there are records from: Cattersty Rocks, near Saltburn in November 1868; Billingham Bottoms in January 1947 and January-February 1970, the latter bird being illegally shot; Charlton's Pond in 1949, 1993 and 1997; Crookfoot Reservoir in September 1951; Stewart Park in February 1958; Poole Hospital lake in December 1968; Scaling Dam from January to March 1986 and South Gare in December 1995 and 1 January 2004.

LITTLE BITTERN *Ixobrychus minutus*

There is only one record where all the details are known. A bird was shot at Redcar on 26 September 1852, but Nelson (1907) mentions a bird in a Redcar collection of mounted birds, which is stated to have almost certainly been shot locally.

(BLACK-CROWNED) NIGHT HERON
Nycticorax nycticorax

There are five records for Cleveland, but it is difficult to be sure if these refer to genuine wild birds or are from the free-living colony that has existed at Edinburgh Zoo since 1950. The first was described as an adult and remained in a Yarm garden for at least a week up to 13 May 1951. Other records concern: a juvenile in Redcar Lane Cemetery, Redcar, on 8 October 1983; another juvenile in Locke Park, Redcar, on 25 September 1996; one on Cowpen Marsh 4-7 July 2005; and a colour-ringed bird on Coulby Newham Pond from 22 May to 22 November 2007 at least.

CATTLE EGRET *Bubulcus ibis*

One at Longnewton Reservoir on the evening of 10 October 1986 is the only record.

LITTLE EGRET *Egretta garzetta*

Prior to 1993, this bird had only been recorded five times in Cleveland at Coatham Marsh on 27 May 1967, Dormans Pool on 3-4 July 1979 and 7-8 June 1983, South Gare on 18 May 1986 and Greatham Creek from 3 to 7 May 1992.

Since 1993, Little Egret has become an annual visitor to the area; this follows the dramatic influx of birds into the British Isles and the establishment of regular breeding colonies (Cambridge and Parr 1992, Brown and Grice 2005). Up to 2001, one or two birds per year were recorded, but there were five in 2002, at least three in 2003, up to eight in 2004, 13 at Greatham Creek on 22 September 2006 and 11 in the same area in September 2007.

The majority of these recent records have been around the North Tees Marshes, although singles have been seen at Hartlepool, South Gare and Scaling Dam. Between 1994 and 2002 the earliest and latest dates were 22 April and 20 October, but in December 2003 one was found in the stream between Dalton Piercy and Greatham. It remained throughout January-March 2004, frequently roosting on the island in Rossmere Park, Hartlepool, and then from April 2004 birds could be seen in the Greatham Creek area in every month of the year, at least two being present in December 2004. An indication of the origin of Little Egrets in Cleveland is given by one ringed as a pullus in the nest in South Wales on 4 June 2006, that was on Portrack Marsh for a week from 26 July 2006, then around North Tees marshes in August and September 2006 and at Spurn, Humberside, on 4 March 2007.

GREAT WHITE EGRET (GREAT EGRET)
Ardea alba

Prior to 1998, there were two records of single birds at Scaling Dam Reservoir, from 28 May to 6 June 1974, and 19 July 1990, but from 1998 it has become an annual visitor.

Whilst the spread of Great White Egret in Western Europe is less dramatic than that of Little Egret the species now breeds more or less regularly in France and the Netherlands.

Recent records in Cleveland are of single birds on: the North Tees Marshes on 17-18 April 1998 and 16-17 June 1999; Coatham Marsh on 12 June 2000; Saltholme Pools from 18 June to 12 October 2001; Portrack Marsh,

Haverton Hole and the Brinefields from 11 October to 9 November 2002; Dormans Pool on 2 December 2002; Saltholme Pools on 11 July 2003; Scaling Dam on 26 June 2004; the North Tees Marshes between 24 April and 29 May 2005, 6 April 2007, 17 June 2007 and 27-28 June 2007.

GREY HERON *Ardea cinerea*

This is the only member of the heron family that breeds throughout Britain and can be found on many streams, rivers and lakes at all times of the year.

It is a resident species in Cleveland, but additional birds are also regularly noted as passage migrants and there is probably a small influx of birds in winter. Its favourite haunts are the reed-fringed edges of ditches, rivers, pools and lakes, consequently the many 'stells' and streams around the Tees Marshes are regularly fished by this stately bird. Garden ponds in many areas are also visited quite often, their stock of fish being easy prey. It is only during severe cold and freezing conditions that Grey Herons vacate the freshwater areas for the tidal reaches of Greatham Creek and Seal Sands. Steep-sided and open reservoirs like Crookfoot and Hart rarely hold Grey Herons, although Scaling Dam with its reed-fringed and marshy south-west corner frequently attracts a number of birds, with up to 17 in recent autumns. Portrack Marsh has been a favourite haunt since about 1990, with up to 31 birds during the autumn.

There are fewer Grey Herons around the Tees Marshes in the early months of the year since breeding adults are usually back at the nest sites by February or March. Numbers around the estuary tend to build up again in July and August when adults return with the young birds of the year. The largest numbers at Teesmouth usually occur in the months of July-September peaking at 30 - 50 birds, although 71 were seen in July 1993, 78 in July 1999 and 83 in August 2000.

While the majority of birds present during autumn and winter are probably local, there are regular sightings of birds passing along the coast or seen arriving from the sea, usually between late July and mid-October. There is no ringing evidence to suggest that these birds are from colonies further north in Britain, although it is quite likely. There are two recoveries to indicate that some Scandinavian birds are involved; a pullus ringed in Norway on 3 June 1947 was found shot at Lockwood Beck in September 1947 and another ringed at Lodbjerg Plantage, Jylland in Central Denmark, on 16 May 1985 was found long dead on Seal Sands on 19 January 1986. Also, one in 'a Yorkshire river' in May 1928 had been ringed in Sweden in June 1927 and one found dead near Whitby, North Yorkshire, in April 1994 had been ringed in Estonia in May 1991. Another pullus, ringed at Grimley, Worcester, on 3 May 1980 was found dead at Marske in April 1981.

Most of the sightings over the sea involve between one to three birds, although a total of 14 passed Hartlepool in July and August 1970, a flock of nine passed on 28 August 1967 and a flock of 14 arrived at Hartlepool on 12 September 1981.

As a breeding bird Nelson (1907) mentions occasional nests in the Liverton and Grinkle Woods area. In the 1960s there may have been one or two nests in trees near Yarm and in more recent years a small colony has been established in Wynyard since 1978, and possibly since 1974, slowly increasing to 18-20 nests in 2004. A larger, though more recent colony, has been established in a wood which straddles the Cleveland boundary near Kirklevington. It was first noted in 1979 and contained two - four nests for some years until 1984 when nine nests were reported, with 12 in 1985, 18-24 in 1989-92 and 27-30 in 2001-03. Also one pair successfully reared young in Wilton Woods in 1987, but failed in 1988. Up to seven pairs have reared young in nearby Court Green Woods since 1989.

There are a few records of melanistic Grey Herons, on Coatham Marsh in 1973, by Greatham Creek in 1978 and Saltholme Pools in 1981 and 1993, as well as up to four oiled birds around the Reclamation Pond in 1998. All of these superficially resembled Purple Heron.

PURPLE HERON Ardea purpurea

There are five records for Cleveland: an adult that flew south-west away from Cowpen Marsh on 10 June 1975; a juvenile found in a weak condition in a field at Moorsholm on 1 August 1976 that died the next day; one that flew west over South Gare on 15 May 1985, this bird appeared to land on Seaton Common but could not be relocated; one on Coatham Marsh 27-28 May 2005 and one that flew south over Hartlepool on 4 June 2006.

BLACK STORK Ciconia nigra

There are four records for Cleveland: the first was shot at Greatham in August 1862, followed in more recent times by singles over Eston Nab on 8 July 1995, Coatham Marsh on 18 April 1996 and Hartlepool on 19 April 1996.

WHITE STORK Ciconia coconia

There are two old records: two observed on Cowpen Marsh in the spring of 1830 and one that was seen first at West Hartlepool and later in the Brambles Farm area of Middlesbrough between October and December 1938.

There are twelve further records, but the presence of a free-flying individual in North Yorkshire undoubtedly clouds the picture. This bird is colour-ringed and has been seen in many places in northern Britain, mainly in the months March-April. However, colour-ringed birds from re-introduction schemes elsewhere in northern Europe have also been noted in Britain in recent years, so the origin of any White Stork is likely to be suspect.

The recent records are singles: at Skelton for two days in late March 1995; over Hartlepool on 3 April 1996; over Boulby Cliffs on 14 April 1996; over Crookfoot Reservoir on 17 April 1997; over the Reclamation Pond on 6 May 2004; over Marske on 14 June 2004; at Skelton Castle on 17 June 2004; over Birk Brow and Ingleby Barwick on 1 May 2005; over Saltburn on 9 June 2005; at Belasis Technology Park 2-3 May 2006; in the Yarm/Durham Tees Valley Airport area between 13 and 16 September 2006 and at Yearby 1-2 April 2007.

GLOSSY IBIS Plegadis falcinellus

There are four records for the Cleveland area: one shot in the Moorsholm and Liverton district about 1860; an adult shot on Billingham Bottoms on 25 November 1900; an immature by Wynyard Lake on 22 October 1988; and an adult at Haverton Hole on 5 May 1992.

(EURASIAN) SPOONBILL Platalea leucorodia

Over the forty years 1956-95, there were sightings in fourteen years, but since 1996 it has become an annual visitor with most records being in the Teesmouth area. There are very few records prior to 1956.

The earliest and latest dates are 19 April (1951 and 2002), and 16 December (1984), though most occurrences fall in the May - August period. There are two winter records, one bird around Seal Sands from 16 November to 16 December 1984 and three on Coatham Marsh on 18-19 November 1997, subsequently moving to Saltholme Pools and staying to 25 November 1997.

Most sightings are of one or two birds but four were seen around Cowpen Marsh from 5 July to 13 August 1972, over South Gare on 21 October 1985, on Dormans Pool on 29 June 2000 and on Cowpen Marsh and Dormans Pool on 25 May 2002.

For such an irregular visitor, the birds that do occur seem to find the Tees Marshes attractive enough to linger up to 56 days in the case of the 1972 birds and 59 days for one in 1998, although since 1956 the average stay has been for about 10 days.

Three different colour-ringed birds have been seen in Cleveland, all being ringed as pulli in Holland. The first was ringed in the nest in May 1990, visited Kent and Norfolk in June 1991, then moved north and south from Holland through France to Spain every year from August 1991 to September 2001, apart from a visit to Coatham Marsh on 27 May 1999 and Dormans Pool from 28 May to 6 June 1999. The second was ringed in the nest in July 1994, but was not seen again until it spent the summer of 1999 touring Britain; it was at Titchwell, Norfolk, on 2 June 1999, Minsmere, Suffolk, on 17 June 1999, Loch of Strathbeg, Aberdeenshire, on 1 July 1999, Dormans Pool from 2 to 5 July 1999, Orfordness, Suffolk on 13 July 1999, back on Dormans Pool on 21 July 1999, Rutland Water on 25 July 1999, again on Dormans Pool on 28 July 1999 and at Orfordness again in August and September 1999. From April 2000 it commuted north and south in Europe, being seen in Spain in April 2001, France in September 2002 and several times in Holland. The third bird was ringed in the nest in June 1996, remained in Holland until August 1996, but was not seen again until it was recorded four years later on Dormans Pool on 29 and 30 June 2000, Ouse Washes, Cambridgeshire, on 16 August 2000 and in Spain in February 2002.

HONEY BUZZARD
(EUROPEAN HONEY-BUZZARD) *Pernis apivorus*

Records for this medium-sized passage migrant bird of prey fall in the period mid-May to mid-October, with earliest and latest dates of 15 May (1972) and 16 October (1976). How-ever, close to 75% of the records fall in the periods of the second half of May and all of September: only one bird has been seen in July and three in August.

Singles have been observed arriving from the sea, or following the coastline at various places between Hartlepool and Boulby in 1896, 1903, 1909, 1911, 1960, 1965, 1971, 1972, 1976, 1981, 1982, 1987, 1990, 1993, 1996, and almost annually since 1999. Single birds have also been seen inland at Acklam, Dunsdale, Skelton, Stockton, Yearby, Guisborough, Nunthorpe, Upleatham, Hart, Elwick and Scaling Dam.

An unprecedented influx of Honey Buzzards occurred between 20 and 29 September 2000, at least 12 and possibly 15 individuals were recorded, part of an estimated 500 Honey Buzzards that passed over eastern England, from Scandinavia during this period (Gantlett and Millington 2000).

BLACK KITE *Milvus migrans*

This bird was recorded three times at South Gare in 1988; flying north-west over the lighthouse on 16 April, hunting around the quarries on 5 May and found dead on the beach on 18 May. It is possible that a single individual was involved; the skin is now deposited in the Dorman Museum, Middlesbrough. Single birds also flew south-west over Wilton on 19 June 1993, north-west over Billingham on 17 August 1994 and east over the Leven Valley on 28 April 1997.

RED KITE *Milvus milvus*

Date	Location
1 November 1994	Seaton Common
At least 5 November to mid December 1994	On farmland between Hartlepool & Dalton Piercy
7 February 1995	Skelton Castle
8 March 1995	Skelton Castle
30 March 1996	Yearby, Grangetown, Middlesbrough and Portrack
5 April 1996	Margrove Ponds
9 April 1996	Cowpen Marsh
11 to 22 November 1997	Sleddale
29 March 1998	Sleddale
28 February 1999	Sleddale
4 April 1999	Upleatham
5 March 2002	Scaling Dam
1 April 2005	North Gare
12 July 2005	Saltburn
26 November 2005 to 5 March 2006	Near Hart
4 February 2006	Guisbourough
20 March 2006	Flatts Lane
17 April 2006	Sleddale
24 April 2006	Near Acklam
29 September 2006	Two birds - Sleddale
30 September 2006	Sleddale
31 October 2006	Guisborough
6 March 2007	Sleddale
9 March 2007	Saltburn
2 April 2007	Boulby
Red Kite Sightings (all singles except one record)	

Prior to 1994, there were only five records of this spectacular bird of prey, three of which are for the 19th century. A single was killed at Redcar in 1837, one was seen at Highfields, near Loftus, in 1868 and a third was killed at Teesmouth on 15 September 1883 (Nelson 1907). More recent records involved singles at Eaglescliffe on 3 November 1985 and Scaling Dam on 6 March 1992.

From 1994 it has become almost an annual visitor, no doubt as a result of the widespread re-introduction to various parts of England and Scotland. The bird seen in Sleddale in November 1997 carried wing-tags and had been ringed in the Inverness area of Scotland as one of 39 young reared in 1997.

As can be seen from the recent records, February to early April and November are the best months to look for this charismatic bird of prey.

WHITE-TAILED EAGLE *Haliaeetus albicilla*

This enormous bird of prey was recorded more often in the 19th century than the 20th century, but with the steady increase in the north-west Scotland population, it might one day become a more frequent visitor.

The records are: one shot at Teesmouth in November 1823; one killed at Marske Church in October 1836; one between Cattersty and Skinningrove in 1860; and two present around Teesmouth in late October 1915. These two birds roosted on Grangetown slag tip; eventually one was killed at Guisborough on 15 November and the other was seen near Great Ayton (North Yorkshire) on 1 December 1915 (Nelson 1907, Temperley 1951).

The only recent record concerns an immature which flew in off the sea at Boulby on 27 October 1985, then headed south-east into North Yorkshire, eventually being recorded on the same day at Scarborough and Flamborough Head and then at Saltfleetby and Gibraltar Point, Lincolnshire.

(EURASIAN) MARSH HARRIER *Circus aeruginosus*

The Marsh Harrier is an annual passage migrant in small numbers, principally from April to September, and is usually recorded around Teesmouth.

The species, in common with most birds of prey, was to be seen in greater numbers prior to the advent of the gamekeeper and the gun and may have bred in the marshy moorland areas along the southern border of Cleveland up to at least the 18th century (Hogg 1845).

There appear to be no records between one seen on Waupley Moor in 1859 and the first 20th century Teesmouth record of 17-23 May 1959. Since 1962 the Marsh Harrier has been seen in all but two years (1969 and 1975) and between April and June in most years. However, single birds occurred in August or September 1965, 1976, 1981, 1982, 1983, and every year since 1987, twice in October 1970, and occasionally in October since 1985. The earliest and latest dates are 5 March (2007) and 25 October (1970).

Very nearly all of the spring records involve birds flying straight through or hunting for a few hours in the Teesmouth reedbeds, but the majority of the autumn records involve birds staying for a few days. In 1979 a pair was seen in suitable breeding habitat from mid-May to mid-June, and in 1996 a pair reared three young at Haverton Hole.

Over 70% of the records are from the North Tees Marshes, with a number of sightings at Scaling Dam and South Gare, There are also records from Hart, Charlton's Pond, Portrack Marsh, Lovell Hill, Lockwood Beck, Margrove Ponds, Hartlepool Headland, Crookfoot Reservoir, Boulby Cliffs, Seaton Carew and Roseberry Topping.

There has been a slow but continuous increase in the number of Marsh Harriers seen in Cleveland since 1959, with an average of just over two per year in the 1970s, five per year in the 1980s, 11 in 1990, 13 in 1991, 15 in 1992 and 18 in 1993. By 1994 it was difficult to ascertain just how many birds were seen, but five or six individuals were recorded on 24 April and 6 May alone. Numbers remained around the 20-30 birds per year mark to 2002, and about 40 passed through Cleveland in 2003, including eight on 5 May 2003. It is hoped that this species may breed with the habitat improvements at the new RSPB reserve at Saltholme.

An unusual plumaged juvenile, showing broad white tips to nearly all of its feathers was around the North Tees Marshes from 4 August to 15 September 2001. A wing-tagged bird seen at Dormans Pool in August 2002 had been ringed in the River Tay area of Scotland in 2000 and a juvenile on the North Tees Marshes on 11-12 August 2005 had been wing-tagged in the same area of the River Tay in June 2005.

HEN HARRIER *Circus cyaneus*

In common with other species, this bird of prey has increased in Cleveland in recent years. Hen Harrier, however, is probably the most persecuted bird of prey in Britain, despite this being illegal.

On the moorland between Scaling Dam and Guisborough Forest, along the southern border of Cleveland, no more than one bird per year was seen between the late 1950s and late 1977, and then two or three birds were reported each winter up to early 1984, up to five in late 1984 and at least nine individuals in early 1986. This last report involved eight "ringtails" seen together in January 1986 on the moorland just south-west of Scaling Dam and an adult male was noted occasionally during the same period. At least six individuals were seen in the early months of 1988, and up to five each winter from 1989 to 1999, but no more than three birds each winter since March 1999.

Nelson (1907) mentions that a few pairs nested annually on the 'Cleveland Hills' up to 1850, which may have included the moorland now in Cleveland. A pair was 'obtained' at Grinkle in 1865 and a pair was recorded on Guisborough Moor on 7 December 1950. More recently, a pair was seen each summer between 1995 and 1999 on moorland around the Cleveland boundary, and reared young in at least two of the years.

It seems likely that the gamekeeping influence on all areas of moorland has kept the numbers of this and other birds of prey very low for many decades. The majority of the records from the moorland occur in the months November-March, with occasional birds seen in September, October and early April. Additionally, singles have been seen in May and August 1979, and May and August 2001.

This bird of prey is rather scarce away from the southern border of Cleveland, and in some years is not recorded in any other locality; however, there are a few records of birds passing Hartlepool Observatory and South Gare in late September and October and singles at South Gare on 10 April 1964, 2 May 1974, 9 December 1978, 21 October 1988, 18 May 1989 and 31 March 2002. In addition, singles have been noted at Boulby in recent winters and around the North Tees Marshes in 16 out of the last 40 years, as well as 28 April 1901 and 24 May 1901. The majority of records are between mid-October and mid-April with the birds remaining only for a single day. However, there are three records of birds staying for longer periods: one between 8 February and 9 March 1980 and one from 26 November 1986 to 14 April 1987, this latter bird being joined by a second individual on 17-18 January 1987. A juvenile ringed in the nest in Geltsdale, Cumbria was seen around the North Tees Marshes from 28 August to 9 November 2005.

Apart from the records already mentioned, there have been singles at Crookfoot Reservoir for three weeks in November-December 1953 and on 11 January 1998, Upleatham and Lovell Hill in late February 1979, Skelton on 25 January 1981, and Eston Moor on 11 September 1987 and 29 December 1997, Upleatham on 25 April 1999, Cattersty Sands on 15 November 2000 and Coatham Marsh on 12 May 2001. There is also a historic record of one shot in Redcar High Street on 14 August 1834.

Chicks ringed in nests in Strathclyde, Orkney and the Netherlands have been found in Yorkshire, each in the winter following ringing and a female at Scaling Dam on 13 March 1993 had been wing-tagged as a chick in the nest in north east Scotland in 1992.

MONTAGU'S HARRIER *Circus pygargus*

This harrier is one of the rarest breeding birds of prey in Britain and the rarest of the three harriers to be recorded in Cleveland, averaging only one record every two years since the 1940s.

A pair was seen with flying young on Waupley Moor in 1935, a nesting pair failed in the same area in 1942, but two young were reared on Girrick Moor in 1943. It is possible that breeding was attempted in other years in the 1930s and 1940s on the area of moorland that is now in Cleveland, as Montagu's Harriers bred in north east Yorkshire for at least 20 years until about 1957 (Mather 1986).

Since the last definite breeding record in 1943 there are only about 30 records of non-breeding birds. There have also been several records of harriers that were very likely this species, but definite proof is lacking.

Date	Location	Notes
18 May 1949	Greatham Creek	Adult male
9 June 1956	Teesmouth	Ringtail
19 and 29 July 1958	Stanghow	Ringtail
20 to 30 August 1959	Teesmouth	Ringtail
10 May 1964	South Gare	Ringtail
21 May 1964	Teesmouth	Ringtail
25 August 1964	Lockwood Beck	Ringtail
11 May 1968	Teesmouth	Ringtail
14 May 1969	Girrick Bank	Ringtail
7 June 1972	Teesmouth	Ringtail and adult male
23 June 1977	Scaling Dam	Ringtail
2-3 May 1984	Teesmouth	Ringtail
11 to 15 August 1989	Teesmouth	Immature male
15-16 May 1992	South Gare	Adult male
21 May 1992	Teesmouth	Immature male
5-6 May 1994	South Gare	Ringtail
6 May 1995	Teesmouth	Ringtail
29 May 1995	Teesmouth	Immature male
10 May 1997	South Gare	Immature male
11 May 1997	Teesmouth	Ringtail
29 May 1997	Aislaby	Ringtail
4 June 1997	Easington High Moor	Ringtail
25 April 1998	Hart	Adult male
4 June 1999	Greenabella Marsh	Adult male
8 June 2000	Saltburn	Adult male
19-20 July 2000	Scaling Dam	Immature male
9 June 2001	Teesmouth	Ringtail
28 to 30 July 2001	Teesmouth	Immature male
9-10 June 2006	Teesmouth	Immature male
Montagu's Harrier records		

(NORTHERN) GOSHAWK *Accipiter gentilis*

The only record prior to the 1980s is of one near Grangetown Station on 2 January 1934 (Almond et al. 1939). The next record is of one over Lovell Hill on 25 May 1981 followed by another on the field between Redcar and Marske on 15 November 1982 and another at Dunsdale on 3 January 1985.

Since early 1985, displaying males have been observed in at least six different localities where breeding could take place, though females have rarely been seen. There are also a very few records of birds away from the presumed breeding sites, especially around the marshes of Teesmouth. Most records fall between mid-February and mid-May.

(EURASIAN) SPARROWHAWK *Accipiter nisus*

About 30-40 years ago, this 'dashing' bird of prey probably did not breed in Cleveland every year and there were less than ten sightings of the species annually in some years. Now there are at least 80-90 pairs spread throughout Cleveland and maybe as many as 120 pairs, although they can be very secretive in summer. Also birds are regularly seen in virtually every area and type of habitat and increasingly in industrial and urban areas.

The very low numbers in the late 1950s and 1960s were attributed to the indiscriminate use of pesticides and toxic seed dressings, the situation being somewhat exacerbated at the time by the apparent general dislike of birds of prey by gamekeepers. This applied throughout most of Britain, not just Cleveland (Prest 1965, Brown and Grise 2005).

In Cleveland, at least, the 'low point' was around 1961-63. Since then numbers have steadily, but slowly, increased during the late 1960s and early 1970s. This was followed by a quite dramatic increase in the late 1970s and early 1980s culminating in the current healthy status now enjoyed by this species.

Up to about 1983, there was a distinct pattern to the coastal sightings, perhaps indicative of immigration from Northern Europe. In recent years, however, so many birds have been seen on the coast in every month of the year that any such sighting, unless the bird has been observed actually arriving from the sea, could just be a local wandering bird.

There is probably a regular movement of birds reared in northern Britain, into and through Cleveland. There are two recoveries; a pullus ringed near Langholm, Dumfries and Galloway, in July 1976 was found dead near Eaglescliffe on 23 January 1977, and an adult ringed at Saltholme on 9 October 1993 was at South Gare on 26 July 1996.

No more than about 180 Sparrowhawks have been ringed in Cleveland, the majority being full-grown birds, rather than young in the nest, and none is known to have moved very far. However a juvenile ringed in Yorkshire in September 1966 was recorded in Norway in the following May and a pullus ringed in Norway in July 1979 was in Yorkshire in late October 1979.

(COMMON) BUZZARD *Buteo buteo*

Formerly a breeding resident in the area (up to the 1860s), this large bird of prey was one of the rarest, with an average of only about two birds per year, but is now increasing. Since the formation of Cleveland County on 1 April 1974, there have been about 160 sightings, mostly of single birds, spread throughout the area and being seen in every month of the year. Of these records few birds are known to have stayed for more than a day. One hunted along the narrow strip of trees alongside the Redcar - Middlesbrough trunk road, adjacent to Wilton International, from at least 18 September to 17 October 1983, and up to three birds have been seen in the Upleatham area in most winters since 1991. A minimum of six was in Cleveland in March 1995, three at Upleatham and three at Crookfoot Reservoir.

Whilst there are records for every month there is a slight preponderance in the months of March-April and August-November, labelling the Buzzard as a passage migrant through Cleveland.

An indication of the origin of this species is given by a bird found dead at Marske on 28 October 1936; it had been ringed in Westmorland (now part of Cumbria) on 28 June 1936. Another found on the Yorkshire coast in September 1962 had flown a long way north from the New Forest, Hampshire.

This species is as likely to be seen over towns and places of habitation as at specific bird-watching localities like Teesmouth or the reservoirs.

ROUGH-LEGGED BUZZARD *Buteo lagopus*

October and November are the principal months for sightings of this raptor, one or two having been seen in these months in 1903, 1915, 1926, 1936, 1938, 1973, 1981, 1982, 1984, 1985 and 1991. Since 1995, it has been almost an annual visitor, up to three birds per year being recorded. Favoured places are the moorland around Scaling Dam, Guisborough Forest and Sleddale for lingering birds, and almost anywhere along the coastline from Hartlepool to Boulby for passage birds.

It is strictly a winter visitor with earliest and latest dates of 18 September (1969) and 30 April (1995 and 2003), although one was found long dead on Redcar beach on 25 May 1877.

OSPREY *Pandion haliaetus*

Between 1960 and 2000 there has been an average of about three records every two years. Prior to 1960, it was recorded on 29 August 1905 at Loftus and 31 August 1955 at Teesmouth and was reputed to be fairly frequent at Teesmouth in the early 19th Century (Stead 1964). Since 2000 it has averaged about seven birds per year.

This recent increase in the number of Ospreys is probably a reflection of the success of the Scottish breeding population, although there are at least five records of birds passing Hartlepool observatory that could indicate a Scandinavian origin.

The earliest record is 8 March (1997), though most records fall between mid-April and mid-May, followed by an even spread through June, July, August and September, and late birds seen on 21 October 1970, 23 October 1999, 25 October 2001 and 6 November 1976. Most records are of single birds seen on one day, although one fished Hemlington Lake regularly from 24 to 31 August 1983, one around Guisborough for at least 5 weeks from early May 1988 regularly fished the pond at Guisborough Priory and singles have fished Scaling Dam and Lockwood Beck for a week or two every August since 1990. In addition, two passed Hartlepool on 17 September 1960 followed by four more birds 12 days later, two were at Crookfoot Reservoir for a few days in early June 1992 and three were over Greatham Creek on 2 October 1999.

Between 1960 and 1976 only four out of 21 records were of birds observed at Teesmouth. The other 17 came mostly from Hartlepool, with one or two at Crookfoot Reservoir, Lockwood Beck, Wynyard, Charlton's Pond, Lovell Hill and Hutton Gate.

Since 1977, 35% of the records have involved birds seen at Teesmouth, and a fairly high proportion of the remainder have occurred at Scaling Dam or Crookfoot Reservoir, both waters sometimes holding birds for two or three weeks. Individuals have also been seen at places like Margrove Ponds, Norton, Cowbar, Cattersty Pond, Leven Valley, Hunt Cliff, Middlesbrough, Hutton Village, Marske and Wilton.

(COMMON) KESTREL *Falco tinnunculus*

A hovering Kestrel is a familiar sight around Cleveland, especially on the Tees Marshes and coastal fields, and the industrialisation of this area has been reasonably beneficial to the Kestrel by providing safe nesting places. More than one pair regularly nest in the chemical works at Billingham, Wilton International, Corus at Redcar and on the pylons around Teesmouth. There are other industrial areas around the River Tees, as well as several bridges and warehouses which almost certainly hold pairs of Kestrels. On a number of industrial sites Kestrels nest in boxes specifically erected for the birds.

The town centres of Middlesbrough, Hartlepool, Stockton and Guisborough probably have a pair or two in each and pairs are known to be present on Boulby Cliffs and several agricultural areas around the south and west of Cleveland. In total the population in the county is about 80-90 pairs.

There is a general dispersal of birds after the breeding season and a distinct increase around the North Tees Marshes. Up to 15 have been seen at one time on Greenabella Marsh and up to 20 have been recorded between Port Clarence and Seaton Carew, both counts being made in August.

Between late July and early November birds are quite regularly seen arriving from the sea or coasting south. The origin of these birds is debatable; the ringing recoveries mentioned below establish that some Scandinavian birds are involved and it is also likely that birds breeding in northern Britain will be generally moving south along the coast. The largest number seen along the coast occurred on 19 August 1978 when 11 passed Hartlepool observatory and four arrived over the coastline at Saltburn. Additionally, 20 passed Hartlepool between August and November 1970 and five arrived at Hartlepool in one hour on 27 September 2000. In most years about five to ten are seen actually crossing the coastline, although occasionally none is reported.

Over 300 Kestrels have been ringed in the county, the vast majority being young in the nest. The random dispersal of recently-fledged juveniles is well-illustrated by 11 known recoveries: four were ringed in June in Cleveland and were recovered between September and December in the same year of ringing, one moving south to Ninfield, East Sussex, one south-west to Manchester, one south-east to Flamborough, Humberside, and one west to Keswick, Cumbria. Another bird ringed in June 1995 in Cleveland had moved south to Pavenham, Bedfordshire, by February of the following year. Another was ringed at Newby, North Yorkshire, in June 1980 and had moved north (albeit only 12 km) being found in Billingham, in January 1981, one had moved north-west from New Holland, Humberside, in June 1957 to Billingham in August 1958. One ringed in Grosmont, North Yorkshire, in June 1996 was found dead in Middlesbrough 40 days later, whilst one ringed at Moorsholm in June 1995 was found dead at Lyndhurst, Hampshire, in December 1996. A bird ringed at Teesport in June 1994 was found dead at Hendon, Tyne & Wear, in June 1997 and one ringed in Thornaby in July 1996 was found dead in York in January 1997.

Two birds ringed in the Swedish province of Norrbotten, the first in July 1961 and the second in July 1976, confirm the Scandinavian origin of some wintering Kestrels. They were both recovered three months later, the first just to the north of Cleveland in Durham, and the second in Hartlepool. A third Scandinavian recovery concerned one ringed in the nest in Lappi, Finland, in July 1998 and found dead on Hartlepool North Sands in October 1998.

The 14 ringing recoveries mentioned above would seem to indicate that Scandinavian Kestrels fledge about one month later than British bred birds, therefore it could be concluded that Kestrels moving along the coast in July and August are British birds, whereas some of those seen in September-November have crossed the North Sea from Scandinavia.

An almost completely white male was observed in the Seaton Common-Greenabella area from August 1997 to March 2000.

RED-FOOTED FALCON *Falco vespertinus*

There are three records of this endearing falcon prior to 1989, a female near North Gare on 30 October 1949, a male at Saltholme Pools on 25 October 1969 and a male at Longnewton on 1 May 1987.

In 1989 single females were seen at Redcar on 17 May, on Coatham Marsh on 18 and 27 May and on Eston Moor on 29-30 May. These records could involve one bird, but since there was a small influx of Red-footed Falcons into Britain at this time, it is possible that two or three individuals were involved.

There have been seven subsequent records. A male was in the Cowpen Marsh-Greenabella area from 10 to 21 May 1990, whilst a female was at Haverton Hole and Cowpen Marsh from 10 to 12 June 1992. A male was seen at Cowpen Marsh on 12 June 1992, with single females over Hartlepool Headland on 24 May 1994 and 24 May 1995, and in Hargreaves Quarry on 9 and 10 June 2000, and a male over Hummersea on 25 April 2004.

MERLIN *Falco columbarius*

For at least the last 30 years, two or three birds have spent the winter hunting over the Tees Marshes, most records being of brown immature/female birds. The small grey-blue adult male is fairly rare.

There is generally a bird seen at Teesmouth in late July, then one or two in August and September and peak numbers are present from November to January. Fewer are seen in February to April and one is occasionally seen in May or June, although birds on passage cloud the picture in spring and autumn. One or two migrating birds are observed in most years passing points such as Hartlepool and South Gare.

Apart from wintering at Teesmouth, a few Merlins are regularly seen in urban areas during winter, although it is quite possible that birds seen around Redcar, Hartlepool or Billingham are the same individuals that hunt at Teesmouth. It would not take many minutes for a Merlin to fly from the Dormans-Saltholme Pools area to Billingham or from Seaton Common-Greenabella area to Hartlepool.

The only area where Merlins are regularly present in the summer is the moorland along the southern edge of Cleveland. There are breeding records for these moors for several years during the 1950s, 1980s and early 1990s.

The BTO 1968-72 Breeding Atlas showed Merlins to be present in nine of the 10 km squares on the North York Moors and in 1974, at least five pairs were known to be in the same area. Since it is not unusual for birds to be on the moorland during the summer, it is most likely that Merlins breed either in Cleveland or just to the south and east of the boundary every year.

There are eight recoveries, seven being ringed in the nest on North York Moors in June or July of 1912, 1970, 1984, 1989, 1996 (two birds) and 1998. All were found dead, at Middlesbrough in October 1914, Billingham in March 1978, Hartlepool in August 1984 and October 1989, Guisborough in November 1996, Billingham in November 1997 and Hartlepool in August 1998 respectively. The 1978 bird was nearly 8 years old, the 1984 bird was found beneath a window, and the seventh bird only lived for six weeks after ringing. One found dead on Cowpen Marsh on 25 August 1995 had been ringed in the nest at Longformacus, Borders, Scotland on 1 July 1995.

It has been suggested that Icelandic Merlins may reach Cleveland in winter, but with only two adult Merlins having been ringed in Cleveland since 1973, nothing definite can be said about the birds seen in winter.

(EURASIAN) HOBBY *Falco subbuteo*

Since 1982 there is an average of two to four records each year of this beautiful falcon. It is a summer visitor and the records for Cleveland are fairly evenly spread through the period early May to late September, with earliest and latest records of 18 April (1970) and 30 October (1975).

The majority of records are of birds seen on only one date, frequently for just a few minutes as it passes overhead. About 60% of the records involve birds seen around Teesmouth. Undoubtedly, the near-continuous birdwatching coverage of Teesmouth, especially between May and October, has an effect on the spread of records, but also the distribution of hirundines and dragonflies, the birds main prey items, during the summer must contribute to where Hobbies are found. One hunted over Dormans Pool from 22 September to 2 October 2000.

Prior to 1968, there were four records, of singles at Greatham in 1868, Hartlepool in September 1960, Redcar in September 1961 and Bousdale in July 1965.

Since then birds have been seen away from Teesmouth at many places, including Norton, Middlesbrough, Ormesby, Greatham, Boulby Cliffs, Eston Moor, Saltburn, Aislaby, Hartlepool, Elwick, Billingham, Scaling Dam, Yarm and Portrack Marsh.

GYR FALCON *Falco rusticolus*

There is only one record of Gyr Falcon, one of the most spectacular European birds of prey. The bird was shot "on the moor between Normanby and Guisborough" in March 1837 and described as an immature male of the Icelandic race. The skin was taken to the Hancock Museum in Newcastle upon Tyne where it remains (Hogg 1845, Stead 1964).

PEREGRINE (FALCON) *Falco peregrinus*

The sight of this particular falcon chasing a duck or wader over Seal Sands must rate as one of the most exhilarating on the Teesmouth 'scene'. Happily, the occurrence of Peregrines around the Tees estuary has been increasing, albeit rather slowly, with a bird or two being seen between early September and early March and occasionally in other months. When present, Peregrines tend to favour Saltholme Pools and the Greatham

Creek - Seal Sands area and seem to be quite at ease hunting amongst the pylons, chimneys and huge buildings around Teesmouth.

Elsewhere, a bird or two is fairly frequently seen around the moorland at Scaling Dam and less frequently along other parts of the coastline, occasionally appearing to have arrived from over the sea in autumn.

There are also records of birds seen over most of the centres of population like Redcar, Middlesbrough, Stockton and Yarm. Considering the vast areas that Peregrines can hunt over, one could be seen virtually anywhere.

In the past Peregrines were much less common; between the early 1940s and late 1970s very few were seen and in some years no birds were recorded. In the earlier years it suffered at the hands of gamekeepers, then from the 1960s to the 1980s the lack of Peregrines was attributed to the use of toxic seed dressing and insecticides which affected many other bird of prey species.

The earliest known breeding record occurred in the early 1700s at Hunt Cliff and since 1999, up to three, and possibly four, pairs have bred in Cleveland. The sight of a family party of five or six Peregrines in the air together is magical.

WATER RAIL *Rallus aquaticus*

This bird is secretive, and probably more numerous than the records suggest. It is quite regularly seen on passage, a few pairs breed in most years, but it is commonest in winter.

There are generally about 10-20 birds seen each winter and doubtless quite a few go unrecorded. Favourite places for this species in recent years have been Guisborough Sewage Farm, Teesmouth Field Centre, South Gare, Coatham Marsh, Haverton Hole, Dormans Pool and Billingham Bottoms. Birds are also seen in many other wetland areas such as Scaling Dam, Wynyard Lake, Hartburn Beck, Hemlington Lake, Charlton's Pond and several marshy areas around Teesmouth.

Passage migrants are seen in each year between September and December along the coastline especially at Hartlepool and South Gare.

It is also likely that birds spend some or all of the winter along the more secluded stretches of streams and beside ponds that are not watched as well as others, especially if there is some waterside cover in which the bird can conceal itself.

Fatalities and stranded or injured birds have been reported. One hit a television aerial in Dormanstown on 11 October 1955 and one that arrived over the sea at Hartlepool on 26 December 1970 was killed by a Great Black-backed Gull. It is not unusual for a bird or two to be stranded inside industrial areas, such as Billingham chemical works and Wilton International at this time of year, or to be found dead under overhead cables.

A pair or two were known to have bred at Teesmouth around the 19th to early 20th centuries and no doubt before and after this period, it being secretive when nesting. In the last 20 years or so, it has certainly bred in some years at Lovell Hill, the Dormans Pool - Hargreaves Quarry area, Haverton Hole, Coatham Marsh and in the Graythorp area.

The vast majority of sightings are of single birds, occasionally two birds are noted, but three were present at Guisborough Sewage Farm during January-March 1970 and eleven were in the Dormans Pool - Reclamation Pond area during freezing conditions on 6 December 1998.

SPOTTED CRAKE *Porzana porzana*

This crake is now a rare passage migrant, but in the 19th century it was an irregular summer visitor and was known to breed on the north side of Teesmouth.

In 1899 a fully-formed egg was taken from a female killed on 25 May and in 1900 a pair was seen with young (Nelson 1907).

Between 1900 and 1961 only one bird was recorded, a male killed against telegraph wires on the north side of Teesmouth on 21 May 1933. From 1962 to 1994, there was an average of one record every two years, although three individuals were seen in 1968 and four in 1989, but none between 1969 and 1977. From 1994, it has been recorded in almost every year, principally on Margrove Ponds, Coatham Marsh and Dormans Pool.

The majority of records refer to autumn birds, the earliest being 5 August (1989) and the latest being 25 November (1968). A few records refer to spring birds, including calling males at Portrack Marsh, Saltholme Pools and Haverton Hole, with the earliest and latest dates of 4 May (2006) and 9 June (2002). There are two records that do not fit spring or autumn passage; one at Haverton Hole on 2 January 1999 and one at Dormans Pool on 3 July 2000.

Spotted Crakes are notorious for being difficult to see and, considering the amount of suitable habitat, it is quite possible that the species may be an annual passage migrant in small numbers.

BAILLON'S CRAKE *Porzana pusilla*

There are two records for Cleveland; one shot with two Spotted Crakes at Saltholme Marsh on 16 September 1882 and an adult in Moordale Beck, between Wilton and Guisborough, from 10 to 12 May 1965.

CORNCRAKE (CORN CRAKE) *Crex crex*

The change in agricultural practices and methods during the last 100 years has been quite dramatic and it is considered that this has been responsible for the complete disappearance of this species as a breeding bird in Cleveland as well as many other counties in Britain. Corncrakes certainly bred in the Redcar area and around the southern boundary of Middlesbrough up to about 1920-1930 and once near Middlesbrough in 1950. It appears to have been quite regular on passage through the area up to the late 1950s, Nelson (1907) recording Corncrakes as late as the first week of November.

Between 1960 and the formation of Cleveland County in 1974, there were eight records, more than half of them on the coast, plus singles at Wilton, Hemlington and Portrack.

From 1974 to 2007, there have been 20 records, nine on the coast, three at Lovell Hill, four at Pinchinthorpe, one near Carlton Carr, one at Portrack and two at Bowesfield. The earliest and latest records in recent years have been 16 April (2004) and 7 October (1969).

(COMMON) MOORHEN *Gallinula chloropus*

This bird has a breeding population in Cleveland of about 350-450 pairs, and is capable of nesting on or by very small waterways and ponds, around the edges of reservoirs (if there is suitable vegetation) and in urban parks and gardens near water. There are probably more pairs per hectare around the North Tees Marshes than anywhere else in Cleveland. Some birds become quite tame in parks and gardens, especially when food is provided.

There is often a general movement of Moorhens in the winter to the south, depending on the severity of the winter. There are two ringing recoveries; a juvenile trapped at Graythorp in October 1972 that was present on Cowpen Marsh on 26 April 1973 and an adult ringed on Coatham Marsh on 14 March 1976 was killed at Moyelles-sur-Mer, Somme, France, on 20 September 1977. Also, single birds ringed in Denmark and the Netherlands have been found in Yorkshire in winter.

In an average winter the Tees Marshes probably hold about 100 wintering birds, compared with the estimated breeding population of about 70-90 pairs. Approximately 50 wintering birds resort to Stewart Park, Middlesbrough in most years.

Occasionally migrating birds are seen along the coastline, with most records being in the months April and August-November. There are at least five records of birds seen on the sea during these months, and several records of presumed migrants found dead beneath overhead cables.

(COMMON) COOT *Fulica atra*

The 1960s and 1970s saw a dramatic increase in the numbers of this water bird in the area, that almost certainly had nothing to do with the increasing numbers of observers or better coverage.

The earliest record of breeding concerns at least three pairs with eggs or young on Cowpen Marsh in 1912. Stead (1964) stated that "parties seldom exceed five birds around Teesmouth" and that breeding was attempted on Cowpen Marsh in 1958. By March 1972, the highest count was 131 and the breeding population at Teesmouth was estimated at 40-50 pairs. Numbers further increased to a maximum count of 356 in March 1977, but the Teesmouth counts have since dropped, levelling off at about 100-150 birds as a winter maximum in the 1980s and 1990s. The number of breeding pairs has also declined with 44 pairs on Cowpen Marsh in 1976, only nine in 1986 and about 20 pairs in 2004. Counts are not available over as many years for other parts of North Tees Marshes, but the present Teesmouth population is about 85-95 breeding pairs.

Breeding is also regular at Scaling Dam, Charlton's Pond, Margrove Ponds, Poole Hospital, Lovell Hill and several other small waters where there is sufficient vegetation to conceal a nest. Each of these areas holds approximately five to ten breeding pairs making the total breeding population in the county about 150-170 pairs. Nests with eggs have been found as early as mid-March, and it is not unusual for small chicks to be seen in mid-April.

The main wintering area since numbers declined at Teesmouth in the late 1970s has been Scaling Dam. Numbers here increased quite dramatically in the early 1960s, from 14 in January 1960 to 155 in December 1961, then 260 in December 1966, 273 in December 1975, 301 in December 1978 and 420 in December 1985. However, winter populations have since declined with no more than 200-250 in the early 1990s, 333 in 1995 and 100-150 in the late 1990s. Charlton's Pond has recently held 100-130 in the winter months and waters such as Lockwood Beck, Cowpen Bewley Pond, Wynyard and Margrove Ponds have held up to 50-60 Coot as winter maxima. Several other small ponds also hold a few birds in winter, the total population in the 1990s probably being about 500-700 birds each winter. However, with increased water levels in the Reclamation Pond, over 800 were present in November 1999, over 1,000 in November 2002 and November-December 2003, 1,200 in November 2004 and over 1,500 in 2006. The winter population in Cleveland is approximately 1% of the winter population of the UK.

During very cold weather it is not unusual for a bird or two to survive in Hartlepool Docks. The Teesmouth birds move to Greatham Creek and the adjacent south-west corner of Seal Sands when the freshwater pools and marshes freeze over, 100 or more being seen here occasionally. The tidal mud close to the Transporter Bridge is also used in very cold weather.

It is extremely unusual to see a Coot on the sea, but single birds were off Saltburn on

11 February 1986, off Cowbar Nab on 2 March 1986, North Gare on 8 January 1995 and South Gare on 16 July 1995.

COMMON CRANE *Grus grus*

There are 17 records of this bird, mostly since 1997, possibly associated with the recent breeding in Norfolk.

Date	Location	Details
May 1865	Dyke House Farm, Hartlepool	Single bird(shot)
4 August to 1 Nov 1959	Teesmouth	Single bird
4 May 1986	Boulby	Single bird
16 August 1987	Stillington	Single bird
29 April 1988	Coatham Marsh	One flew over
13 to22 June 1988	Durham Tees Valley Airport - Aislaby area	Two birds
9 May 1997	Haverton Hole	one over
14 – 15 May 1999	Cowpen Marsh	two
2 October 1999	Greatham Creek	one over
10 March 2002	Saltburn	Single bird
17 March 2002	North Tees Marshes, Wilton and Dunsdale	Five flew over
7 April 2002	Dormans Pool	One flew over
13 to 20 May 2002	near Cowpen Bewley	Single bird
14 - 15 September 2002	Cowpen Marsh	Two
5 January 2003	Hartlepool Docks	One flew over
7 January 2006	Redcar, Seal Sands & Hartlepool	Four flew over
15 March 2006	Coatham Marsh	Four flew over

Common Crane records

MACQUEEN'S BUSTARD *Chlamydotis macqueenii*

This species was formerly known as Houbara Bustard and is one of eight species that have not been recorded in Cleveland since its formation in 1974.

A single bird was seen and subsequently shot at Windy Hill, Marske, on 5 October 1892, at the time being the second British record. The skin resides in the Hancock Museum, Newcastle upon Tyne (Nelson 1907).

(EURASIAN) OYSTERCATCHER
Haematopus ostralegus

Nationally the Oystercatcher is one of the commonest breeding waders, but in Cleveland, it is one of the county's rarest with only one to four pairs nesting in most years since 1933. Single pairs occasionally nest inland, and have been recorded breeding by Hart Reservoir, Wynyard and Longnewton Reservoir. A pair also nested on the Billingham chemical works site in 2004. However, most nesting pairs are around the mouth of the Tees, principally on areas of tipped slag near Greatham Creek.

At the same time as the local birds are breeding, there is a gathering of non-breeding birds around Teesmouth and along the coastline as far south as Hummersea. This is usually about 200-400, although 600 were present in July 1985, these birds being considered to be immatures. Individuals from this gathering have been ringed at Teesmouth and found in Shetland in following summers. One ringed on Seal Sands on 2 May 1988 was found dead on the Isle of Sheppey, Kent, in December 1996, another ringed on the same day was killed by a Peregrine on Seal Sands on 8 February 1998 and a third bird ringed on 2 May 1988 was found dead at Saltburn on 2 March 2000.

Throughout August and September there is a steady passage of birds through Teesmouth, 100-200 being seen passing Hartlepool on some days with flocks of tens and twenties frequently heading south-west from Teesmouth during autumn evenings.

Birds ringed at Teesmouth in the autumn have been recovered on the Mersey and in France in the following winter, as well as in Norfolk and France during the following autumn and in the Shetlands in summer. One ringed in July 1983 was seen in the Netherlands in November-December 1989, August-September 1990, December 1992, October 1996, 1997 and 2000, December 2001 and September 2003. Another bird ringed in July 1983 was found dead at Wells, Norfolk, in January 2002, having reached the age of 20, very similar to the age of the previous bird. Another ringed in August 1986 was recorded at Wrangle, Lincolnshire, in August 1995.

Most autumn immigrants stay through the winter and 133 Oystercatchers caught on Bran Sands on 6 December 1976 included a bird ringed as a pullus in Norway earlier in 1976. Another bird from that catch was recovered in Norway in March 1978, and yet another was found dead at Skinningrove on 6 December 1985. At least nine other birds have either been ringed as pulli in Norway or recovered in summer there, as well as two recovered on the Faeroe Islands in summer. A bird ringed as a pullus on the Isle of May, Fife, was recorded at Teesmouth over seven years later.

In some years the autumn numbers at Teesmouth are higher than those in winter, though the highest counts are 1,648 in November 1956, 2,168 in September 1993, 2,261 in October 2000 and 2,635 in February 2005.

About 700-900 has been the usual winter maximum, birds beginning to depart by March. Their favourite high-tide roost sites are the rocks and islands around South Gare, the Seal Sands peninsula and Seaton Snook.

The favoured feeding areas seem to be the rocks revealed as the tide recedes at Coatham, Redcar, Saltburn and Skinningrove and around Hartlepool Headland. Co-ordinated counts along the coastline and Teesmouth in November 1990 and 1991 revealed close to 2,300 birds in Cleveland, and 2,600 in January 1994, around 75% of which were in the Saltburn-Skinningrove area.

At least 900 birds have been ringed in Cleveland, most by the Durham University teams, and there are at least 30 recoveries/controls of birds moving to or from Teesmouth as detailed above. In most years, there are one or two records of birds at inland localities, generally Crookfoot Reservoir and Scaling Dam and usually in spring. Breeding may have occurred at the former locality in the recent past.

A white individual was seen regularly south of the Tees between April 1968 and September 1971, and an almost completely white bird was at Saltburn each winter from August 1993 to January 2002.

BLACK-WINGED STILT *Himantopus himantopus*

There are two records of this spectacular wader, one on Coatham Marsh on 17 May 1986 and one on the North Tees Marshes from 23 April to 5 May 1993.

(PIED) AVOCET *Recurvirostra avosetta*

This beautiful wader has become an annual visitor to Teesmouth, most records falling in the months March to May, and with many of the birds occurring in the Seal Sands - Greatham Creek area or on Saltholme Pools.

Nelson (1907) recorded three single birds shot at Teesmouth in the 19th century. Also, one was seen in late May 1931, one was on a pool near Dormanstown on 9 September 1947 and one or two appeared at Teesmouth in late May 1960.

Most records are of one-two birds, although 17 were on the Reclamation Pond on 4 May 1974, 14 or 15 flew over Seaton Snook on 26 April 1998 and 20 were on Saltholme Pools on 30 September 2000.

Very few Avocets are recorded in Cleveland away from Teesmouth, the only records being one in a flooded field beside Wilton Lane, Guisborough, on 7 April 1979, nine on Scaling Dam on 26 September 1998 and one at Longnewton Reservoir from 2 to 4 April 2001.

Whilst most birds are seen in the months March to May, it is quite frequently recorded in the winter months, and occasionally in September.

STONE CURLEW (STONE-CURLEW)
Burhinus oedicnemus

While it is not certain that this bird ever bred in what is now Cleveland, it did breed quite commonly in Yorkshire up to the early part of the 19th century, but declined during the following 100 years.

There are seven records for this area, all singles. The first four involved birds being killed: between Saltburn and Brotton in about 1840; at Saltholme in 1843; at Redcar on 16 December 1899; and at Coatham on 10 or 11 January 1901. The recent records are South Gare on 13 September 1987, Coatham Marsh from 4 to 6 May 1993 and South Gare on 25 October 1994.

LITTLE RINGED PLOVER (LITTLE PLOVER)
Charadrius dubius

This wader is now a regular summer visitor to Cleveland, most birds being seen north of the Tees, and between early April and mid-August.

Little Ringed Plovers first bred in Britain in 1938 (Ledley and Pedlar 1938) in Yorkshire in 1948 and Durham in 1962, but it took another ten years before breeding was proven in Cleveland, when a pair successfully reared young on the North Tees Marshes in 1972. Breeding has been attempted every year since then, and since 1978 pairs have been known or considered to be breeding on occasion at Crookfoot Reservoir, Hartlepool Docks, Billingham Beck Valley, Portrack, Bowesfield, Eaglescliffe, Teesdale development site at Thornaby, Scaling Dam and Stillington. Single pairs also bred on Coatham Marsh in 1976 and 1978, young being seen in both years. It is likely that the present Cleveland breeding population is four-six pairs and has probably reached its maximum.

The first record for Cleveland was an immature on Cowpen Marsh from 27 to 31 July 1963, followed by four immatures at Scaling Dam in July 1964 and one or two every year thereafter until breeding was proven in 1972. Since then small groups of adults and juveniles are often seen in July and August eight or nine together being quite frequent, though ten were at Billingham Beck Valley on 17 July 1981, up to 11 around the North Tees Marshes in July 1991 and July 2000, 12 were on Portrack Marsh on 27 July 1994, Longnewton Reservoir on 26 June 2004, and Saltholme Pools on 13 July 2006.

The earliest and latest dates are 12 March (2007) and 29 September (1972).

RINGED PLOVER *Charadrius hiaticula*

May and August are the months when most Ringed Plovers are seen in Cleveland mainly around Teesmouth, although it can be found at other places along the coastline throughout the year, and every year a few birds are seen at inland localities.

Around 400-600 is the usual high count in May, though 1,137 were counted in May 1997; these birds are thought to have been headed for Iceland and Greenland, having wintered in southern Europe and West Africa. Up to 600 are seen in August-September, and most are thought to have come from Iceland and Greenland, although some originate in north Europe, including Sweden and the Netherlands. The current National Significance Threshold for passage Ringed Plover is 300 birds, a figure that has been easily surpassed every spring and most autumns since 1994.

While counts show several hundreds present on any one day, it is thought that well over 1,000 birds pass through in spring and autumn. Throughout the winter, about 50-100 are present, although 200-300 have been counted very occasionally, perhaps in response to cold weather.

The Cleveland breeding population is about 30-50 pairs, most being around Teesmouth, especially the Brinefields, Seal Sands Peninsula, North Gare Sands and South Gare. Single pairs are known to have bred at places like Scaling Dam, Billingham chemical works, and Hartlepool Docks, and up to three pairs nested on the Teesdale development site, Thornaby in the 1990s.

After the breeding season the adults moult, some staying in the area throughout the winter, but others disperse, single Teesmouth-ringed birds having been noted on the Clyde Estuary in September and in East Lothian in October. The young birds generally move south, some being recorded in France two-three months after fledging and in the winter near Cardiff. This last bird was caught again, nesting at Coatham Sands three years after hatching there.

Several birds ringed as nestlings at other east coast sites have been seen around Teesmouth in the following autumns, indicating that not all birds passing through in spring and autumn are necessarily bound for, or have come from, nesting grounds outside Britain. Birds in this category have been ringed at Holy Island and Beadnell in Northumberland, Spurn in Humberside and Gibraltar Point in Lincolnshire. At least three ringed in Norfolk had moved north to Seal Sands, by the autumn of the same year.

Most of the known ringing recoveries and controls have been obtained by Durham University, which has established the passage routes of this species, but relatively little, has been determined with regard to the wintering grounds or breeding areas. Birds ringed at Teesmouth during spring or autumn passage have been recorded during the following years at Walney Island in Cumbria, Portsmouth, Canvey Island in Essex, near Bristol, Cornwall, north France, south Norway, Sweden, Portugal and Iceland. Also, a bird ringed in May 1983 was recovered in Senegal in January 1984 and one ringed in August 1980 was recovered in West Sahara in April 1986.

Birds controlled at Teesmouth during spring or autumn passage have been ringed in previous springs or autumns in Finland, Norway, Poland, Denmark, France, Spain, Highland, Dumfries, Essex, Cornwall and Cumbria.

The only bird known to move any great distance during the same period of migration was a juvenile ringed at Teesmouth on 8 September 1980 and recovered near Bangor, Gwynedd, North Wales, 20 days later.

One ringed at Washington Ponds, Tyne & Wear, on 5 October 1974 was dead 'near Middlesbrough' over 17 years later on 5 June 1991; a considerable age for a small wader.

Approximately 3,000 birds have been ringed at Teesmouth, almost all as full grown birds, by Durham University, and many of these during the 1980s, so there should be more recoveries and controls in the future and perhaps more indication of the origin of some of the thousands of Ringed Plover that use the Tees estuary.

KENTISH PLOVER *Charadrius alexandrinus*

There are 15 records of this plover for Cleveland, three records involving four birds in the first half of the 20th Century, five birds between 1954 and 1974 and another seven since then. All concern spring birds between 30 April (1961) and 18 June (1972), except for one on Bran Sands on 9 September 1963. Of the spring records, nine fall in the period 11-29 May. In the early records, two are labelled as "Teesmouth", but the species has been seen once at North Gare, Seaton Snook, Cowpen Marsh, the Brinefields, Saltholme Pools, Scaling Dam and Redcar beach and three times at both Bran Sands and beside the Long Drag. Since 1974, the Long Drag has been the favourite locality.

All but three of the records concern birds seen on only one or two days, but a bird by the Long Drag in May 1980 remained for three days, one on Scaling Dam in May 1973 stayed for four days and one on Seaton Snook was present from 16 to 23 May 1994.

All but one of the records involved single birds, but two were at Teesmouth on 11 May 1924.

(EURASIAN) DOTTEREL
Charadrius morinellus

Up to 1939, this bird was a regular passage migrant to one particular undisclosed area of grassland. The secrecy was almost certainly to prevent the birds being shot.

They are normally very tame and approachable, and Dotterel shooting was quite commonplace.

The species is now scarce in the area though there are signs of a modest recovery, with small trips (groups of Dotterel) regularly being seen in Yorkshire, sometimes at Danby Beacon, only two kilometres south of Cleveland and there are now records of passage birds in Cleveland for almost every year since 1987.

The spring records up to 1939 were usually in the period 25 April to 6 May and the autumn sightings between 15 August and 7 September, although the latest is 29 November 1900 on Coatham Marsh. A party of 30 at the unknown locality in May 1903 is the largest number mentioned.

Since 1959 the earliest and latest dates have been 2 April (2005) and 18 November (2001).

Date	No.	Location
12 September 1959	1	between Redcar & Marske
4 to 6 September 1965	1	South Gare
23 October 1982	1	between Redcar & Marske
14 August 1983	1	Greatham Creek
6 May 1983	1	Boulby Cliffs
2 October 1984	2	Boulby Cliffs
18 April 1987	3	Boulby Cliffs
20 - 21 May 1989	2	Seaton Carew
20 May 1991	1	Long Drag
13 - 14 May 1992	4	North Gare
28 to 30 May 1992	2	North Gare
14 April 1993	1	Boulby Cliffs
15 ~ 16 May 1993	9	Boulby Cliffs
12 May 1994	1	South Gare
14 May 1994	1	Boulby Cliffs
17-26 May 1997	1	South Gare
7 May 1998	1	between Redcar & Marske
8 May 1998	8	between Redcar & Marske
1 October 1998	1	South Gare
6 October 1998	1	Coatham Marsh
29 May 1999	1	Long Drag
29 August 1999	1	Boulby Cliffs
18 November 2001	1	Saltholme Pools
20 April 2002	1	Boulby Cliffs
10 September 2002	1	Boulby Cliffs
24 April 2003	1	Boulby Cliffs
30 October 2003	1	Saltholme Pools
2 April 2005	2	Cowbar, 1 next day
21 September 2005	1	Hummersea
6 October 2007	1	Boulby
Dotterel Records since 1959		

Species

AMERICAN GOLDEN PLOVER *Pluvialis dominica*

There are seven records for Cleveland of this American wader. The first was an adult in full breeding plumage present around Greenabella Marsh and on the reclaimed part of Seal Sands from 2 to 9 July 1979, but the remaining six have all been juvenile or first-summer birds.

Singles were seen on the coastal fields between Redcar and Marske from 14 to 19 October 1981 and on 30 September 2000, and on the North Tees Marshes from 23 August to 4 October 1984, 30 September to 1 October 1988, 11 to 13 June 1995, and 31 August to 2 September 1995.

More birds have been noted on or beside Greatham Creek than any other location in Cleveland.

PACIFIC GOLDEN PLOVER *Pluvialis fulva*

The only Cleveland record for this species concerns an adult moulting out of summer plumage in the Greatham Creek - Seal Sands - Reclamation Pond area from 5 to 15 August 1995. Details are given by Joynt (1996).

(EURASIAN) GOLDEN PLOVER *Pluvialis apricaria*

The coastal plain around Teesside appears to be one of the main wintering areas for this wader in northern England. Their favourite area in recent years is the fields around Saltholme Pools, and to a lesser extent those between Redcar and Marske, Durham Tees Valley Airport - Longnewton area, Bowesfield, Scaling Dam and Seaton Common.

Very few Golden Plover are seen during the summer months, but quite large numbers begin to appear in August and several hundred are often present at favoured sites from December to March, when there is a steady decline with most birds having gone by mid-April. In recent winters, the maximum count has been about 1,500-2,000 at Teesmouth, around 1,000 on the Redcar fields, with smaller numbers at the other localities. However, there is probably a certain amount of interchange between the areas mentioned. In total it is estimated that there are likely to be 3,000-4,000 Golden Plover in Cleveland in winter. The highest estimates at Saltholme Pools have been 2,350 in October 1994, 2,650 in November 1996, 3,000 in December 2001 and 4,000 on 23 November 2002. The current National Significance Threshold for this bird is 2,500.

Migrating flocks of birds are sometimes seen at other suitable locations, but almost any field in Cleveland could hold Golden Plover at times.

There are three ringing recoveries: a pullus ringed on the moorland 2km south of Lockwood Beck on 17 May 1980 was killed at Rabat, Morocco in December 1981; an adult ringed at Drente, Holland on 28 December 1990 was present on Seal Sands on 14 July 1993; and an adult ringed on Seal Sands on 14 July 1993 was killed in Biera Litoral, Portugal, in Feb 1996. Also, a pullus ringed just south of Cleveland, on Lealholm Moor on 16 June 1990 was killed in Cantabria, Spain, in February 1991.

In most springs birds of the race *P.a.altifrons* are seen, which breeds in the north and east of the species' range, although it is only in breeding plumage that this race can be readily identified.

The moorland of the North York Moors above about 300 metres is ideal Golden Plover breeding habitat. However, only a small strip of this occurs in Cleveland and the present breeding estimate is 25-30 pairs and it seems likely that the breeding population in this area has not changed for many years.

An individual with white primaries was seen at Dormans Pool and Bowesfield in October 2000.

GREY PLOVER *Pluvialis squatarola*

Seal Sands is the favourite haunt of this wader, although some birds feed on Bran Sands and North Gare Sands, and it is here that Durham University has carried out extensive studies of this and other common waders. About 500 have been ringed since the mid-1970s, giving a reasonable insight into the life of Teesmouth's Grey Plovers.

Very few Grey Plover are seen in the summer, the first returning birds, all of which are adults, generally appearing in August. Some of these birds stay to moult, but others move further south, as far as western France. Here they are joined by some of the birds which have moved on after moulting, one being recovered in north west Spain in January.

Juvenile birds begin to arrive at Teesmouth in September, some staying, but others moving south again as far as western France. A juvenile ringed on Seal Sands on 16 December 1975 was seen again on Seal Sands in October 1997, aged 22, and one ringed on Seal Sands on 19 September 1978 was in Luneberg, Germany, in April 1988.

More adults arrive in November, after having moulted on the Wadden Sea in north Germany, some of these birds staying and displacing some of the juveniles that have taken up feeding territories. An adult ringed on Bran Sands on 23 October 1985 was recorded in Norfolk in August 1995.

There is another distinct influx in late January and February as birds begin to move north. Up to 300 can be present at this time in some years, but most have departed by March for their breeding grounds in Siberia, Usually only a few young birds remain in April and May, although a few adults in full breeding dress are occasionally seen in May. One ringed at North Gare on 28 January 1979 was found in western Siberia, in July 1985.

The highest counts at Teesmouth have been 340 on 28 September 1957, 368 on 1 November 1964 and 367 in mid-February 1977, indicating that Teesmouth can hold no more than 300-400 at any time. This could be due to the fact that the available mud has diminished considerably during the 1960s-1970s or that Grey Plover are much more territorial on their feeding grounds than other waders, hence the lower carrying capacity of Seal Sands.

Very few Grey Plover are seen in Cleveland away from Teesmouth, birds being noted passing Hartlepool in most autumns, and one or two are occasionally seen at inland waters such as Scaling Dam, Longnewton Reservoir and Crookfoot Reservoir. Up to five were at Scaling Dam in September 1960.

(NORTHERN) LAPWING *Vanellus vanellus*

While this bird is a member of the wader family, Lapwing breed in a greater variety of habitats than other waders nesting in Cleveland. Apart from breeding alongside Redshank and Snipe around the Tees Marshes, Lapwing also nest on tipped slag, and sand and gravel habitats with Ringed Plover and Oystercatcher, on upland fields with Curlew and on suitable agricultural land throughout Cleveland.

The highest density of Lapwings is in the fields and marshes between Seaton Carew and Port Clarence, over 100 pairs being in this area at least in the 1980s.

Taking the BTO's Common Birds Census 1972 figure of 3.4 pairs of Lapwing per square km of agricultural land, the 300 square km in Cleveland should hold approximately 1,000 pairs although the intensive farming techniques used since the 1980s may well have reduced the overall density. The Cleveland Lapwing nesting population is now probably about 700 pairs.

Immediately after the breeding season, the adults generally gather in favoured fields to moult. There is a distinct build up of birds around Saltholme Pools and Cowpen Marsh at Teesmouth with up to 1,000 present in July. After this the numbers sometimes drop before building up again to a winter peak of around 3,000-5,000 birds. The highest counts are: 9,800 in December 1990; 10,500 in December 1995; and 9,000-10,000 in November 2002. Gatherings of 1,000-2,000 have been noted in the Longnewton area, Hartlepool Docks, Portrack Marsh, Bowesfield, Redcar coastal fields, Lovell Hill and Scaling Dam, and flocks numbering a few hundred can frequently be seen in autumn and winter in many fields throughout the area.

In October and November there is an influx of birds, sometimes appearing as flocks, which arrive from over the sea anywhere along the coastline. Some are known to have come from northern Europe and at about the same time the local birds tend to move south, some flying as far as France and Spain. Flocks of birds can usually be seen heading south or west as soon as severe cold weather reaches the area. On an unspecified date in October 1899, approximately 1,000 Lapwings arrived at Teesmouth in fifteen minutes (Nelson 1907).

Over 1,000 Lapwing have been ringed in Cleveland, and there are at least 20 recoveries of birds to or from Cleveland, most being ringed as pulli. Those ringed in Cleveland in one summer have been recovered in following winters in France (three) and Spain, but a bird ringed in 1980 was found in December 1983 at Marske no more than 15 km from its ringing location and a bird ringed as a juvenile at South Gare on 21 August 1986 was found dead at Redcar in November 1999. Another, ringed on Moorsholm Moor in June 1977, lived almost 13 years before being found dead at Rosedale, North Yorkshire, in April 1990. One bird ringed at Marske in January 1986 was present at Sunderland in July 1987. Birds recovered in Cleveland in autumn and winter have been ringed the previous summer in Norway (three), the Netherlands and Shetland. A bird ringed in Suffolk in 1969 was present at Teesmouth in September 1970 and a colour-ringed bird at Saltholme Pools in August 1993 had bred in Upper Teesdale, County Durham, in 1992 and 1993.

That some birds return to their natal area is indicated by one ringed at Stanghow in 1956 that was found to be breeding in 1959 only ten metres from the point at which it hatched. Equally, some do not return to their hatching areas, birds ringed as pulli in Northumberland and Durham have been reported in their 3rd-5th summers in Russia, Sweden, Norway and Finland, all between late April and mid-June.

A cinnamon-coloured bird was at Redcar in December 1892 and leucistic birds were on Dormans Pool in February 1991 and Saltholme Pools in December 2005, January 2006 and October 2006.

GREAT KNOT *Calidris tenuirostris*

An adult was seen on Greenabella Marsh on 13 October 1996, Seal Sands from 14 October to 2 November and Bran Sands from 2 to 5 November 1996. This is the second record of this species for Britain. Details of this record are given by Gee (1997).

(RED) KNOT *Calidris canutus*

To many Teesmouth birdwatchers, this bird epitomises winter. It used to be the commonest wader in the winter months, with a regular population of between 4,000-7,000 birds during the 1980s, but since 1995 peak counts have been about 1,000-4,000. Approximately 19,000 were recorded in December 1970.

Knot can be seen in every month of the year, though very few occur in May and June and it is usually the latter half of July before some (adults) start to congregate around the Tees. Large scale ringing, mainly by Durham University, has shown that these birds do not usually stay long, but move to their traditional moulting grounds on the Wash, having bred in Greenland and Arctic Canada. Some move back to Teesmouth in November after completing their moult on the Wash, but others arrive in November having moulted in the Wadden Sea (Denmark, Germany, and The Netherlands). An adult ringed at Princess Marie Bay, Ellesmere Island, in the extreme north of Canada on 24 June 1980 was present on Bran Sands on 22 November 1985. Some of the birds that arrive in November move into Northumberland and to the Firth of Forth and Stranraer in Scotland. However, departing birds are more than replaced into December by arrivals from other areas; consequently the peak numbers at Teesmouth usually occur in January.

The juveniles generally begin to arrive at Teesmouth in September, but almost all of these birds move on, being recorded later, on the Humber, the Solway Firth and in north and west France. The most remarkable recovery from Teesmouth concerns a juvenile bird ringed on 23 September 1983 and recovered at Langebaan Lagoon, Cape Province, South Africa, on 14 April 1985. Birds from the Siberian breeding population winter in southern and West Africa, but do not normally pass through Britain on migration with only a few records for East Anglia. If the Teesmouth bird was from the Greenland population, South Africa was far outside its normal wintering range.

Some juveniles move on from the Tees in their first autumn, whilst others ringed at such places as Fair Isle, Highland, Fife, Kent, Norfolk, Dorset, Lothian, North Wales, Norway, Poland and Holland have been recorded at Teesmouth in the following winters, as well as juveniles ringed in March in Gwynedd and April in Germany.

Almost all of the wintering Knot leave Teesmouth within one or two weeks at the beginning of March, travelling to the Wash, Morecambe Bay or the Wadden Sea to gain summer plumage and thence back to Greenland, via Iceland in May. A small proportion of the birds heading for Greenland/Arctic Canada travel via northern Norway, stopping to feed mainly in two fjords near Troms. Seven birds ringed at Teesmouth in winter have been re-caught there in May 1985 and 1986, one of which was recorded back at Teesmouth in the following winter. Another was recorded near Troms in August 1997, having been ringed at Hartlepool in December 1994, and two other adults, ringed in Norway in August, have been controlled at Hartlepool in February.

Other interesting recoveries and controls include two aged at least 17 years; one ringed as an adult at South Gare in November 1985 was taken by a cat at Hartlepool in December 2001 and the other ringed as an adult at Hartlepool in January 1987 was found in Holland in January 2003. Some birds seem not to be faithful to one wintering site: one ringed on the Cromarty Firth on 17 January 1987 was at Hartlepool on 1 December 1994 and 7 January 1997; one ringed in Norfolk on 10 February 1990 was at Hartlepool on 7 January 1997; one ringed on Tayside on 11 December 1988 was at Hartlepool on 8 December 2001 and another ringed at Hartlepool on 7 January 1997 was in Holland on 12 January 2003.

Whilst Knot mainly feed on Seal Sands and Bran Sands, flocks can be found feeding along most of Cleveland's shoreline, and some birds roost in these areas during high tide. Hartlepool North Sands has become a favourite site in recent years.

Occasionally one or two Knot resort to the marshes at Teesmouth, especially Dormans Pool, these birds usually being seen in late spring and autumn, and occasionally birds are noted on the inland waters, up to five being at Scaling Dam in August 1962 and seven at Longnewton Reservoir on 28 August 2000.

SANDERLING Calidris alba

This wader can be found on virtually any section of sandy beach in Cleveland. It is reasonably tolerant of disturbance, occurring on the beaches at Redcar and Seaton Carew, but also frequenting the beaches between Crimdon Dene and Hartlepool Headland, at North Gare, Bran Sands and between Redcar and Saltburn. There has been a noticeable decline in birds seen in Cleveland since about 1999.

Work conducted by Durham University since the 1980s has shown that Cleveland's Sanderlings can be divided into four groups: passage migrants in August and September; adults that moult here in August-October and mostly stay through the winter; adults that moult elsewhere in Britain and then winter at Teesmouth; and passage migrants in April and May. Over 2,200 had been ringed by 2003 and the oldest known bird was ringed as an adult in November 1980 and controlled in December 1993, aged at least 14.

The passage migrants in autumn begin to arrive in late July, but most adults generally appear in August, followed by juveniles in September, and then move on to wintering grounds, perhaps in Europe or West Africa. One bird ringed on autumn passage has been recovered in mid-winter in southern Spain. At this time, peak counts are generally 500-700 birds, and up to 200 birds have been seen passing Hartlepool in a day.

The adults that arrive in August usually number about 300-400 and stay at Teesmouth to moult. Most of them remain throughout the winter, being joined by adults that have moulted elsewhere in Britain (in particular the Wash in Norfolk) and swelling the numbers of over-wintering birds to 800 in most years. The birds which arrive from other moulting areas do so in late October and early November, whilst a few birds that have moulted and/or been seen at Teesmouth in autumn, move north to spend some of the winter at places such as Whitburn, and St. Mary's Island, in Tyne & Wear. A bird presumed to be wintering when ringed at Saltburn in November 1982 was controlled near Workington, Cumbria, in November 1987, and another ringed at Saltburn on 7 February 1995 was at Filey Brigg, North Yorkshire, on 22 January 2000.

The fourth category concerns birds that have wintered to the south of Teesmouth, including those from southern Europe, and move through Cleveland in April and May. This is usually when the highest counts are made, about 600-900 being usual, although 1,078 were around Teesmouth on 24 May 1998. Some of these birds may well have passed through Teesmouth in the previous autumn, as indicated by a bird ringed at Seaton Carew on 10 September 1984, controlled at Teesmouth on 21 May 1985 and noted on Handa Island in north-west Scotland three days later.

Colour-marking of birds wintering at Teesmouth has indicated that both Greenland/Arctic Canadian breeding birds and Siberian breeding birds are using Teesmouth in winter. Birds marked on spring passage have been seen in Iceland and in the German part of the Wadden Sea, and birds marked on autumn passage recorded in Sweden, Germany, Norway and the Netherlands.

It is not unusual for a few birds to be seen on the marshes at Teesmouth in spring and autumn, but in the first week of June 1975 up to 20 were seen on Coatham Marsh and up to 54 on Dormans Pool.

Up to four have been observed at Scaling Dam in spring or autumn in at least eight years since the reservoir was built, and singles were at Crookfoot Reservoir in November 1993 and Longnewton Reservoir in July 2000 and May 2004.

SEMI-PALMATED SANDPIPER *Calidris pusilla*

There are four records of this small American wader: singles on Saltholme Pools from 7 to 10 May 1989; Greenabella Marsh from 23 to 25 July 1989; Dormans Pool on 14 July 2002 and Saltholme Pools from 5 to 11 July 2006.

Birds of Cleveland

LITTLE STINT *Calidris minuta*

In common with many species of wader, the records each year are predominantly from Teesmouth, although it is sometimes seen at Scaling Dam and occasionally elsewhere.

Autumn passage is the time when most Little Stints are noted, most records falling between early August and early October, although a few birds are quite frequently seen in May and early June and occasionally in early July and November. There are also records of single birds at Teesmouth in January, February and April 1966, late November 1975 and November and December 1984, as well as a sighting of three birds at Hartlepool on 19 February 1950.

Prior to 1974, the highest count was at least 113 at Teesmouth on 24 September 1960, there being 48 at Scaling Dam seven days earlier. Nelson (1907) recorded 40-50 in some years, with earliest and latest 'autumn' dates of 12 August and 14 November, and an occasional bird in spring.

Since 1974, the annual autumn peak count has varied widely from four to 140 with an average of about 30, the peak occurring between late August and early October and sometimes there are two distinct influxes during this period. The highest count of 140 was on 9 September 1978 and up to 18 were at Scaling Dam in September 1996.

Favoured areas are invariably the North Tees Marshes, but a few birds usually appear south of the river at South Gare and Coatham Marsh.

Inland records include birds at Scaling Dam and very occasionally at other waters such as Crookfoot Reservoir, Portrack Marsh, Margrove Ponds and Longnewton Reservoir. Birds also occasionally pass along the coast at Hartlepool.

In autumn nearly all of the birds are in immature plumage, but occasionally an adult bird is noted in winter or transitional plumage. The birds seen in spring generally appear to be in near-summer plumage and are probably one year old.

Only 23 Little Stints have been ringed at Teesmouth, and a further bird was trapped on Dormans Pool on 29 September 1984 having been ringed seven days earlier at Tjorveneset (Vest Agder) on the extreme southern tip of Norway.

TEMMINCK'S STINT *Calidris temminckii*

Since Cleveland was formed on 1 April 1974, this wader has averaged five birds per year and occurrences have varied between two and eight birds annually apart from only one in 1984 and 1991, none in 1995, 1997 and 1998, and 15 in 2004.

Prior to 1974, Temminck's Stints had been recorded in autumn 1833, autumn 1954, three times in 1963, singles in 1966 and 1967 and annually since 1969. It is certain that some birds will have been overlooked in the past, but there does seem to have been a real increase in the number visiting Teesmouth.

Since 1969, just over half of the birds have occurred in May, the remainder being about equally spread between June, July and August, with very few in September and October. The earliest and latest records are 22 April (2003) and 24 October (1969).

Not surprisingly the majority of birds have been recorded around the marshes of Teesmouth, though single birds have been seen at Scaling Dam on 20 May 1971, 18 to 21 May 2004 and 24 August 2004, Crookfoot Reservoir from 10 to 12 August 1984 and Longnewton Reservoir on 30 June 2004.

Most records involve one or two birds, although three together have been seen on more than one occasion, four were on Saltholme Pools on 22 May 1978 and six were on the North Tees Marshes on 6 June 1977.

LONG-TOED STINT *Calidris subminuta*

An immature present on Saltholme Marsh on 28, 30, 31 August and 1 September 1982 was accepted as the first record for Britain at the time and was seen by hundreds of birdwatchers during its stay (Dunnett 1992, Dunnett 2005).

A wader on Saltholme Pools from 30 September to 21 October 1989 was originally identified as a Long-toed Stint, but when caught midway through its stay, the measurements suggested it was most probably an extremely small Pectoral Sandpiper.

WHITE-RUMPED SANDPIPER *Calidris fuscicollis*

This is the most frequently recorded of the five American small waders, collectively known as 'peeps', to occur in Britain and is the only one to have occurred more than four times in Cleveland. Semi-palmated and Baird's Sandpipers have been seen four times, but

Birds of Cleveland

Least and Western Sandpipers have yet to be recorded.

There are 17 records, all falling in the period 13 July to 19 August, or 29 September to 21 October, with over 60% staying for five days or more.

The first White-rumped Sandpiper was on Seaton Carew tip pool from 13 to 17 August 1963, followed by:

Date	No.	Location
4 to 14 August 1973	1	Dormans Pool
16 August 1975	1	Reclamation Pond
10 October 1977	1	Reclamation Pond
26 - 27 July 1980	1	Long Drag Pools
4 to 21 October 1980	1-3	Dormans Pool (3 seen 5-6 October)
30 July to 9 August 1983	1	Dormans Pool and Reclamation Pond
7 to 17 August 1986	1	South Gare/Bran Sands/Seal Sands
5 to 14 August 1989	1	Reclamation Pond area
13 July 1990	1	Bran Sands
23 July to 3 August 1990	1	Saltholme Pools
13 to 19 October 1995	1	Dormans Pool
13 to 18 August 1998	1	Dormans Pool to 17th, then Coatham Marsh
29 September to 11 October 2001	1	Saltholme Pools
13 July 2002	1	Greatham Creek - Seal Sands
8 to 19 August 2002	1	Seaton Snook - Seal Sands
26 July to 5 August 2006	1-2	Seaton Snook (2 seen 30 July - 3 August)
White-rumped Sandpiper Records		

BAIRD'S SANDPIPER *Calidris bairdii*

There are four records of this American 'peep': one on Saltholme on 5 May 1979, one first seen on Greenabella Marsh on 29 September 1986, then present on the Long Drag Pools for three days and finally spending the next 11 days on South Gare lagoon, being last seen on 13 October 1986; one on Coatham Marsh on 10 August 1997 and one on Saltholme Pools 2 - 8 September 2005.

PECTORAL SANDPIPER *Calidris melanotos*

This American wader has been recorded in all but three years since 1975, almost always at Teesmouth and principally in the months May and September, although it has been seen in every month from April to December with a total of about 95 birds occurring to the end of 2007.

The first record was in October 1841, when one was shot near Hartlepool, then two were shot in 1853; one on 30 August 1853 at Teesmouth and one on 17 October 1853 at Coatham (Nelson 1907, Temperley 1951).

There was a gap of more than 100 years before the next record, one on Cowpen Marsh from 12 to 17 September 1962. Since then; one was seen at Teesmouth in July 1963 and October 1967; two in October 1969; up to six in September 1970, the peak of six occurring on 19 September; and up to four in September 1971. Two were seen in 1973, one of which occurred in mid-June and was displayed to by several male Ruff.

Since 1975, one to four have been observed annually (except for none in 1987, 1990 and 1998), usually on Dormans Pool, Saltholme Pools or Long Drag, but almost every area of marsh and mud at Teesmouth has been visited by the species. The earliest and latest dates are 19 April (2004) and 25 December (1975).

Away from Teesmouth singles were at: Margrove Ponds from 2 to 6 September 1989; Scaling Dam from 19 September to 13 October 1989 (two birds 23-26 September); Scaling Dam from 14 to 27 September 1991; Portrack from 4 to 9 September 1994; Margrove Ponds on 18 September 1994; Bowesfield Marsh on 3 August 2001; and Scaling Dam on 21 September 2003.

Since 1974, 75% have stayed for more than one day and 30% have stayed ten days or more.

SHARP-TAILED SANDPIPER *Calidris acuminata*

This is one of the rarest waders to be recorded in Cleveland, single adults being seen on Cowpen Marsh from 21 to 24 August 1963 and beside the Long Drag on 3 September 1977 and 26 August 1997.

CURLEW SANDPIPER *Calidris ferruginea*

This wader follows a very similar pattern of occurrence to that of Little Stint although it is not as frequent in spring and has never been recorded in winter.

Apart from single birds seen at Teesmouth on 30 March 1969 and 26 April 1981, the earliest birds are seen from mid-May, although very few are seen in spring and early summer. It is usually late July before there are signs of increased numbers with a peak usually between late August and mid-September. There are very few records in October and the latest is 29 November (1963).

Nelson (1907) did not report any spring records, the earliest being 27 July 1894, and the highest number being about 100 shot in the autumn of 1890. One cannot help but wonder just how many birds passed through Teesmouth in that autumn.

The highest count is 230 spread around Teesmouth on 28 August 1969, but since 1974 the annual peak has varied between five and 84, with an average of 33 birds. This is quite similar to the average for Little Stint (30), but comparison of the annual peaks shows that a good autumn for one is not necessarily a good one for the other. The two worst autumns for Little Stint were 1973 and 1982, which were poor and average respectively for Curlew Sandpipers, but 1976 and 1983 were the worst for Curlew Sandpipers, both of which were much better than average for Little Stint.

The few birds seen in spring are generally in winter plumage or very washed-out summer plumage suggesting one-year old birds. However, birds observed in July and early August are sometimes in beautiful brick-red summer dress. It is from mid-August onwards that the immature birds appear.

Away from the North Tees Marshes, there are several records from the saltwater locations such as Seal Sands and North Gare Sands and a few from Hartlepool and the South Gare - Coatham Marsh - Redcar beach area.

Very few are seen inland, with no more than four at Scaling Dam, Bowesfield Marsh, Longnewton Reservoir and Hart Reservoir, although flocks of Curlew Sandpipers have been seen to leave Teesmouth heading inland on autumn evenings.

An indication of the wintering range of birds passing through Cleveland is given by one ringed on Seal Sands on 12 August 1989 and noted at Merja Zerga, Morocco, on 7 December 1989.

PURPLE SANDPIPER *Calidris maritima*

As a winter visitor, this rather nondescript wader has declined in recent years, and is rarely recorded away from its chosen habitat of tidal rocks. The favourite wintering areas are Hartlepool Headland and South Gare, and to a lesser extent, North Gare and along the coast from Saltburn to Cowbar.

Counts of up to 50 were normal from at least as far back as 1893 to the early 1960s, then 80 were recorded in December 1964, 140 in March 1973, 178 in January 1976, 200 in December 1979, 246 in January 1982, 278 in April 1983, up to 360 in the 1986/87 winter and 277 in March 1991. The winter peaks between 1991 and 1999 remained around the 160-200 figure, and then 130-140 were seen in 2000 and 2001, but no more than 120 since 2002.

The Teesmouth-Hartlepool area was a nationally important site for this species because it regularly held more than 1% of the British wintering population. For Purple Sandpiper, the National Significance Threshold was 160 birds, a figure which was exceeded in almost every winter from about 1980 to 1999. Recently this threshold has been increased to 180, a figure which has not been reached since April 1999.

The high counts since 1964 have all been at Hartlepool, one of the favourite high-tide roosts being the West Harbour. This area was slowly being eroded by the sea and as such it made an ideal roost-site for this wader as well as for Turnstone and Oystercatcher, since large parts of the walls were totally inaccessible to people at high tide. Restoration of the Hartlepool Harbour was completed in 1992 and, as mitigation, the restoration work has included an island specifically for roosting birds.

Whilst mainly a winter visitor it is also a passage migrant, birds being seen from late July to mid-May; sometimes there is a distinct increase in early May, presumably as birds that have wintered further south in Britain move north. The occasional bird or two has also been seen in June or early July.

Birds have been observed on the slag walls at the edge of Seal Sands during onshore gales on more than one occasion, and a single bird was on Reclamation Pond on 14 August 1961.

Less than 100 Purple Sandpipers have been ringed in Cleveland. Two birds ringed at Rhos-on-Sea, North Wales, on 10 November 1979 were re-caught together at Hartlepool on 29 December 1988, and another ringed at Hartlepool on 4 March 1993 was on the Farne Islands, Northumberland, on 20 July 1995.

DUNLIN *Calidris alpina*

A visit to Teesmouth on any day of the year will reveal some Dunlin, although relatively few are present in June. The tidal mudflats of Seal Sands are this small wader's favourite area, though Dunlin can be found on virtually all wet and muddy parts of Teesmouth at various times of the year.

Extensive trapping has revealed that three races of Dunlin visit Teesmouth: *C.a.alpina* breeding in northern Scandinavia and Russia, occurs in winter; *C.a.schinzii* from Iceland, is seen on migration in spring and autumn; and *C.a.arctica* from Greenland is also recorded on passage, but is uncommon.

Wader studies conducted by Durham University since autumn 1976 have shown that adults of *C.a.arctica* and *C.a.schinzii* are the first to arrive at Teesmouth, in July and early August, passing through en route for wintering areas in north west Africa, the birds following the French, Spanish and Portuguese coastlines. Juvenile *C.a.schinzii* pass through in August and early September, followed by juvenile *C.a.alpina* in September and

October, some of which remain at Teesmouth throughout the winter, but others move further south and west, as far as the Irish Sea coasts. One ringed at Teesmouth on 17 September 1988 had flown north-west to South Uist, Western Isles by 11 November 1988. However, juvenile *C.a.alpina* follow a route from Russia either via northern and western Norway or through the southern Baltic regions of Poland and Germany. Adult *C.a.alpina* rarely occur at Teesmouth until they have finished moulting in the Wadden Sea (Denmark, Germany, Holland), or The Wash, in late October. Quite large numbers of these birds travel north to Teesmouth from The Wash in October and November, and sometimes the autumn passage peak count is higher than the spring passage and mid-winter counts; 1,600-2,000 having been seen in August in recent autumns.

Further arrivals of Dunlin from the continent, either via the Wash or directly over the North Sea occur through November and December, so the peak numbers are often reached in January. In recent years, the winter counts have been about 2,500-6,000, although 8,000 were recorded in January 1974 and just over 10,000 in November 1973.

Adult Dunlin are extremely site-faithful, although unusually mild or harsh weather may influence some birds, which either stay further north or east, or further south and west respectively. An adult ringed at Saltburn in February 1981 was in the Danish Wadden Sea in February 1982 and another ringed at Teesmouth in February 1977 was controlled in the Dutch Wadden Sea in February 1981.

Most *C.a.alpina* leave Teesmouth in early March, although some stay until late May and others pass through in May, including birds known to have wintered in Ireland.

Passage of *C.a.schinzii* and *C.a.arctica* occurs briefly in mid-May, some birds being recorded at Teesmouth having been ringed in Morocco and western France in April. However, most passage of these races occurs along the Irish Sea coasts in spring as shown by birds ringed at Teesmouth in July and August and controlled in later Mays on the Severn, Morecambe Bay, Walney Island and the Solway. An adult ringed on South Uist, Western Isles, on 4 May 1986 was dead on Cowpen Marsh on 24 July 1986 and another ringed at North Gare in August 1979 was found dead at sea off Durafjordur, Iceland, on 5 June 1986. A few *C.a.schinzii* tend to migrate in a southerly direction in autumn through western Britain, but move north to Iceland via the Tees, as shown by two juveniles ringed in August, one in Co Cork, Eire, and the other on the Dee estuary and found at Teesmouth in the following May.

A total of over 12,000 Dunlin has been caught and/or ringed in Cleveland, more than half by Durham University since 1976, resulting in at least 70 reports of Teesmouth-ringed birds and at least 90 birds ringed elsewhere and subsequently reported in Cleveland. One ringed in February 1976 at Teesmouth as a one year old was killed at Estremadura, Portugal, on 3 May 1993, this being the oldest known Dunlin for Cleveland.

It is not unusual to observe Dunlin on inland waters such as Scaling Dam or Crookfoot Reservoir, nor is it unusual to see them passing along the coastline in autumn in company with other waders such as Sanderling, Knot and Redshank. The highest count from Hartlepool Headland concerns about 800 flying north into a gale on 3 November 1984. A few birds are sometimes seen on the coastal fields to the south-east of Redcar, principally in autumn and winter.

Nelson (1907) stated that a few pairs nested on the Tees Marshes, implying that this was an annual occurrence, and single nests were certainly found on Cowpen Marsh in 1899 and 1902. A family party of five was recorded in July 1909 and a pair was seen on 29 June 1947, again on Cowpen Marsh, but no nest found. With the knowledge we have today these later records would indicate passage rather than breeding birds.

BROAD-BILLED SANDPIPER *Limicola falcinellus*

There are 14 records of this European wader, all single birds. They have been seen: on Seal Sands and Saltholme Pools from 13 to 19 August 1961; Greenabella Marsh from 23 to 29 June 1974; beside the Long Drag on 31 May and 1 June 1981; on the Brinefields on 13 June 1986; by Greatham Creek and North Gare Sands on 3-4 May 1987; on the Brinefields on 23 June 1990; in the Greatham Creek area from 3 to 6 June 1992; on Greenabella Marsh on 26 June 1992; at Saltholme Pools from 5 to 7 May 1994; on the Brinefields from 22 to 26 July 1994; in the Greatham Creek area from 27 September to 3 October 1994; at Dormans Pool on 15 June 2002; at Saltholme Pools on 6 June 2003 and at Saltholme Pools from 27 May to 1 June 2007.

BUFF-BREASTED SANDPIPER *Tryngites subruficollis*

There are 11 records of this American wader, more birds being seen at Saltholme Pools than any other location. Singles were here on 10 September 1977, 18 to 21 September and twice in October 1980, 3-4 September 1994 and 25 September 1995, (this last bird also appearing at Belasis Technology Park the next day), and 2 and 6 October 2007.

Two were at Marske on 11 September 1977, one was on the Brinefields from 17 August to 4 September 1985, one was at Haverton Hole from 1 to 3 June 1989, one was at Marske on 7 and 8 October 2000, one was at Greatham Creek on 13 August 2007 and another was at North Gare from 23 to 25 September 2007.

RUFF *Philomachus pugnax*

A visit to Teesmouth in any month of the year will probably yield this species. It is a spring and autumn passage migrant, a regular wintering bird and it is not unusual for one or two to be seen during the summer.

Ruff nested at Teesmouth in 1902 and 1903, one or two nests being found in both years approximately where Hartlepool Power Station is now situated. They were also suspected of nesting in 1901 (Nelson 1907, Templerley 1951). It is feasible that the species could nest again in the area, since lekking males are sometimes reported in June though this could be difficult to establish as females can be very secretive when nesting.

In the winter months some or all of the Teesmouth Ruff can frequently be found on the fields between Redcar and Marske with up to 30 in recent years. However, there are usually no more than three or four birds around Teesmouth during early summer. There then follows a steady build-up from mid-July, peaking usually in August or early September at about 60-90 in most years. However, 176 were counted on 8 August 1980. Since the passage of Ruff is noted from July to October, it is probable that several hundred birds are involved during each autumn.

In common with almost every species of wader, the majority of records concern birds seen at Teesmouth, but Ruff are also frequently observed at: Scaling Dam, with up to 11 in recent years; Bowesfield Marsh, up to 28 recently; and Longnewton Reservoir, where 55 were seen in September 1985.

Almost any water or wet field can support individuals or small flocks and birds have been seen beside Charlton's Pond, Crookfoot Reservoir, Portrack Marsh, Margrove Ponds, Lockwood Beck, Lovell Hill, in fields by Billingham and Norton and on the beach at Hartlepool, Redcar and Saltburn.

At least 120 Ruff have been ringed in Cleveland and there are four known recoveries: one ringed at Soppero in Swedish Lapland, on 2 June 1948 was present at Redcar on 23 October 1948; a first-year bird ringed at Saltholme Pools on 19 August 1974 was killed at Matera in Italy on 25 March 1975; another first-year bird ringed at Saltholme Pools on 25 August 1980 was reported in the West Flanders part of Belgium on 31 July 1981 and then at Dialloube in Mali, on 15 April 1982; and an adult ringed on Coatham Marsh on 8 December 1985 was controlled in Belgium on 5 September 1986.

JACK SNIPE *Lymnocryptes minimus*

This beautifully marked and well-camouflaged bird is probably the most under-recorded wader to be seen in Cleveland. It likes marshy areas; consequently the majority of records are of birds around the North Tees Marshes. It is very difficult to see when on the ground and will only fly up when somebody or something approaches to within a metre or two.

Whilst the earliest and latest dates are 9 August (1969) and 21 May (1972), it is generally late September before Jack Snipe are reported, with the majority arriving in October and November and almost all of the high counts being in this period. Between 13 and 17 birds have been recorded in the Dormans Pool - Saltholme - Cowpen Marsh area on at least six occasions during the last 25 years and 19 were counted on 10 November 1973, 20 were on Portrack Marsh on 27 November 1994 and in late January 2003, whilst 20 were at Haverton Hole on 26 October 2005. The highest number recorded by Nelson (1907) was six on 23 October 1900.

It is not unusual to see a bird or two arriving from the sea along the coastline in October and November, and a few birds usually over-winter in Cleveland. There is sometimes a small influx in April, with the occasional late bird in May.

Away from the North Tees Marshes, it is observed in most winters on Haverton Hole, Coatham Marsh and Portrack Marsh, and there are records from most of the other areas of water and marsh including Scaling Dam, Lockwood Beck, Margrove Ponds, Hemlington Lake, Bowesfield and Charlton's Pond.

At least 26 Jack Snipe have been ringed in Cleveland, but none has been recovered.

(COMMON) SNIPE *Gallinago gallinago*

With changes in land management and the reduction of the Tees Marshes there has been a dramatic reduction in the numbers of breeding Snipe in Cleveland. As late as the 1960s about 15-20 pairs were breeding on Tees Marshes, but since the 1980s, no more than five-ten pairs have been present in the summer months.

A total of about five to ten pairs probably breed in other areas including the low-lying fields between Guisborough and Nunthorpe, and the moorland edge.

Outside the breeding season quite large numbers of Snipe use the Tees Marshes, and to a lesser extent other areas of marshland. In most years there is a distinct influx of birds in August and again in October and November. The August influx is thought to involve birds from the other parts of North East England, whereas the October-November influx probably contains a fairly large percentage of Scandinavian and northern European birds. Certainly it is not unusual to see Snipe arriving over the sea in October, November and December often with Fieldfare, Redwing, and Woodcock.

In most winters, about 100-150 is the normal maximum count, although in view of its secretive habits it is probably under recorded. The highest counts are 340 on Haverton Hole and Dormans Pool combined on 1 November 1973 and 400 on Portrack Marsh on 9 March 2003.

About 50-100 is the normal autumn or winter maxima for other areas such as Coatham Marsh, Billingham Beck Valley and Bowesfield Marsh, and small numbers can frequently be found on most other area of marsh such as Margrove Ponds, Lovell Hill, Carlton Carr, Scaling Dam and South Gare. In some winters birds occasionally resort to the coastal fields during severe weather.

There are at least five recoveries, single birds ringed in the Redcar area in December were recorded in Norway in the following September and in Russia 17 months later. Another ringed at Billingham in August 1971 was in Co. Kerry in Ireland in January 1973. Two birds have been controlled at Teesmouth; one ringed at Wareham in Dorset in June 1982 was caught in August 1983 and another ringed near Pori in Finland in August 1975 was caught in February 1976. Birds ringed in summer in Finland, Czechoslovakia and West Germany have been found in Yorkshire in winter months.

GREAT SNIPE *Gallinaga media*

There are four records for Cleveland for this rare British bird and all are singles: about 1825 shot at Newport; 1 September 1901 shot at Teesmouth; 21 August 1976 on Cowpen Marsh; and 23 September 1976 on Hartlepool Headland.

SHORT-BILLED DOWITCHER *Limnodromus griseus*

The second record for Britain concerns a bird around Teesmouth from 29 September to 30 October 1999. It was first seen on Greenabella Marsh, and spent most of its time feeding on the mud of Greatham Creek, but was seen on Bran Sands on several occasions. Details of this record are given by Beck (2000). This same individual had been observed in the Grampian region of Scotland in mid-September 1999, before arriving at Teesmouth.

LONG-BILLED DOWITCHER *Limnodromus scolopaceus*

The only record for Cleveland concerns one seen on Seal Sands on 13 November 2007, and on Seal Sands and North Gare Sands the next day.

(EURASIAN) WOODCOCK Scolopax rusticola

Although a member of the wader family, this bird inhabits woodland in the summer, whilst in winter it can be found almost anywhere on dry land.

Woodcock breed in several places in Cleveland, including Wynyard, Grinkle Park, Guisborough Forest, Newton Woods, Flatts Lane, Wilton Woods, Stanghow, Kirklevington, Lockwood Beck, Margrove Park and Saltburn, the total number of breeding pairs probably being about 70-90.

More are usually recorded during the autumn migration period than at any other time, birds regularly being observed to arrive from the North Sea in October and November. At least 32 were seen on 5 November 1994, but many must be missed so it is likely that 100-200 arrive along the Cleveland coastline each autumn. Occasionally there is a distinct movement in December-February, probably linked to the severity of the winter, when birds are more likely to be seen in towns and urban parks. About 60 individuals were thought to be involved in one such movement in January-February 1979. Much smaller numbers are seen in March and April as presumed continental birds begin to drift north and east on their return migration.

Chicks ringed in North East England have been recorded in Cumbria, the Isle of Man and Ireland during following winters indicating a southerly and westerly movement of local birds. A bird ringed as full-grown at Graythorp on 8 November 1975 was shot in Sweden on 2 July 1977 (presumably whilst breeding). Another bird ringed on Isle of May on 15 May 1978 (probably whilst returning to its breeding grounds in northern Europe) was at Saltburn on 4 January 1979. A bird shot near Guisborough on 4 January 1975 had been ringed in Finland as a chick on 2 June 1974. Also, one ringed at Hartlepool on 28 October 2004 was killed in Gwynedd, Wales, 23 days later.

An almost white Woodcock with faint yellow markings was seen at Ormesby in November 1904.

BLACK-TAILED GODWIT Limosa limosa

This wader fitted neatly into the category of spring and autumn passage migrant in small numbers until the late 1970s. Since then a few birds have been observed in the summer months and from the 1980/81 winter, up to 39 birds have been seen in the winter months at Teesmouth. In recent years this wader has been recorded in every month of the year.

There is usually a small influx of birds in April, about 15-40 being the norm, then generally up to 70-80 pass through Teesmouth from July to September, although 153 were present on the North Tees Marshes in July 1999, 109 in April 2001, 163 on 30 July 2001,

126 in September 2002, 158 in August 2003, 174 on 28 June 2005, and 281 on 13 July 2006.

Most birds favour the marshes and mudflats to the north of the Tees, although they occasionally visit Bowesfield, Portrack and Coatham Marshes, and less frequently, the reservoirs such as Crookfoot, Longnewton and Scaling Dam. Small flocks and single birds are occasionally seen passing Hartlepool Headland in spring and autumn, and flocks sometimes leave the Tees Marshes on autumn evenings, heading high to the south-west.

A pair successfully reared one young on Cowpen Marsh in 1969, and a pair may have nested in the same area in 2003, but no young was seen.

Two colour-ringed birds were present on Seal Sands in August 1994, one being ringed on The Wash in autumn 1993 and the other in Fife in spring 1994. A third bird, colour-ringed as a chick in Iceland in July 1999, was in Fife in November 1999, Northern Ireland in May 2000 and subsequently at Teesmouth in June 2000. A fourth bird, ringed on Golf du Morbihan, France, on 26 October 2001, was seen in France in November - December 2001 and April 2002, and on Dormans Pool on 26 July 2002.

BAR-TAILED GODWIT *Limosa lapponica*

The mudflats of Seal Sands and Bran Sands are the only places in Cleveland where one can be reasonably sure of seeing this wader, between late July and late April, although it is not unusual for a few birds to be seen in May and June. About 400 were noted on 7 September 1895 indicating that numbers have changed little over the last 100 years. In recent years the highest counts have been approximately 200-400 and generally in the months September, December, January or February. About 600 were seen in September 1953 and 927 in January 1970.

Some birds arrive to moult in July and August, most staying through the winter and in some years large numbers of juveniles arrive in September and October, some staying and others flying further south.

The return migration is usually underway in February and many of the Bar-tailed Godwits have left by late March, heading for the Wadden Sea. Relatively few birds have been ringed and recovered/controlled, but those that have indicate that some pass through southern Norway and Holland *en route* to Teesmouth in autumn, and birds that have been ringed in autumn at Teesmouth can take as little as five days to reach the western edge of the Sahara. Others have been found wintering in France, Morocco, the Channel Islands, the Dutch Friesian Islands and on the Humber. A juvenile ringed at Teesmouth in October 1980 was seen in Schleswig-Holstein, Germany, in August 1992 and wintered on Jersey every year to 2003, when it had reached the age of 22. One ringed at South Gare on 9 October 1980 was killed in Murmansk, Russia, in September 1984, and two one-year old birds ringed on Seal Sands on 2 July 1992 were site-faithful, one being at Dawlish Warren, Devon, in November 1992 and January 1997, and the other was on the Wadden Sea, Germany, in March 1994 and April 1997.

About 400 birds have been ringed at Teesmouth, 161 of these in 1985.

A few birds regularly pass along the coastline in autumn and it is not unusual to see them heading south-west away from Teesmouth on autumn evenings, together with Curlew, Whimbrel and Oystercatcher. Single birds are very occasionally seen in August and September at or over inland localities and on the edge of reservoirs, particularly Scaling Dam where up to four were noted in August 1960.

An off-white bird was observed at South Gare and Seal Sands in November 1990 and January 1991, and a male in full breeding plumage was at South Gare in late December 2002.

WHIMBREL Numenius phaeopus

The Whimbrel is a regular passage migrant through Cleveland, specifically around the mouth of the Tees and associated marshes. It is usually recorded between early April and late May, and again between mid-July and late September, although there are several records of birds in March, June and October. Apart from singles at Teesmouth on 3 February 1945 and 9 December 1992, the earliest and latest dates are 10 March (1957) and 14 November (1989).

Spring numbers seldom exceed 20-30 birds, but there are regularly flocks of 30-50 birds seen in autumn and occasionally 70-100. The highest count is of 212 flying south over Seal Sands on 1 August 1970. Peak passage is almost invariably recorded between the last few days of July and mid- August.

Whimbrel along with most other waders leave Teesmouth on autumn passage heading just west of south over the centre of Teesside. It is not unusual therefore to hear Whimbrel calling as they fly over Middlesbrough, Norton, Stockton and Billingham, sometimes at night and probably at a great height. There are several records of birds at Scaling Dam recently and two records of birds over Hutton Gate, including eight on 19 August 1969.

A colour-ringed bird on Seal Sands on 6 July 1994 was ringed whilst breeding on Fetlar, Shetland, in summer 1986.

(EURASIAN) CURLEW *Numenius arquata*

This is the largest of the ten wader species that breed in Cleveland and is one of the commonest waders to be found at Teesmouth. It breeds sparingly along the moorland edge between Scaling Dam and Guisborough Forest and in several agricultural areas including Crookfoot Reservoir, Wynyard, Morton Carr, Pinchinthorpe and Eston Moor. The overall population is considered to be about 50 pairs and whilst the local birds are nesting, up to 100 birds spend the summer at Teesmouth, presumably immature birds. There is a distinct influx of birds in July, these being adults moving into Teesmouth to moult, and it is not unusual to see flocks of 100-200 flying over the Billingham-Norton area in July towards Teesmouth. More birds arrive in August and September, some being juveniles from Scandinavia, as shown by four birds ringed as pulli in Norway and Finland and recovered (two shot) at Teesmouth in the following August, September and October. Two pulli ringed in Cleveland (Loftus and Wynyard) were recovered in Ireland the following winter, the first in Cork and second in Galway.

In some years quite large numbers spend the winter at Teesmouth, close to 1,000 being seen in February 1984, March 1993, January and March 1994, January 1995, January 2000, February 2002 and February 2004, although over 1,000 had frequently been recorded prior to the 1950s. The actual highest counts are 1,219 in August 1994 and 1,617 in January 2003.

Some of Cleveland's wintering Curlew feed on inland fields, flying to the Tees marshes/mudflats in the last hour of daylight; about 100 have been seen at Upsall Carr, Wynyard and Preston Park in recent winters. As is the case with almost all waders, the males are smaller than the females and have shorter bills; severe winter weather sometimes causes the shorter-billed males to move from the inland fields back to the mudflats.

Several hundred birds regularly feed around Saltholme and Cowpen Marsh during the winter. The numbers decrease in March and April as the birds move back to their breeding grounds. One ringed in March 1992 was recaptured whilst breeding in Finland in May 1994. Other recoveries include birds ringed at Teesmouth in winter and found in Denmark, Finland and Sweden during the summer. A bird ringed in June was recovered in Northumberland in the following February, another ringed on Seal Sands in July was found dead two years later in Sweden in July, and one ringed on Seal Sands in August was noted 36 km to the north at Washington, Tyne and Wear, in December of the same year. Five birds ringed at South Gare in August and September 1980, were all controlled again at South Gare on 23 October 1985.

Virtually all of the full-grown birds have been ringed as part of the Durham University work at Teesmouth.

It is quite normal to see a few birds passing along the coastline in most months of the year, but a count of 111 flying south off Hartlepool on 24 September 1981 was exceptional.

At least 600 Curlew have been ringed in Cleveland, at least 120 being chicks in the nest.

A completely white bird was at Scaling Dam on 12 March 1972.

SPOTTED REDSHANK *Tringa erythropus*

A Spotted Redshank in its almost black breeding dress is one of the most beautiful waders to be observed in Britain and it is seen in such plumage at Teesmouth in some years, usually in May, but also occasionally in June. However, it is rare for more than three or four birds to be present in spring. Most Spotted Redshank are seen in autumn, when a trickle of birds pass through the county from July to October.

There was one bird seen in almost every winter from the early 1960s to January 1995, the favoured location being the Seal Sands - Greatham Creek - Greenabella Marsh area. There has never been more than a single individual staying throughout the winter, although a second bird has been seen on occasional winter days.

In some years no more than three or four are seen together at Teesmouth but 13 were recorded in August 1964 and August 1986 and 14 were noted in August and September 1973.

A bird or two is seen on passage in some years at places such as Scaling Dam, Crookfoot Reservoir and Billingham Beck Valley, as well as passing along the coastline. The highest counts away from Teesmouth are four at Scaling Dam in September 1960 and Hart Reservoir in September 1969.

(COMMON) REDSHANK *Tringa totanus*

The alarm call of the Redshank is the most frequent sound to be heard around Teesmouth, this wader being known as the 'sentinel of the marshes' as it is usually the first bird to fly up when a potential predator is about, be it human, animal or bird.

At Teesmouth it is a resident, breeding in fair numbers, a regular passage migrant in spring and autumn, and a winter visitor.

The stronghold of the breeding birds are the various marshes between Seaton Common and Hargreaves Quarry on the north side of the Tees, there being about 30 pairs in this area. Single pairs have been known to breed on Coatham Marsh in recent years, although more bred there in the 1950s and 1960s. There used to be a pair or two in the Billingham Beck Valley area, but there is no recent record for the site. Redshank may have nested at Scaling Dam in the last 15-20 years.

As a passage migrant large numbers arrive in July, August and September. Some of these move on, presumably to estuaries to the south and west of Teesmouth, but others stay throughout the winter. However, ringing has shown that there is a certain amount of movement between estuaries even in the middle of the winter. One bird ringed at Teesmouth in December 1975 had moved north to Eyemouth on the Scottish border one month later; another ringed in November at Teesmouth was on the Humber two years later. One ringed at Saltburn in January 1983 was on the Eden Estuary, Fife, Scotland, in November 1983 and one ringed on Seal Sands on 1 April 1990 was found dead at Lealholm, near Whitby, North Yorkshire, on 26 June 1990, presumably whilst breeding.

Apart from the months of May and June, several hundred Redshank can always be found around Teesmouth, the highest numbers usually being recorded in August and September, 1,900 being present in August and September 1984, September 1991 and November 1995, and 2,450 were noted in October 2003. In most years there is a slight decline in October-December as the birds move south. This is followed by a distinct increase in March and April as the birds fly back north with at times over 1,000 being seen in spring. The National Significance Threshold for Redshank is currently 1,200, a figure that has been bettered every year between September and December since 1997.

Although a few birds from the Scandinavian breeding population are reported to pass along the east coast of Britain during passage times (Prater 1981), the only recovery to support this involves a bird ringed on Seal Sands in October 1978 and found at sea off south western Norway in August 1986. Conversely, there are known to be at least three recoveries of the Icelandic race (T.t.robusta), these birds being ringed at Teesmouth and recovered in Iceland in May, June or July. A bird ringed as pullus in Iceland on 9 June 1995 was found dead under the wires at South Gare on 3 February 1996. Another bird ringed at Saltburn in January 1982 and controlled in north-west Holland in October 1984 could have been from either population. There are also quite a few records of birds moving up and down Great Britain, via Teesmouth, from as far south as Cornwall and as far north as the Grampian region of Scotland. One ringed at Teesmouth in September 1982 was on the Ythan estuary, Aberdeen, on 22 July 1983, but was back on Seal Sands on 30 December 1988.

Over 3,000 full-grown Redshank have been ringed at Teesmouth since 1979. However, only a few pulli have been ringed in Cleveland, and none is known to have moved any great distance.

Passage of Redshank along the coastline is regularly noted in July and August, the highest count being 268 flying south off Hartlepool Headland on 19 July 1980.

Whilst most birds feed around Teesmouth, quite large numbers are sometimes seen feeding on inland fields, on the tidal banks of the River Tees between Middlesbrough and Portrack, on the rocky shoreline from Saltburn to Cowbar and on several of the inland waters, especially during the autumn and winter.

The age that a Redshank can reach is indicated by the following three records. A bird that had completely white primaries, as well as the usual white wing-bar, wintered every year in the Brinefields area and was seen between 25 December 1970 and April 1978. A first-year bird ringed in Scotland in October 1978 was controlled on Seal Sands in August 1985, and an adult ringed on Seal Sands in July 1978 was controlled at Hartlepool in January 1990.

MARSH SANDPIPER Tringa stagnatilis

There are two records of this delicate wader, one on Cowpen Marsh from 25 to 29 May 1963 and one on Saltholme Pools on 5 and 6 May 2003.

(COMMON) GREENSHANK Tringa nebularia

The first Greenshank on Dormans Pool in mid- April is the sign to the Teesmouth bird-watchers that spring is in the air. This wader is a regular spring and autumn passage migrant at Teesmouth and is quite frequently seen in autumn at Scaling Dam and to a lesser extent on other inland waters. Also, single birds are sometimes observed at Teesmouth in December, January or February and very occasionally right through the winter.

In an average year, the first Greenshank is seen in mid-April, usually on the North Tees Marshes, and five to ten are seen during the spring. There are generally no birds present in June, but the autumn passage begins in July with peaks of about 15-20 birds in mid to late August, or early September. The highest count is 61 around the North Tees Marshes on 9 September 1979, about half of which were seen to leave to the south-west during the day. There is a general departure throughout September, and very few are left into October and November.

Most inland waters hold a bird or two in spring or autumn, but of the inland localities it is usually Scaling Dam that holds the most Greenshank, the highest count being 15 there on 11 August 1981. Also, up to 11 were on Bowesfield Marsh in August 2000 and up to 16 at Longnewton Reservoir in August 2004.

While the annual autumn peak count may not be any higher than 20, the constant arrivals from the north and the departures to the south indicates that perhaps 100 or so Greenshank pass through Teesmouth during each autumn. It is not unusual for a few birds to be seen flying south over the sea during the autumn, generally at Hartlepool Headland, although 15 passed there on 19 August 2001.

At least 40 Greenshank have been ringed in Cleveland, one of which was ringed at South Gare on 4 October 1981 and killed at Minho in the extreme north-west of Portugal on 30 November 1981. Another ringed at Saltholme Pools on 26 July 1999 was killed in Calvados, France, on 21 September 2003.

LESSER YELLOWLEGS *Tringa flavipes*

There are two records of this North American wader: singles on Dormans Pool on 13 and 14 August 2003 and Cowpen Marsh from 22 September to 19 October 2003.

GREEN SANDPIPER *Tringa ochropus*

This wader has a very similar status to Greenshank, being a regular spring and autumn passage migrant at Teesmouth. It differs from Greenshank in that one or two regularly winter in Cleveland and it is just as happy feeding by an inland stream as on the Tees Marshes.

A few birds are usually seen for a day or two in April, although they are rarely present in May and the first returning birds almost always appear in the last few days of June or the beginning of July. Usually five or six birds are seen around Teesmouth in the autumn, although 11 were present on 14 August 1964, 25 August 1991 and 28 August 1999, 12 on 18 August 1995 and 22 at Teesmouth plus five at Scaling Dam on 19 August 2001.

If inland streams, marshes and ponds were watched as well as the North Tees Marshes, it could well be that this wader is nearly as frequent inland as it is along the coast. Certainly it has been reported from a wide variety of localities, including Portrack Marsh, Billingham Beck, Dalton Piercy, Hart Reservoir, Skelton Beck, Margrove Ponds and Marton in autumn as well as the winter months. In the 1970s and 1980s up to four Green Sandpipers were seen in winter along the inland part of Greatham Creek, in particular near to Cowpen Bewley and Billingham Sewage Works and, in January-March 1999, up to five were at Haverton Hole.

Unlike the Greenshank, this wader does not favour Scaling Dam over other inland waters, although one or two are seen there in most autumns.

WOOD SANDPIPER *Tringa glareola*

This species is a regular spring and autumn visitor to the Tees Marshes, usually two to six birds are seen in spring and five to twelve birds in autumn. However, 38 were on the North Tees Marshes on 8 August 1963, 24 on 2 August 1980 and 15 on Seaton Common on 5 August 2002.

In spring, most birds stay for no more than three or four days, and are usually observed between early May and mid-June. In autumn birds can be seen almost continuously from late July to mid-September, although there is probably a steady trickle of birds moving in and out of the area.

There are at least four records of birds singing and displaying over Saltholme, Dormans Pool and Cowpen Marsh in late May and June, but there is very little likelihood of this wader breeding in Cleveland. Its breeding range is far to the north where it nests in secluded marshy moorland. A few pairs breed in northern Scotland but the bird's main breeding area is northern Europe.

Apart from the North Tees Marshes, birds are seen in most years on Coatham Marsh, and occasionally at Scaling Dam, Portrack Marsh, Longnewton Reservoir, Lovell Hill, Margrove Ponds, Crookfoot Reservoir and Hart Reservoir.

The earliest and latest dates are 10 April (1997) and 31 October (1981).

TEREK SANDPIPER *Xenus cinereus*

This is a rare wader in Britain and has been seen in Cleveland on only three occasions: near Greatham Creek on 27 and 28 September 1952 (Evans 1973), Scaling Dam on 4 August 1971 and beside the Long Drag from 20 to 22 June 1979.

COMMON SANDPIPER *Actitis hypoleucos*

This bird and Little Ringed Plover are the only two waders that breed in Cleveland as summer visitors. The other eight wader species that nest in the county can all be found throughout the year.

In most years the first Common Sandpiper is recorded in the latter half of April, although the earliest is 27 March (2007) and there is a distinct passage in May, but generally no more than 10-20 birds are seen in total. Return passage can be seen from early July, with peak counts of 15-25 birds on any one day and perhaps up to 200-300 birds passing through Cleveland in the season. The highest counts are about 40 on Scaling Dam on 4 September 1958, 38 on Scaling Dam and 18 by Wynyard Lake on 10 August 1975, 41 beside the Long Drag on 8 August 1980, at least 40 at Lockwood Beck and 12 at Charlton's Pond on 27 August 1996, about 80 combined on several waters in Cleveland on 12 and 25 August 1997, at least 140 around Cleveland on 11 August 1997 and at least 185 around Cleveland on 10-11 August 2004, including 57 at Scaling Dam. Most birds have passed through by early September and very few are seen in late September or early October. There are occasional records of birds in late October and one remained by Greatham Creek to 14 November 1954.

Common Sandpiper probably does not breed every year, although it has bred at Charlton's Pond, Cowpen Marsh, Portrack Marsh, Crookfoot Reservoir and Lockwood Beck in at least 15 years in the 20th century and has been thought to breed at Scaling Dam and along the Cleveland reaches of River Tees on more than one occasion.

Virtually any area of water, with its associated edge, can hold a few birds during times of passage, from the tidal rocks at South Gare and Hartlepool through the Tees Marshes to all of the inland waters and along the length of the River Tees. Odd birds have been seen in flooded fields and by park lakes on more than one occasion and it is not unusual to hear Common Sandpipers calling whilst flying overhead at night in autumn. One was even watched walking along a busy road in Middlesbrough Centre on 29 August 1966, although it flew off after a few minutes.

SPOTTED SANDPIPER *Actitis macularius*

There are three records for Cleveland: a bird in breeding plumage at South Gare on 16 June 1995, a juvenile beside the Long Drag from 16 to 29 September 1997 and another in breeding plumage on Saltholme Pools on 11 August 2004. Details of the first record are given by Cowton (1996).

(RUDDY) TURNSTONE *Arenaria interpres*

A summer-plumaged adult seen in May-August must rate as one of the most beautiful of the common waders to be observed in Cleveland. Not many Turnstones stay throughout the summer, and of those that do, not all attain breeding dress, but a fairly high percentage of the returning birds in July and August are adults. These generally moult locally and stay throughout the winter; very few birds ringed in

Cleveland have been found wintering elsewhere. A bird ringed at South Gare on 23 November 1976 returned in many winters until it was found dead on North Gare on 12 January 1986. Another ringed at Redcar, on 30 November 1976 was controlled at Saltburn in December 1993 at least 17 years old; however, the oldest bird recorded locally involved an individual ringed at North Gare on 5 May 1977 and controlled in Finistere, France, on 1 May 1997 making it at least 21 years old.

Wetland Bird Survey records for Teesmouth do not reveal the full picture for Turnstone because a number of birds are regularly present outside of the survey area. There are often between 30-60 birds in the Hunt Cliff area in winter, and sometimes small numbers can be found from Skinningrove to Cowbar. The Teesmouth counts show a regular wintering population of about 150-250, which seems to have remained quite stable since at least the 1950s, though the highest count was 466 around Teesmouth on 10 November 1985. Over 250 have quite frequently been seen at Hartlepool during the winter months, so the total wintering in Cleveland is probably near to 500 birds. Higher numbers have been seen at Hartlepool during autumn passage, 686 being counted in September 1991 and a combined total of 843 was noted at Hartlepool and Teesmouth on 17 October 1993.

It is thought that most, if not all, of the Turnstone seen in Cleveland are part of the Greenland and Arctic Canada populations; one bird ringed at Teesmouth on 23 November 1976 was seen at Kroksfjardenes in western Iceland on 6 August 1982, no doubt on its way back to Teesmouth. Another ringed at Teesmouth in August 1976 was recorded in the Netherlands on 6 August 1977, probably part of the moulting flock of Greenland birds that use the Wadden Sea and then fly to Britain in late autumn. A juvenile ringed in western Norway on 18 August 1970 was at Teesmouth five years later and seen regularly there in several subsequent winters. This individual was no doubt part of the population that flies from Greenland to the North Sea coastlines via Norway in their first autumn. However, a pullus ringed at Pori, Finland, on 14 July 1989 was dead at Skinningrove in January 1991, and one ringed at Saltburn on 23 December 1986 was present at Terrington Marsh, Norfolk, on 18 August 1989.

Very nearly all of the birds leave Cleveland in April and May, at which time some passage birds are observed. These include one ringed at Morecambe Bay in August 1970 and seen at Hartlepool in May 1972, one which wintered on the Wirral, Merseyside, for several years after it had been ringed at Teesmouth in May 1977, one which was ringed in Mauritania (west Africa) in April 1985 and seen at Teesmouth in May 1985 and one ringed on Jersey on 11 January 1989 that was dead at Teesmouth on 14 May 1996.

While the main habitat is the coastal rocks and beaches around the tide-line, a few birds quite frequently visit the marshes in spring. Up to 100 birds are occasionally seen on Coatham Marsh, Dormans Pool and Seaton Common and up to 150 have been seen on the grassy areas to the north of Seaton Carew (part of the old Seaton Tip).

A few birds are occasionally seen at inland sites such as Scaling Dam, Bowesfield Marsh and Longnewton Reservoir; however, no more than six have been involved. There are also records of birds on corrugated roof tops at the Hartlepool fish quay and also on the Hartlepool breakwater well above the high tide-line.

At least 1,000 Turnstone have been ringed in Cleveland, the vast majority by Durham University teams with more than half since the 1980s.

WILSON'S PHALAROPE *Phalaropus tricolor*

This American wader was recorded for the first time in Britain in 1954 and in Cleveland in 1963, however, it is now an annual British visitor, albeit in very small numbers. There are 13 Cleveland records, an average of one bird every four years. The records are:

Date	Location
12-13 October 1963 (the latest date)	Reclamation Pond
20-21 June 1965 and 22 June 1966	Scaling Dam (dead on last date)
5 June 1971 (the earliest date)	Dormans Pool
4 to 8 September 1971	Dormans Pool
7 to 10 Sept & 17 to 28 Sept 1977	Saltholme Pools
31 August to 2 September 1979	Two birds on Long Drag and Dormans Pool, one staying until 3 September
13 to 20 September 1980	Long Drag and Dormans Pool
15 to 27 September 1983	Reclamation Pond
26 Aug to 11 Sept 1985 (the longest stay)	Reclamation Pond
27-29 September 2001	Coatham Marsh
9 January 2005 (first mid-winter record in Britain)	Seaton Carew golf course
Wilson's Phalarope Records	

Apart from the three June, the January and the October records, the remaining sightings have occurred between late August and late September. Some of these have taken place during or after westerly gales, indicating a recent passage from America, but some birds have appeared during easterlies, with Pectoral and/or White-rumped Sandpipers, indicating that a few follow the European wader routes. It is possible that Wilson's Phalarope breeds somewhere in Europe or Asia, as has been suggested for other American waders.

RED-NECKED PHALAROPE *Phalaropus lobatus*

Despite the fact that this bird breeds in Britain, it is as rare as Wilson's Phalarope in Cleveland. The majority of the records are of birds on the various marshes around Teesmouth with Dormans Pool being the most favoured locality in recent years.

Singles were recorded in the Redcar-South Gare area on 22 November 1851, 12 October 1947, 9-23 December 1962, 6-8 August 1979, 13 September 1988, 15 September 1993 and 29 August 1996.

Singles were in the Hartlepool area on 14 September 1969, 23-24 September 1998, 13 October 1988 and 13 and 15 September 2002.

Singles were in the North Tees marshes area on 23 October 1891, 21-23 September 1968, 15 September 1969, 11 August 1970, 14 August 1973, 7 September 1981, 26 August 1986, 29 June 1988 and 14 June 2007.

Other singles were noted at Seaton Carew on 6 September 1901, Graythorp shipyard on 2 October 1943, Scaling Dam on 14 September 1958, Margrove Ponds on 28-29 August 1986 and Crookfoot Reservoir on 14 September 1997.

As can be seen by the records, early August to mid October is the prime time period, although the earliest and latest dates are 14 June (2007) and 23 December (1962).

GREY PHALAROPE *Phalaropus fulicarius*

Since 1962, this winter visitor has averaged four birds every three years, although it is not seen every year. The majority of the records fall between mid-October and late January, with a few in February and March, and earliest and latest dates of 11 September (1954) and 14 May (1977). This last bird was showing signs of summer plumage and is one of only four records of birds in freshwater areas, being on a pool behind the dunes by North Gare Sands. The other three concern singles over Cowpen Marsh on 11 September 1954, on Scaling Dam on 6 November 1965 and on the Tidal Pool beside Greatham Creek on 12 September 1983. There are also historic records of single birds seen in June and August.

The majority of birds occur during, or immediately after, winter storms and are usually seen singly, although two together have been noted on several occasions, and four were observed at South Gare on 25 November 1969. Most stay only a day or two, but one of two birds at Hartlepool in 1970 remained from 16 February to 31 March. The majority are seen either around Hartlepool Headland or at South Gare, partly as a result of relatively intense observer coverage of these areas, but also because both areas offer some shelter during onshore gales. Odd birds have been noted on Seaton Sands, Redcar seafront, Saltburn and in Greatham Creek. There are a few old records, which seem to follow a similar pattern to the modern-day; two were reported to have been shot at Haverton Hill in 1824.

It is interesting that all three species of phalarope have never been seen in Cleveland in the same year.

POMARINE SKUA *Stercorarius pomarinus*

This skua is an irregular passage bird along the coast, being seen in quite large numbers in some years and very scarce in others. Virtually all birds occur between August and November with the highest numbers in October and early November. The occasional juvenile skua seen during the winter months along the coast is frequently thought to be Pomarine, although they can be difficult to identify with certainty in this plumage. Also, single adults passed Hartlepool on 3 June 2001 and 6 May 2002.

Details of high counts over the last 50 years are: 195 flew south at Hartlepool on 26 October 1962; 76 flew north at Hartlepool on 10 October 1973; at least 175 out of 200 skuas that passed the coastline between Saltburn and Cowbar on 10 November 1985 were Pomarine; at least 160 passed South Gare on 1 November 1986; and at least 850 passed South Gare on 9 October 1992. However, all these figures pale into insignificance compared to the number that passed on 14 October 1879 when an estimated five to six thousand flew south over Tees Bay. Details of this enormous passage are vividly recorded by Nelson (1907).

There are only three records of live birds further inland than Seal Sands; an immature that flew south-west over Wynyard on 21 November 1985, two adults that flew west over Dormans Pool on 12 September 1987 and a juvenile present around the Saltholme - Dormans Pool area on 16 and 17 September 2000. Immature birds have also been found dead on Coatham Marsh in December 1985 and in Hargreaves Quarry in January 1986.

ARCTIC SKUA *Stercorarius parasiticus*

This is the commonest of the four species of skua, being seen around the mouth of the Tees from late June to late September where they often chase terns. Birds are also recorded passing offshore from July to late October especially during onshore winds. Occasionally, depending on the wind and weather conditions, birds are seen in the months of November-May.

The regular build-up of terns around the mouth of the river in July and August gener-
ally attracts about 15-30 Arctic Skuas, although about 80 were in the river mouth on 15
August 1985, the day after heavy sea passage along the coast. About 150 were present dur-
ing a large sprat wreck in August 1962, and 230-264 were counted on several days in mid-
August 1988. However, no more than four were seen here in July-August 2004 and 7 in
July - August 2006.

The biggest numbers of Arctic Skuas are always recorded passing at sea, usually being
observed from Hartlepool Headland or South Gare. In most years about 80-150 is the
maximum count, but 220-350 have been seen on several dates in the last 30 years and
the highest counts are about 600 passing on 23 August 1962 and 440 on 30 August 1980.
Virtually all of the high counts are between mid-August and early October.

Any skua passage in the last three months of the year is usually rather small even if the
wind is gale-force and the picture is clouded still further by the appearance of Pomarine
Skuas in some years. The identification of juvenile/immature Pomarine and Arctic Skuas
is sometimes rather difficult, so the occasional skua seen offshore in the winter months
could be either species.

During, or just after onshore gales, some birds are occasionally seen around the Tees
Marshes such as Coatham Marsh and Dormans Pool. Usually only one or two birds are
involved, but on 26 August 1986, a gathering of 44 birds was noted on the Cowpen Tip
and at the same time about 25 Arctic Skuas flew inland over Cowpen Marsh.

Single birds have also been seen occasionally at Lockwood Beck, Scaling Dam and
Crookfoot Reservoir.

LONG-TAILED SKUA *Stercorarius longicaudus*

July, August and September are the months to see this skua, although it is not recorded every year and is very unpredictable in its appearance compared to other skuas. It
is as likely to be seen on fine sunny days along the coastline as during onshore winds.

Nelson (1907) recorded Long-tailed Skua quite regularly with earliest and latest dates
of 20 July and 6 November, and with a highest count of 15 adults 'taken' off Redcar and
others seen during the violent gale of 14-15 October 1879. Between 1955 and 1973 the
species was noted in most years with a maximum of four on 21 August 1969, with earliest and latest dates of 7 August and 28 October.

Since 1974, the earliest and latest dates have been 22 May (2004) and 27 November
(2005). The highest counts are up to 139 off the coastline from 5 to 8 September 1991
and about 100 passing Hartlepool on 7 August 1995.

Very nearly all of the records are of birds over the sea in the Hartlepool-Teesmouth
area, although single birds have been seen over Cowpen Marsh, bathing on Greenabella

Marsh, on Seaton Common, Dormans Pool and on the coastal fields at Redcar and Marske, with most of them in September being immatures.

GREAT SKUA *Stercorarius skua*

This is the most powerful member of the skua family, sometimes known as the 'Bonxie' and is quite capable of forcing a flying Gannet into the sea.

It is generally observed offshore only during strong winds, almost never venturing into the estuary mouth in the same manner as Arctic Skuas, although one or two birds have been seen on Seal Sands and North Gare Sands as well as flying over Cowpen Marsh, Coatham Marsh, Dormans Pool and the Long Drag during severe weather conditions.

A few birds are sometimes present in the first six months of the year, but more are seen in July and August and still more in the months September-November. The peak count in most years is about 20-50 birds in a day, although 235 passed Hartlepool and 283 passed Redcar on 11 September 1976, and 254 passed Hartlepool on 6 November 2000.

There are three recoveries of this bird, all being ringed as pulli on Foula, Shetland Islands. The first was ringed in July 1974 and found dead at Hartlepool in June 1981; the second in July 1976, found dead at Redcar in October 1976; and the third in July 1984 was dead at Hartlepool in June 1986. Virtually all of the British Great Skuas breed on the islands of Orkney and Shetland with the biggest colony on Foula.

MEDITERRANEAN GULL *Larus melanocephalus*

The history of this gull in Cleveland has been relatively well-documented after the first known record in 1956. It is an annual visitor in small numbers and, between 1973 and 2000, there were up to five adults and ten immatures each year. Since 2000, it has been difficult to ascertain the exact number of birds seen, but it is probably about 20-25 per year.

The first record was of an adult at Hartlepool on 29 October 1956 which then wintered in the Hartlepool area for 15 consecutive winters, generally arriving in August and leaving in late March. If it was the same bird throughout, it had reached at least 17 years of age. The first record of a different bird concerned a sub-adult on Seaton Snook in mid-August 1964, followed by four other pre-1973 records: an immature around Hartlepool in March 1969; an adult found dead on Brenda Road, Hartlepool on 25 February 1970; one near Hart Reservoir on 12 October 1970; and an immature around Teesmouth between early May and early July 1971.

Since 1973, birds have been seen in every month, though adults rarely appear between April and June, but are quite evenly spread throughout the rest of the year. Juveniles generally are noted from late August with usually two or three birds per year.

The Tees Marshes and coastline between Hartlepool and Saltburn are favoured locations, but birds have been seen at many inland localities, including Scaling Dam, Crookfoot Reservoir, Stockton, Lazenby Reservoir, Hemlington Lake, Belasis Technology Park, Longnewton Reservoir, Portrack Marsh and Margrove Ponds. Several localities have had adults regularly returning for 10-20 winters including South Gare and Hartlepool.

An adult in the Redcar - Marske area between 31 July and 3 November 2004 had been colour- ringed as a pullus in the nest at Gambshein, Germany, on 15 May 1999, and was breeding at Saxonia, in eastern Germany, in May 2004. An adult at Seaton Carew on 8 January 2007 and 18 December 2007 was colour-ringed as a 3rd-year bird at Paczkowski Reservoir, in southern Poland on 7 May 2006.

A first-summer gull at South Gare in June 1992 showed the characteristics of a hybrid between Black-headed Gull and Mediterranean Gull

LAUGHING GULL *Larus atricilla*

There are two records for Cleveland of this North American species. A bird considered to be in second summer plumage was beside the Long Drag on the evening of 21 June and morning of 22 June 1981, and a similar-plumaged bird was at Port Clarence on the evening of 16 July 2003 and around Dormans Pool next day.

FRANKLIN'S GULL *Larus pipixcan*

There are four records of this North American gull in Cleveland: an adult which flew inland at North Gare on 24 July 1977; adults seen on the Reclamation Pond from 19 to 23 June and 28 August to 1 September 1991; and an adult on Longnewton Reservoir on 4 September 1991. The last three records are likely to involve the same individual.

LITTLE GULL *Larus minutus*

This bird fits into four categories of occurrence: an irregular winter visitor to the coastline with usually one or two birds being seen in most years; a regular summer visitor to the North Tees Marshes in somewhat larger numbers; a regular passage migrant at sea in the autumn in still larger numbers; and an occasional straggler to almost any inland water at any time of the year.

About 100 years ago, it was a passage migrant along the coast in small numbers only (Nelson 1907). The appearance of the summering flock of mainly one year-old birds was first noted about 1970, the first birds usually being seen in early to mid-April, building up to a peak of about 20 in late June or early July. A total of 42 on 3 July 1986 is the highest count in this category. They then depart, usually all having vacated the marshes by late August. It is not unusual for one or two adults in full breeding dress to be seen among this gathering.

At sea, passage is recorded between late July and late October, although they have been noted passing Hartlepool in windy conditions in the months October to January. In some years very few are seen, probably due to weather conditions, since the highest numbers recorded have been during strong northerly or north-easterly winds. The highest counts passing Hartlepool are 711 on 23 September 1988, 655 on 27 September 1995, 840 on 16 September 2000, 1,106 on 1 October 2003, 3,891 on 3 October 2003 and 2,500 on 4 October 2003. Juveniles figure quite heavily in these movements, the first usually being seen in the latter half of August or early September.

Winter records usually involve only single birds and in some winters no Little Gulls at all are recorded between the last passage bird in September or October and the first of the summering birds in April or May. However, ten were present in Hartlepool Harbour on 31 December 1978.

Inland sightings are also infrequent with some years producing no records at all. Scaling Dam and Crookfoot Reservoir are favoured localities, although the highest inland counts are 12 at Hart Reservoir on 4 September 1958 and up to 16 at Bowesfield in June-July 2003.

The origin of these birds is uncertain. However, it is likely that the majority come from the nearest breeding grounds to Britain which are in Holland and Denmark. There is a recovery of a one-year old bird in Durham that was ringed as a pullus in Finland. It is not apparent why one year old birds should summer in the same area of Teesmouth for so many years, without there being any suggestion of attempted breeding.

A completely white bird passed Hartlepool on 3 September 2000 and one with a white mantle, rump and underwing was on Saltholme Pools on 12 June 2003.

SABINE'S GULL *Larus sabini*

The first known Cleveland record concerns an immature shot in the Tees Bay on 6 October 1889, the skin of which is in the Dorman Museum, Middlesbrough. Owing to a labelling error it was thought that the bird concerned was a Little Gull, but it is now known that the original identification was correct.

There were records in 1911 and 1954, then in the 45 years between 1960 and 2004, approximately 90 Sabine's Gulls were recorded, equally divided between adults and immatures.

All the records fall between 20 July (1971) and 24 November (1963) with the exception of a single bird at Hartlepool on 22 June 1985, one passing Redcar on 30 December 1978 and one in the Saltburn-Brotton area from 12 November to 14 December 2000, the latter frequently being seen on inland fields.

Virtually all records concern birds along the coastline, the majority occurring during or immediately after strong north-westerly, northerly or north-easterly winds. However, in 1971 two or three birds were around North Gare Sands between 20 July and 9 September associating with large numbers of other gulls, terns and skuas during a prolonged sprat wreck. Over 60% of the records of Sabine's Gull come from Hartlepool, but this is probably biased since most sea watching is carried out from the Headland. The remainder of the records are equally shared between Redcar, South Gare, Tees Bay and Seaton Carew.

Most sightings concern single birds, though three were recorded on 30 September 1911, 23 September 1984, 1 November 1986, 14 September 1988, 9 September 1989, 13 September 1993 and 3 October 1994. Four passed Hartlepool on 9 September 2005 and six were observed from the same location on 16 September 2005.

BONAPARTE'S GULL *Larus philadelphia*

There are two records of this American gull, a first-summer bird moulting into second winter plumage that was present on Saltholme Pools from 12 August to 2 October 1977 and an adult was at Saltburn 13-14 November 2006.

BLACK-HEADED GULL *Larus ridibundus*

For inland birdwatchers this is the commonest 'seagull', being the main species which follows the plough in autumn, is inclined to feed in fields and to come to the bread-throwing public in parks. At times it is also the commonest gull along the coastline, with influxes in autumn and winter, especially during sprat wrecks and extremely cold weather.

Whilst the birds spread themselves out along the entire coastline, the biggest estimates at Teesmouth have been about 25,000 in August 1962 and 11,000-12,000 in January 1977 and 1978. In most years, the Wetland Birds Survey counts show up to 4,000 around Teesmouth, but more use the beaches and rocks to the north and south, so about 6,000-7,000 is probably a reasonable estimate of the numbers using Cleveland's coastline between August-March. Many also roost overnight on some of the inland waters, especially Longnewton Reservoir and Scaling Dam.

Ringing recoveries have shown that a large proportion of the birds present in Cleveland in autumn and winter originate in the countries of northern and central Europe, such as Norway, Sweden, Finland, Denmark, Lithuania, Belgium, the Netherlands, Poland, Germany and Russia. There are also at least 14 known recoveries in Cleveland of birds ringed as pulli in Britain, ten of these from Ravenglass, Cumbria (one as early as June 1909), and others from Nidderdale, North Yorkshire, Hallington Reservoir, Northumberland, and Baston Fen, Lincolnshire.

Despite being a noisy and conspicuous bird when breeding it is not known if this species breeds in Cleveland every year, although there are several colonies on the North York Moors very close to the county boundary. One of these colonies has the Cleveland boundary running through the middle and in 1986 this colony held about 550 breeding pairs, just over half of which were considered to be in Cleveland. Up to about 15 pairs have been known to nest at Scaling Dam in recent years and at Teesmouth a few pairs nested between 1930 and 1938, in 1971, 1979 and 2004. The recently-created tern islands on RSPB Saltholme have proven attractive to this species, 20-30 pairs being noted in 2006. Also, single pairs nested at Margrove Ponds in 1977 and 1979. The brown juveniles begin to appear at the coast in very late June or early July.

This bird seems to be more vulnerable to extreme cold than the other common species of gull. It is not unusual to find dead birds in winter and, over 200 were located between Hartlepool and Crimdon Dene in early January 1971, during an exceptionally cold spell.

Individuals with a faint pink flush on their breast can sometimes be seen, but a winter-plumaged adult at Charlton's Pond on 27 December 1992 had its entire underparts and head suffused with a bright pink colouration. There are also records since 1960 of at least four leucistic individuals.

Approximately 500 birds have been ringed in Cleveland as full-grown adults. Three ringed at Teesmouth in September 1975, October 1981 and September 1989 were found dead in Germany in May 1976, June 1982 and July 1990 respectively. One ringed on the Reclamation Pond in August 1976 was found dead in Finland in May 1979. Another ringed on Seal Sands in September 1989 was dead in Denmark in July 1990 and one ringed on Seal Sands in August 1999 was present in Denmark in March 2003. Wing-tagged birds have been seen occasionally. One marked in Durham City in November

1983 was noted at Crookfoot Reservoir in October 1984 and January 1986 and another marked at Coxhoe, Durham, in December 1983 was observed in North Humberside in January 1984 and Hartlepool Docks in January 1986.

RING-BILLED GULL *Larus delawarensis*

There are 13 records of this gull, which was first recorded in Britain as recently as 1973, but is now the most frequently observed American gull.

Date	Age/plumage	Locations
19 December 1978	first-winter bird	Coatham Marsh
20 April 1982	adult	Long Drag Pools
21 July 1983	first-summer bird	Redcar
24 June to 15 July 1990	first-summer bird	Reclamation Pond
5 to 13 May 1991	second-summer bird	Reclamation Pond
9 to 26 September 1992	adult	Reclamation Pond
19-20 July 1995	second-summer bird	Seaton Snook
20 October 1995	second-summer bird	Reclamation Pond
16 to 19 January 2001	second-winter bird	River Tees at Stockton
13 to 19 February 2001	second-winter bird	Portrack Marsh
19 Feb to 26 Mar 2002	adult	Belasis Technology Park
12 to 14 March 2002	adult (2nd bird)	Belasis Technology Park
18 January 2003	adult	Belasis Technology Park
21 Feb to 23 Mar 2005	adult	Belasis Technology Park
Ring-billed Gull Records		

COMMON GULL (MEW GULL) *Larus canus*

Although frequently outnumbered by other gulls, this can be the commonest gull around the river mouth. The Wetland Birds Survey counts are the only regular source of information and in most years the highest counts of the Common Gull are in the region of 2,000-8,000, generally in January-March. However, about 12,000 were present in February 1977, 15,000 in August 1962 and an estimated 34,000 on 22 January 1978.

Most, if not all, of the birds at Teesmouth originate from more northerly parts of Britain and Europe and it is the severity of the northern winter that is probably the main determining factor of Common Gull numbers in the county.

Totals generally decline in March and April, but a small number of one-year old birds spend the summer around Teesmouth. The adults begin to reappear in late July and

August, usually accompanied by juveniles. If a 'sprat wreck' occurs in August, there can be a rapid build-up of numbers of Common Gulls, as well as other gulls and terns. The Common Gull tends to be more of an estuarine bird than the Black-headed Gull, although some move inland with the Black-headed Gulls each year.

There are many records of birds ringed in northern Europe and recovered on the east coast of Britain, but there are only eight known recoveries in Cleveland. Seven of these were ringed as pulli: in Denmark in June 1928; in Norway in July 1963, July 1988 and June 1991; near Pori in Finland in June 1971, in the Murmansk region of Russia in June 1982; and on Yell, Shetland, in July 1993. Most were recovered in the year following ringing around the Hartlepool-Teesmouth-Redcar area. Another bird ringed in Finland in June 1931 was found at an unknown locality in Durham in February 1933, one ringed in Norway in July 1985 was found dead at Teesmouth in December 1990, one ringed in Nunthorpe in January 1996 was dead in Norway in July 1997 and one ringed at South Gare in March 1997 was dead in Sweden in June 2006.

White individuals have been seen in most years at Teesmouth and occasionally elsewhere in Cleveland since April 1976.

LESSER BLACK-BACKED GULL *Larus fuscus*

This gull is never very numerous as a passage migrant, from March to May and again from July to September. However, there are increasing numbers of pairs nesting each year.

In most years, a few birds are seen on the coast and inland waters in January and February with a small trickle of birds moving north in March-May, but generally involving no more than 50-100 individuals in total. In some years there is a build-up of non-breeding birds, mostly immatures, at Teesmouth in the summer. By mid-July, numbers are again beginning to increase as birds move south and in most years 20-30 can be seen with the terns around the river mouth. Prior to 1988 the maximum was 56 on 7 August 1971. However, in August 1988, a large influx of gulls and terns brought an exceptional number of Lesser Black-backed Gulls to Teesmouth. A count of 106 on 3 August was nearly twice the previous maximum and numbers steadily increased peaking at about 920 on 19 August, the birds being spread over most of Teesmouth. Birds were seen moving inland between the two dates, so well over 1,000 birds were involved in this significant influx.

Most birds have left by early September, although a few are sometimes seen in October and November, and occasionally during the winter months. There seems to be no obvious reason for the departure of the Lesser Black-backed Gull to warmer waters, when the Herring Gull appear to be perfectly capable of staying throughout the winter in Cleveland.

Until recently, breeding records have been very scarce; Nelson (1907) stated that the species probably nested at Boulby occasionally. In more recent times two pairs were there in 1947, with single pairs in 1949 and 1954. A pair also nested on Hunt Cliff in 1955 and the recent surveying of the cliffs has revealed one or two pairs at Cowbar between 1996 and 1999. In 1979 a pair nested on a rooftop in Hartlepool and others have been nesting on the roofs of the chemical plant at the Wilton International site since at least 1985, about seven pairs being present in 1986 and about nine pairs in 1987. Also a pair laid eggs on the Brinefields in 1987, but failed to raise any young, at least two pairs nested at Hartlepool Docks in 1990 and 1991, and one or two pairs have attempted to breed at Longnewton Reservoir since 1994. The number of pairs in Hartlepool increased to at least 22 in 1997, and there were about 20-30 pairs at Portrack in 1998 and 47 pairs in 1999. It is possible that small numbers could be nesting unseen on any of the many warehouses and industrial complexes in the area. It is likely that there are over 100 pairs in Cleveland since 2001-2002.

A few birds occasionally move inland to the larger waters such as Scaling Dam, and Crookfoot Reservoir in summer, autumn and occasionally winter. A night-time roost on Longnewton Reservoir has built up in recent years, 490 being there in late June and July 1993, 780 in September 1997, 2,600 in September 1998, 2,765 in September 2000, 3,000-3,500 in late August - early September 2002, 2,930 in September 2004 and 3,310 in September 2005. A few hundred have also been seen here in March in recent years.

At least nine ringed birds have been recorded in Cleveland, five being ringed as pulli on the Farne Islands in August and recovered around Teesmouth up to seven years later. Two ringed at Foulshaw, Cumbria, in July 1916 and July 1920 were found at Middlesbrough 11 weeks later and Seaton Carew five weeks later respectively, one ringed as a pullus on the Isle of May in July 1982 was dead at Redcar in August 1984 and another ringed as a pullus on the island of Flatholm, South Glamorgan, in July 1990 was dead at Pinchinthorpe in July 1995.

The above information concerns the race *Larus fuscus graellsii*, but in most years, a few birds of the race *Larus fuscus intermedius* are reported.

HERRING GULL *Larus argentatus*

During the 20th century this gull increased significantly in this area, almost certainly as a result of increased fishing activity and the practice of tipping large amounts of domestic refuse on open sites.

A fishing boat at sea with an attendant flock of mostly Herring Gulls is a common sight and many follow these boats into Hartlepool Harbour to loaf around the fish quay area, several hundred Herring Gulls frequently being seen here in winter.

Local refuse tips had almost disappeared in the 1990s, mainly due to the provision of the Portrack/Haverton Hill Incinerator, but landfill sites at Hargreaves Quarry and Cowpen Marsh have attracted several hundred (mainly Herring) gulls, since 2000-01.

The main breeding area in Cleveland, the coastal cliffs between Saltburn and Cowbar, has seen a drop in numbers of breeding Herring Gulls since the early 1970s, although there had been a tremendous increase during the first half of the 20th century. In about 1900 only 20-30 pairs were breeding on Hunt Cliff, but by 1969 just over 1,000 pairs were noted between Saltburn and Cowbar. This area held about 330 pairs in 1977, 625 pairs in 1986, 825 pairs in 1987, and 470-600 in the years 1988-2003. Perhaps the warmer and more sheltered inland breeding sites have drawn breeding pairs away from the coast. This gull is known to nest on the Wilton International site (about 100 pairs in 1986), North Tees chemical works (about 20 pairs), on buildings in Hartlepool (about 20 pairs in 1973, 40 pairs in 1979 and 60 pairs in 1986), Poole Hospital (about five to seven pairs in the mid-1980s), Portrack (about 60 pairs in 1999) and Longnewton Reservoir (one pair in 1991, three pairs in 1992, 11 pairs in 1994 and 28 pairs in 1997). It is likely that unrecorded pairs nest on other high buildings in the area.

After the breeding season there is a general dispersal with quite large numbers sometimes building up around Teesmouth in August, especially during sprat wrecks. Also many are sometimes noted in the middle of winter during severe weather conditions, about 17,000-18,000 being present in January 1977 and January 1978.

The beaches and rocks to the north and south of Teesmouth frequently hold large numbers of Herring Gulls, particularly at low tide and especially in autumn and winter. However, immature/non-breeding birds can be found along the entire coastline at any time of the year. The average wintering population is probably in the region of 6,000-10,000 birds increasing at times to perhaps 20,000-25,000.

The origin of many of these birds is shown by approximately 30 known recoveries, about 20 of which were ringed as pulli in northern Britain (Fair Isle, Bass Rock, Isle of May and Firth of Forth). Another four were ringed as pulli in western Norway, Denmark, and northern Russia. One was ringed in Co Down, Ireland, and another (first year bird) was ringed near Ipswich, Suffolk, in December 1987 and found dead at Hunt Cliff in June 1990. Two ringed in Cleveland in November were recovered in north-west Norway within two years and one ringed in October 1978 was recovered at Kandalaksha Bay, Murmansk, Russia, on 30 August 1983. Four pulli ringed in Wilton in June 1995 were seen in later years, one dead at Blakeney Point, Norfolk, a year later, one in Belgium in March 1996, one in Cheshire in April 1997 and one at Blyth, Northumberland, in February 2002. The birds ringed as pulli elsewhere were mostly recovered in Cleveland within two years, although a Fair Isle bird was found dead on Coatham Marsh just over 11 years after fledging, the Co Down bird was ringed in June 1977 and dead at Hartlepool in July 1993, and one ringed in Lincolnshire in November 1987 was found dead on Cowbar Nab in January 2000. Also two ringed in Co. Durham in winter have been located in Iceland in April, two and five years later.

Individuals with white wings or white primaries have been seen on more than one occasion and at least one completely white Herring Gull has occurred in Cleveland.

YELLOW-LEGGED GULL *Larus michahellis*

Before 2004 Yellow-legged Gulls were treated as Herring Gulls of the race *L.a.michahellis*, but since then they have been regarded as a separate species *Larus michahellis*.

As long ago as 1966 an adult with yellow legs was seen, at South Gare. Since at least 1994, Yellow-legged Gull has been observed in Cleveland and it is now an annual visitor in very small numbers.

CASPIAN GULL *Larus cachinnans*

Prior to 2007 this bird was regarded as a race of Herring Gull *L.a.cachinnans*, but is now a full species.

First recorded in 2001, there are now a few records each year, primarily first year birds.

ICELAND GULL *Larus glaucoides*

Of the three white-winged gulls (Iceland, Glaucous and Mediterranean), the Iceland Gull is the least common in Cleveland. Iceland Gulls tend to be recorded on only one day, whereas the other two species usually stay for days or even weeks. However, one adult was seen occasionally through each winter at South Gare from at least November 1984 to February 1988. A bird presumed to be the same individual was also observed at Saltburn in some winter months between April 1962 and May 1967. When last seen it was in adult plumage.

Adult Iceland Gulls are quite unusual in Cleveland, the majority of records being of first and second-year birds. They are generally located along the coastline between Hartlepool and Redcar and especially around the Hartlepool fish quay. Up to three birds have been found in the gull roosts at Longnewton Reservoir and on the Tees Marshes, usually around Dormans Pool. There is more than one record of single birds at Lockwood Beck, Scaling Dam, Dunsdale Tip, Hemlington Lake and Crookfoot Reservoir.

Approximately 85% of the records refer to birds seen in the months December-April with a few observations in November and May, and even less in June-October. The only July record concerns a bird found dead at Seaton Carew in 1951 that had been ringed as a juvenile in western Greenland in August 1949.

GLAUCOUS GULL *Larus hyperboreus*

This annual visitor has averaged ten birds per year since 1974, about 75% of which have occurred between mid-November and mid-May, with more being seen in January than any other month.

It is virtually impossible to be sure just how many individual Glaucous Gulls are in Cleveland in any single year, but judging by the records, between eight and fifteen have been noted almost every year since 1974. They fall into three categories, 70% of the records have been 1st/2nd year birds, 16% have been 3rd/4th year birds and 14% have been adults.

In most years four to six birds are seen along the coastline between December and March. High counts include five off Hartlepool on 31 January 1976 during a strong northerly gale and 16 flew north off Hartlepool on 9 December 1967, followed by four more off South Gare next day.

The favoured area for the Glaucous Gull is Hartlepool with its associated fish quay and boats. One, probably the same, adult was seen here every winter from 1985 to 2003, returning in late August or September and leaving in March. Glaucous Gulls can be found at times virtually anywhere along the coastline wherever numbers of the larger gulls gather, particularly around Seal Sands, Dormans Pool and the river mouth between the Gares. During the 1950s and 1960s, Coatham Tip, Dunsdale Tip and Seaton Tip were used by one or two birds each winter and occasionally up to four birds, but with the capping of Coatham Tip in the early 1970s and the Seaton Tip in about 1980 these sites now rarely attract Glaucous Gulls. Smaller waste disposal sites have existed at one time or another at Thorpe Thewles, Dunsdale and reclaimed parts of Seal Sands; all three sites have attracted this gull on occasion. There are also a few records from most inland waters including Hart Reservoir, Crookfoot Reservoir, Charlton's Pond, Longnewton Reservoir and Lockwood Beck as well as Scaling Dam, where it occurs almost annually.

There are six records of gulls thought to be Glaucous/Herring hybrids, single 1st/2nd winter birds at Skinningrove on 24 February 1990 and 5 April 1990, Loftus Tip on 21 February 1991, and South Gare on 6 May 2000. A 3rd winter bird was observed near Guisborough Cemetery on 15 February 1992 and single adults were at Redcar on 7 August 1975 and Seaton Tip on 20 January 1979.

GREAT BLACK-BACKED GULL _Larus marinus_

Peak numbers of this large gull are always recorded between August and January, but it is generally outnumbered by the other common gulls and in some years the peak count is under 1,000 birds. The occasional sprat wreck in the river mouth in autumn attracts very large numbers of gulls including Great Black-backed and strong onshore winds in the months August-December often lead to the gulls seeking shelter around Hartlepool and Teesmouth. At such times 2,000-3,000 Great Black-backs can be involved. The highest counts are 4,200 on 14 October 1973, 4,860 on 16 November 1975 and 4,700 on 22 January 1978.

As is the case with Herring Gulls, quite a large percentage of the birds are seen away from Teesmouth, so it is probable 3,000-4,000 Great Black-backed Gulls are usually present in Cleveland during autumn and winter. This gull is equally as likely as the Herring Gull to be seen following fishing boats, feeding on refuse tips and bathing in reservoirs.

It is a potential breeding species for Cleveland, as there is plenty of suitable habitat between Saltburn and Cowbar. It spread to the east coast of Scotland as recently as 1960, but so far does not regularly breed any nearer to Cleveland than the Firth of Forth to the north and the Isle of Wight to the south.

There are about 25 known recoveries of this species in Cleveland, all of which were ringed as pulli, including five from Hoy, Orkney, two from the Moray Firth, 12 from the west coast of Norway and one from the Great Ainov Islands in northern Russia. Another two were ringed as full-grown birds near Thorpe Thewles and recovered less than one year later in Norway. A third bird ringed as an adult on Seaton Tip in December 1978 was found dead on the west coast of Iceland on 30 March 1990. These records suggest that the majority of Great Black-backed Gulls seen in Cleveland originate in either north-eastern Scotland or Norway, those from Scotland being recorded at Teesmouth as early as mid-August and those from Norway, as early as mid-September, although one individual ringed as a pullus in Norway during summer was found dead at Teesmouth in the following May. The few immature birds that can be seen in April-July are as likely to be Norwegian as Scottish in origin.

The scavenging nature of this gull is well-known, but it has also been known to attack Wigeon and Pochard on Seal Sands and is equally well-known for chasing migrant thrushes as they arrive over the sea and for attacking auks close inshore.

A leucistic immature was seen around Hartlepool and Seaton Carew in October 1979 and March 1980, an unusual pale brown-backed adult was on Seaton Tip in February 1979 and December 1980, a pale grey-backed adult was at South Gare on 1 October 1987 and a pale, coffee-coloured juvenile was at Hartlepool on 14 November 2002.

ROSS'S GULL *Rhodostethia rosea*

There are six records for Cleveland of this attractive gull. Single adults have been observed in Hartlepool Bay on 6 and 9 April 1975; at Hartlepool fish quay on 7 May 1976 (and probably on the previous two days); in Hartlepool Bay on 9 February 1983 and 11 October 1992; and on the Brinefields and Dormans Pool from 12 to 27 June 1995. Also an immature was at Hartlepool on 11 April 1994.

KITTIWAKE (BLACK-LEGGED KITTIWAKE) *Rissa tridactyla*

This pelagic gull can be found throughout the year and is the most numerous of the breeding gulls in Cleveland, although this appears to be a fairly recent development.

The first mention of breeding concerns about 20 pairs between Cowbar and Boulby on the cliffs in 1947, increasing to about 80 pairs in 1950 (Chislett 1952) although Kittiwakes were described as very numerous on 'some' cliffs in Yorkshire as far back as in the 1770s and early 1800s (Nelson 1907). A colony on Hunt Cliff was found in 1962 (and may have been in existence in 1961), containing six or seven nests. The increase in numbers at Hunt Cliff is well-documented, with 67 nests in 1963, 586 in 1969, 1,780 in 1974, 2,842 in 1977, 3,270 in 1985, 4,620 in 1989 and 4,300 in 1997. The figures available for the section of cliffs between Skinningrove and Cowbar, including Boulby Cliffs, are 1,227 pairs in 1969, 3,350 in 1977, 3,400 in 1985, 3,980 in 1989 and 3,000 in 1997. However, there has recently been a significant fall, with only 1,900 breeding pairs on Hunt Cliff and 2,660 pairs at Boulby in the summer of 2004. A few pairs have attempted to breed around Hartlepool in some years; on buildings in the docks in 1959, 1972 and annually since 1992 and on the Steetley Magnesite Pier in several years since 1969. The colony in the fish quay numbered 50-70 pairs in the late 1990s and over 100 more recently. Since at least 2002, birds have bred on the oil jetties at North Tees and by 2005 the colony had increased to over 100 pairs.

Approximately 8,000 pairs were breeding in Cleveland in the mid 1990s, so with fair breeding success there could be at least 25,000 birds, including young leaving the colonies in the late summer.

Very large numbers pass along the coast in severe onshore winds in some years, mainly in autumn and winter. The figures available include about 10,000 flying north at Hartlepool on 9 November 1957, with similar numbers on 14 August 1977 and 12 January 1978.

Hundreds, and sometimes thousands, gather in the Tees Bay during sprat wrecks and during onshore gales, the largest numbers usually occurring in the autumn, although there are always some Kittiwakes around the river mouth and a few records each year of birds around the Tees Marshes. However, the species is much more unusual further inland, there being a few records of singles at places such as Scaling Dam and Crookfoot Reservoir. A flock of 56 flew inland over the Long Drag on 22 February 1999, up to eight were by the Tees Barrage in July-August 2000, one flew over Sleddale on 10 November 2002 and 45 were on Scaling Dam on 28 March 2006.

Very few have been ringed in Cleveland, although there are several recoveries of birds ringed elsewhere. At least six concern birds ringed on the Farne Islands, Northumberland, and found dead on the tide lines in Cleveland. Three ringed beside the River Tyne have been found dead up to 12 years later at Saltburn and Redcar. Another ringed at Vindfarholmen in central Norway on 28 June 1978 was dead at Hartlepool on 8 October 1978, whilst one ringed on the west coast of Iceland on 16 July 1987 was dead at Hartlepool on 8 June 1989. Two ringed at Cruden Bay, Grampian, Scotland, in July 1979 and July 1987 were dead at Hartlepool in January 1980 and Skinningrove in August 1987 respectively.

An average of 24 birds are found dead during each winter's Beached Birds Survey, which began in 1978, although 75 were noted during an "auk wreck" in February 1983. By contrast, no more than four Kittiwakes were found dead on the beaches of Cleveland in each of the Februarys of 1982, and 1984-91.

It is not unusual to see individuals with pinkish or reddish legs, but one at South Gare on 18 August 1989 had bright orange legs.

IVORY GULL *Pagophila eburnea*

This is probably the only gull to visit Britain as a vagrant that has suffered a decline in records since the beginning of the 20th century. The three records for Cleveland all concern immatures, shot at Seaton Carew in March 1837, shot at Redcar on 2 November 1879 (Nelson 1907) and seen at Saltburn from 31 January to 8 February 1986.

GULL-BILLED TERN *Gelochelidon nilotica*

There are three records of this southern European tern, one on the Reclamation Pond on 5 June 1991, two flying north at Hartlepool on 9 May 2006 and one, also flying north at Hartlepool, on 29 September 2007.

CASPIAN TERN *Sterna caspia*

There are five records of this very large tern all involving single birds: at South Gare on 26 September 1965; on Coatham Sands on 7 August 1972; over the Long Drag on 12 July 1981; commuting between Saltholme Pools and Seaton Snook from 2 to 5 August 2000; and flying south at Hartlepool on 2 July 2006.

LESSER CRESTED TERN *Sterna bengalensis*

One bird of this species was seen along the east coast of Britain from Norfolk to Northumberland from 1983 to 1997 where it usually associated with Sandwich Terns, especially when visiting the Farne Islands. One, assumed to be the above-mentioned bird, was seen on both sides of the Tees estuary between 17 and 20 June 1984, 13-14 June 1987 and 23 August 1987, at Hartlepool on 10 June 1990, again on the Tees estuary from 9 to 12 July 1990, 16 June 1991, 12-28 May 1994, 14-15 May 1995, 11-16 June 1995 and 15 July 1995.

SANDWICH TERN *Sterna sandvicensis*

This tern is a common passage migrant along the coastline from mid-April to early September with some birds spending the summer months around the mouth of the Tees. The earliest and latest dates are 13 March (2000), and 10 December (1996). Odd birds have been seen elsewhere in Britain during the winter months in recent years, so one may winter locally in the future.

Spring passage is much less conspicuous than that in the autumn, the birds generally flying north without stopping and many must pass unseen. The return passage begins as early as mid-June, virtually overlapping the spring passage, but it is early to mid-July before birds of the year appear. By August hundreds of birds gather around the mouth of the Tees with favoured roost sites being North Gare Sands, Seal Sands and Bran Sands. In most years between 1,000 and 1,500 is the normal maximum count, these numbers usually occurring between late July and mid-August, although 3,300 were present at Teesmouth on 29 July 1973, 3,650 on 13 August 1995, 3,770 in mid-August 1995 and approximately 4,000 on 16 July 2002. While 1,000 or more may be the annual maximum count, it is certain that several thousand birds use Teesmouth as a staging post, staying only a few days or weeks. It is estimated that a total about 10,000 birds move through the estuary in autumn. Small flocks of terns (Common, Arctic and Sandwich) can sometimes be seen leaving Teesmouth on August evenings, heading south-west over land and occasionally they can be heard passing over towns such as Middlesbrough and Billingham.

Colour-ringing of birds at their nesting sites and trapping on passage has shown that many using Teesmouth in autumn set off from the Farne Islands and Coquet Island, in Northumberland. Birds from Aberdeen, Fife, Orkney, Norfolk, Essex, Holland, Belgium, Northern Ireland and Denmark have also been seen or recovered here in autumn. Birds ringed or noted at Teesmouth have been known to move north in autumn to Coquet Island and Fife. Two birds ringed in the nest on Coquet Island in 1967 and two others from Farne Island nests were all re-trapped at Teesmouth in 1986, having reached the age of 19 years. Another ringed on Coquet Island in 1970 was re-trapped in 1993, aged 23 years. One ringed at Strangford Lough, Co. Down, in 1983 was re-trapped in 1995, aged 22, and another ringed at Newburgh, Grampian, in 1978 was re-trapped in 1999, aged 21 years.

The migration routes used by Sandwich Terns can be shown by the following recoveries of birds ringed at Teesmouth: Portugal on 1 September; Mauretania on 30 October; Ghana on 5 October; Senegal on 2 October, 10 October, 29 December, 4 January and 18 January; Cape Town, South Africa on 3 January; Spain on 2 February; Senegal on 14 March, 27 June and 15 August; Angola on 19 March and Ivory Coast on 16 February and 30 March. The Spanish record on 2 February probably indicates that a few birds winter around the western Mediterranean: similarly the June and August records for Senegal indicate that birds sometimes stay or return very early to their wintering areas.

Apart from migrating birds flying overhead, this tern is rarely encountered any further inland than Dormans Pool, Coatham Marsh or Hartlepool Docks. Singles near Lockwood Beck on 1 July 1956, at Charlton's Pond on the very unusual date of 10 December 1996 and four at Portrack Marsh on 24 July 2000 appear to be the only inland records.

Up to six pairs attempted to nest in the North Gare area between 1929 and 1931, but with very little success (Stead 1964), and five pairs laid eggs at Saltholme Pools in July 2006, but only reared one young.

A leucistic juvenile with yellowish legs and bill was at South Gare in late July 1998.

Moorland

Moorland view from Stanghow Moor. *Steve Ashton*

Woodland

One of Tees Valley Wildlife Trust's nature reserves - Saltburn Gill. *Steve Ashton*

Coast

Part of the Cleveland Coast. *Steve Ashton*

Industry

Seal Sands *Huntsman Pigments*

Shelduck

Teesmouth is still an important Shelduck habitat, but internationally significant numbers are no longer regularly present during the winter months. *Geoff Iceton*

Goosander

There has been a slight but distinct, increase in the numbers of this duck being recorded in Cleveland over the last 20-30 years. *John Bridges*

Red Grouse

Red Grouse breeds on intensively managed heather moors of southern Cleveland.
Wayne Richardson

White-billed Diver

White-billed Diver, Hartlepool Fish Quay in February 1981. This was the first county record. The bird stayed for 9 days and was seen by numerous observers. *Martin Blick*

Great Crested Grebe

This grebe is a regular breeding species in a variety of wetland habitats within the county of Cleveland. *Geoff Iceton*

Double-crested Cormorant

Double-crested Cormorant at Billingham Pond 1989. This long-staying bird was the first ever European record of this North American species.   *Martin Blick*

Little Egret

Little Egret is an increasingly frequent visitor to Teesmouth. *Wayne Richardson*

Gyr Falcon

There is only a single record for Gyr Falcon, the specimen was collected in 1837 and now resides in the Hancock Museum in Newcastle-upon-Tyne.
Hancock Museum

Macqueen's Bustard

There is only a single county record of Macqueen's Bustard, (formerly known as Houbara Bustard) a specimen collected at Marske in October 1892 which now resides in the Hancock Museum in Newcastle-upon-Tyne. *Hancock Museum*

Ringed Plover

Ringed Plover is a regular passage migrant and nesting species. Areas covered in hard-core aggregate on industrial sites are frequently used as breeding habitat.
Wayne Richardson

Lapwing

Large numbers of Lapwings frequently over-winter on the wet meadows and marshes of Teesmouth.   *John Bridges*

Great Knot

Great Knot at Bran Sands, November 1996. This was the second record of this species for Britain. *Jim Pattinson*

Long-toed Stint

Long-toed Stint at Saltholme Marsh, August 1982. This was the first British record for this species. *Paul Doherty*

Buff-breasted Sandpiper

Buff-breasted Sandpiper is a rare visitor occurring mainly during autumn migration.
Jeff Youngs

Short-billed Dowitcher

Taken at Greatham Creek in October 1999. This was the second British record for this species. *Wayne Richardson*

Mediterranean Gull

This gull is uncommon but an increasingly frequent visitor to Cleveland.   *Geoff Iceton*

Ross's Gull

There are six records of this attractive gull in Cleveland; this picture was taken at North Tees Brinefields in June 1995.   *Jeff Youngs*

Ivory Gull

This picture was taken at Saltburn in February 1986. This is the only record of this species in the county since the late 19th century.   *Martin Blick*

Little Tern

Little Tern breeds in nationally significant numbers, but their nests are very prone to disturbance. *Peter Evans*

Little Auk

Little Auk is regularly recorded moving along the coast during gales in autumn and winter. At times birds are "wrecked" on inland pools.   *Wayne Richardson*

Short-eared Owl

Short-eared Owl is a regular winter visitor to the Tees Marshes, but numbers can vary considerably from year to year. *Wayne Richardson*

Kingfisher

This beautiful bird breeds regularly in small numbers in Cleveland and has probably benefited from a series of mild winters.   *Kenny Crooks*

Waxwing

Waxwing is a frequent winter visitor but numbers vary greatly from year to year. Feeding flocks often exploit berry-bearing trees planted in urban areas. *Jeff Youngs*

Dusky Thrush

This bird has only been recorded once in Cleveland in Hartlepool, 1960. This was the second British record for this very rare vagrant at the time. *Brian Coates*

Radde's Warbler

Radde's Warbler is a rare vagrant to the area. *Richard Hart*

Nuthatch

Nuthatch is an uncommon but increasingly frequent nesting species in Cleveland.
John Bridges

Lapland Bunting

Lapland Bunting is a frequent winter visitor in varying numbers. *Jeff Youngs*

Snow Bunting

Snow Bunting is a frequent winter visitor to the beaches and sand dune habitats on both sides of the Tees Estuary. *John Bridges*

ROSEATE TERN *Sterna dougallii*

Although an annual passage migrant, this bird is the rarest of the regular terns seen in Cleveland. It has never been recorded inland and about 90% of the records involve birds between Hartlepool Headland and the river mouth.

In an average year, one or two birds appear in June and five to ten birds, including two or three juveniles, are reported in July and/or August, though occasionally more are seen. In 1975, up to 13 birds could be observed fishing off Hartlepool during the latter half of July. Up to 12 were seen together at South Gare and Seaton Snook between 29 August and 4 September 1999, 39 flew up-river past Seaton Snook in three hours on the evening of 30 August 1999, and 28 were on Seaton Snook on 22 August 2001.

The earliest and latest dates are 1 May (2003) and 22 October (1977), although there are very few records after the first week of September. The origin of birds passing Teesmouth is indicated by a juvenile found dead at South Gare in August 1949, having been ringed as a pullus on the Farne Islands a month earlier. The majority of the birds seen here probably originate in Northumberland, although there are a few small colonies in eastern Scotland, the birds from which presumably also pass the Cleveland coastline.

A pair laid eggs at Teesmouth in the summer of 1997, but bad weather in late June rendered the first known breeding attempt in Cleveland a failure. However, a pair successfully reared two young at the same place in 2002.

COMMON TERN *Sterna hirundo*

The Common Tern is usually first seen in late April and the last birds of the year are generally recorded in early October. It is most common around Teesmouth from May to September, however, the earliest and latest dates are 5 April (1975) and a very unusual late record for South Gare on 15 December (1984).

The majority of the birds visible in spring continue north to breeding grounds in Northumberland and Scotland, but currently about 500 pairs nest in the county, mainly on the northern side of the river. For many years until the 1980s a few pairs of birds attempted, often unsuccessfully, to nest on the Tees Marshes, but through the 1970s and 1980s up to 15 pairs were more successful on a nesting raft on Charlton's Pond. In 1991 about ten pairs bred very successfully on islands specially created in a lagoon in the

Wilton International chemical complex. This colony continued to increase, often with a productivity of two or more chicks per nest, with 50 pairs in 1992 and 79 pairs in 1993. It had risen to over 200 pairs by 1996, 301 pairs by 1999 and 400 pairs in 2001. The colony was located on an operational chemical production area and it was always accepted that the owners would eventually require the site for development. In 2002 the owners, together with conservation organisations, began constructing alternative nesting sites for the birds in more secure areas around the North Tees Marshes, the objective being to encourage the birds to move the breeding colony by a phased removal of the original nesting islands during the next three winter periods. The result of this co-operative venture between industry and nature conservation was the successful natural relocation of nearly 480 pairs of birds on to protected sites north of the Tees by 2004.

From mid-July onwards Common Tern numbers start to increase around the mouth of the Tees as the birds from northern breeding grounds, together with their young, start their southerly migration. Peak numbers are generally reached in mid-August, up to 1,000 birds being the usual maximum count, although 2,500 were present on 15 August 1985, 4,000 on 16 August 1999, 5,000 on 30 August 1999 and 3,000 on 21 August 2001.

On August evenings it is not unusual to see and hear small flocks of Common Terns heading south-west from the Tees Estuary. Birds ringed at Teesmouth in one autumn have been recovered or controlled in the Liverpool area in following autumns, but whether they have crossed the country from Teesmouth or moved along the east coast in one autumn and the west coast in another is open to speculation.

Over 7,000 Common Terns have been ringed in Cleveland. Recoveries for the area include pulli ringed in the Grampian Region, Tyne & Wear, Essex, Lancashire, Lincolnshire, Orkney, Norfolk, North Wales, Ireland, south and western Norway, southern Sweden, Belgium, Germany, Lithuania, Finland and the Farne Islands, a Norfolk-bred bird being ringed and recovered as early as 1912. The origin of the Charlton's Pond birds is indicated by two entangled in fishing line there in 1969 and 1971 that had been ringed as pulli on Coquet Island, Northumberland, in 1965 and 1966 respectively. Not all pulli ringed in Cleveland necessarily return there to breed; one ringed at Wilton International on 1 July 1998 was found in Aberdeen in June 2001.

Birds ringed at Teesmouth in autumn have been found one month later in Portugal, Spain and Togo, West Africa, and two months later off Equatorial Guinea, Namibia and Gabon, 15 days and three months later in Morocco, four months later in Ghana and up to 11 years later in Guinea-Bissau, Senegal, South Africa, Liberia, Nigeria, Norway and Sweden. Another bird was found dead at Langstone Harbour, Hampshire, on the unusual date of 21 February.

Occasionally immature terns aged one or perhaps two years old with darker, heavily worn flight feathers are seen at Teesmouth in summer; these are sometimes referred to as 'portlandica' terns. A wholly white Common Tern was seen at South Gare on 21 August 1988.

ARCTIC TERN *Sterna paradisaea*

One of the anomalies of Teesmouth is the small number of Arctic Terns that are seen compared to Common Terns. About twice as many Arctic as Common Terns breed in Britain and a higher percentage of the former bird's colonies are to the north of Teesmouth. There are large breeding colonies on the Farne Islands and along the east coast of Scotland as well as in Orkney and Shetland, yet relatively few Arctic Terns seem to pass Cleveland. In some years no more than 50-100 birds are recorded, though some are undoubtedly missed, so perhaps Arctic Terns pass further out to sea or most move north and south along the west coast of Britain.

At Teesmouth, the species is recorded between mid-April and mid-October and occasionally into November, although one was identified at Redcar on 2 December 1905. The maximum count is 1,200 in August 1962, but when large numbers of terns are present it is very difficult to ascertain the real proportions of Common and Arctic Terns, and sometimes a bird seen very early or late in the year cannot be satisfactorily identified.

Arctic Terns are rarely recorded any further inland than the Tees Marshes and Saltholme Pools. However, Scaling Dam attracts a bird or two in some years. Other inland records include one that was found dead at Birk Brow on 17 May 1962 and another dead bird at Crookfoot Reservoir on 6 May 1960. This bird had been ringed on the Farne Islands in the summer of 1957. The largest inland count was of 21 birds that visited Longnewton Reservoir briefly on 27 April 2004.

Ringing records include: pulli ringed on Coquet Island and the Farne Islands and reported at Teesmouth in the same year and 14 years later; a bird ringed in Germany in June 1957 was found dead at Redcar on 1 August 1958; and another bird from Schleswig – Holstein in Germany was recovered at Teesmouth 13 years after being ringed. Other European ringed birds include an adult ringed in Jylland, Denmark, on 1 July 1974 that was controlled at North Gare on 22 July 1986 and singles ringed in Finland in July 1989 and June 1999 that were controlled at Teesmouth two months later.

BRIDLED TERN *Sterna anaethetus*

An individual of this species was seen fishing off Hartlepool on 9 August 1988. It was assumed to be the same bird observed intermittently off Northumberland between 11 July and 28 August and as such is the twelfth record for Britain and the first for Cleveland.

LITTLE TERN *Sterna albifrons*

As a breeding summer visitor, this tern is prone to very erratic breeding success and the Cleveland colonies have been wardened in recent years to try to increase the number of young reared.

The first documented nesting was in 1908, at Teesmouth, the number of birds increasing to about 25-30 pairs in 1916 and 1931. From then until 1985 no more than 12 pairs were recorded as breeding at Teesmouth, and most of these were unsuccessful. In 1986 about 30 pairs nested, rising to 45 pairs in 1987, but falling again to 35 pairs in 1988 and about 25 pairs in the years 1989-92. There was an increase to 45 pairs in the years 1993-95, 65 pairs in 1997, 50 pairs in 1998-99, 40 pairs in 2002-03 and 61 pairs in 2004.

Prior to 1996, most pairs nested in the Coatham Sands - South Gare area and a very few pairs had sometimes laid eggs in the North Gare Sands area. From 1997 almost all of the pairs have been nesting at Crimdon Dene, approximately 200-300 metres north of the Cleveland boundary, but a very few pairs still lay eggs around North and South Gares in some years.

This increase is mostly due to sterling protection work by local organisations including the Industry and Nature Conservation Association (INCA), Tees Valley Wildlife Trust and the RSPB with the involvement of local people acting as volunteer wardens. Fox, human predation and high tides have frequently been responsible for part or complete failure of the colony in recent years. A high number of breeding pairs is no guarantee of a large number of young fledged: six young fledging in 1995; 11 in 1997; two in 1999 mainly due to illegal egg-collecting; and none in 2004 because of fox predation.

In most years, the first returning Little Terns are seen in late April or early May, birds being present through to mid-August and occasionally September. The earliest and latest dates are 15 April (1979) and 2 October (1972 and 2005).

Being a seabird, it rarely ventures further inland than Seal Sands, though one or two have been recorded over Cowpen Marsh, Haverton Hole, Scaling Dam and Longnewton Reservoir, and eight were at Crookfoot Reservoir on 7 July 2000.

Prior to the mid-1980s, the highest counts were in late July and mid-August with 20-50 birds being the norm. In 1987 and 1993 the 45 pairs reared at least 60 young, so in the region of 150 birds were known to have been in the South Gare area for a short period before they began to leave for their wintering grounds.

A pullus ringed at Tentsmuir, Fifeshire, in July 1949 was present at Teesmouth in August 1949, an adult ringed at Inverkeilor, Tayside, in July 1979 was found breeding at Teesmouth in June 1990 and three adults breeding in 1991 at Teesmouth had being ringed as pulli at Teesmouth in July 1976, Carnoustie, Tayside, in June 1980 and near Spurn, Humberside, in June 1987 respectively. The Carnoustie bird was still at Teesmouth on 13 May 1995, aged 15 and a pullus ringed at Brora, Highland, in June 1991 was also at Teesmouth on 13 May 1995. One ringed in the nest at South Gare in July 1976 was still at Teesmouth in June 1991, it also having reached the age of 15. Two pulli ringed in Cleveland on 11 July 1997 were both recorded in Senegal, the first on 8 October 1997 and the other on 16 May 1998.

A total of about 800 Little Terns has been ringed in Cleveland.

BLACK TERN *Chlidonias niger*

This is an annual passage migrant, although numbers fluctuate quite markedly from year to year. Relatively few are seen in spring, when generally one to five birds but occasionally none are recorded. In autumn, five to ten birds are the norm and sometimes there are many more. The highest counts have been: 55 on the Reclamation Pond on 28 August 1958; 39 passing Hartlepool on 28 August 1960; 65 around North Gare Sands during the sprat wreck in August 1962; 49 passing South Gare on 16 August 1967; and at least 87 passing Hartlepool on 2 September 1974. However, on 2 May 1990, very large numbers passed through the eastern half of Britain, with at least 80 being seen in Cleveland including 53 on Longnewton Reservoir.

In spring most birds are seen in May with a few in June and July, whilst in autumn most are observed in August and September with a straggler into October in some years. The earliest and latest dates are 17 April (1968) and 10 November (1984).

Most are seen on the Tees Marshes, with some along the coastline and on inland reservoirs. Other waters, such as Charlton's Pond, Margrove Pond and Wynyard have all recorded a bird or two in recent years.

The spring birds are invariably adults in breeding plumage, while those in autumn are predominantly immatures, but with the occasional adult in moult.

WHITE-WINGED BLACK TERN *Chlidonias leucopterus*

This bird has become a frequent visitor to Cleveland, there being 21 records in the 35 years (1970-2004) with all but six of these on the North Tees Marshes. The earliest and latest dates are 9 May (2002) and 5 October (1982), though more birds have been seen in August than any other month.

The recent records are about equally divided between adults in complete or part-breeding plumage and young birds of the year, although it was not until 1977 that one of the latter was recorded.

The only historic record concerns an adult shot 'near Port Clarence' on 15 May 1869 (Temperley 1951). It was very nearly 100 years before the next record

Date	Location
13 to 18 August 1967	Reclamation Pond
13 to 16 May 1972	Saltholme Pools
26 to 30 May 1976	Coatham Marsh
10 and 11 August 1977	Saltholme Pools
20 August 1977	Seal Sands
11 August 1979	Dormans Pool
3 September 1979	Saltholme Pools
17 August 1980	Saltholme & Haverton Hole
30 Sept to 5 Oct 1982	Greatham Creek area
31 July to 5 Aug 1984	Long Drag - Seal Sands area
29 June 1985	Saltholme Pools
1 September 1985	Dormans Pool
19 August 1992	Scaling Dam
10 July 1995	off Hartlepool
29 June to 7 July 1996	Saltholme & Haverton Hole
7 August 1999	off Hartlepool
25 June 2000	Dormans & Saltholme Pools
19 September 2000	South Gare
4 to 10 June 2001	Dormans Pool & Saltholme
9 May 2002	Coatham Marsh
10 June 2002	Dormans - Saltholme Pools
3 August 2002	Seaton Common
White-winged Black Tern Records	

(COMMON) GUILLEMOT *Uria aalge*

The separation of this auk from Razorbill is sometimes difficult at anything other than close range, although in certain light conditions the back colour of flying auks can be diagnostic. Because of this difficulty most observers record these two species together under 'auk sp' when studying passage at sea; consequently the proportion of Guillemots and Razorbills passing Cleveland is not known exactly and the history of the occurrence of these two birds in the county is not very precise. However, when the two species can be distinguished, it seems that Guillemot outnumbers Razorbill by about four or five to one.

One or two pairs have been observed in recent years sitting on the sea off Boulby with the breeding Razorbills, but none has ever been seen on the cliffs.

Adults pass along the coast throughout the year, but most passage is recorded in January and early February and from late May through to early November. During strong onshore winds about 1,000 auks in a day have been recorded passing along the coast in January and June-October, but the highest counts are 13,400 on 31 January 1976, 3,650 on 29 January 1978 and 3,740 on 3 October 2003. All of these were recorded passing Hartlepool. During times of passage it is quite normal to see birds sitting on the sea, particularly in early autumn and especially around Boulby. Birds occasionally feed and shelter in Hartlepool Harbour, in the river mouth around Seal Sands and on the River Tees as far upstream as Newport Bridge. However, a count of 378 Guillemots by the Seal Sands peninsula on 13 February 1983 was exceptional.

Occasional birds sometimes appear in Hartlepool Docks in winter and singles have been found on Charlton's Pond, Billingham Bottoms, Coatham Marsh and on the River Tees at Stockton. However, these could have been birds blown inland during gales or found on the coast, 'rescued' by well-meaning people, and later released in unsuitable areas.

Every year a few birds, both dead and alive, are found oiled along the beaches, and occasionally large numbers of clean, but very emaciated, birds are washed ashore. Due to oil pollution off the mouth of the Tees in January 1964 about 400 Guillemots died and in February 1983 at least 600 died along the Cleveland coastline with many more to the north and south. Very few were oiled and this is the one occasion when Razorbills outnumbered Guillemots, about 900 of the former being found dead during the RSPB Beached Bird Survey in February 1983. In a normal February approximately 30-50 Guillemots are found dead during this survey. Since at least 1987, relatively large numbers of dead Guillemots have been found on occasion in Paddy's Hole at South Gare. It has been established that these were birds caught and drowned in fishing nets at sea and brought to this locality on a boat before being thrown overboard.

Ringed birds have been found in Cleveland on at least 15 occasions, all birds being ringed on the breeding grounds: Isle of Canna in Hebrides; Isle of May; Grampian and Highland Regions; Fair Isle; Orkney; Shetland; Faeroe Islands and Farne Islands. One of the race *Uria aalge hyperborea* ringed in Murmansk, Russia, in July 1940 was found dead at Hartlepool in May 1950.

A leucistic bird was off South Gare on 10 January 1998.

RAZORBILL *Alca torda*

This account should be read in conjunction with that of the previous species, since many auks pass along the coastline unidentified. The Razorbill seems to stay further out to sea than the Guillemot and when the two species can be distinguished, the Razorbill is almost always outnumbered by the Guillemot.

In late summer and autumn fairly large numbers of auks can be seen sitting on the sea in the south-east of Cleveland. These are mostly Guillemots, but in recent years adult Razorbills with fairly small young still being fed by their parents have been observed. In the summers of 1994, 1995 and 1996 between eight and 23 birds were regularly seen close inshore at Cowbar. Breeding was suspected, but not proven, until the summer of 1997. At least ten pairs have been seen on Cowbar cliffs every spring and summer since 1998, and the breeding population was in the vicinity of 15-20 pairs by 2003-2004.

The Beached Bird Survey, mentioned under the entry for Guillemot, almost always shows very few dead Razorbills on Cleveland's tide lines. Since 1978, between one and 40 birds have been recorded in the four winter months of the year in which the survey took place, with 1983 being exceptional. In February 1983 a phenomenal 'wreck' of auks brought at least 967 Razorbills on to the tide lines, virtually the only occasion when this auk has outnumbered the Guillemot. Very few Razorbills were seen alive at this time although several hundred Guillemots were present in the river mouth.

Three of the February 1983 corpses carried rings. These were pulli ringed in Iceland in July 1982 and the Shiant Islands, Scotland, in June 1979, and a bird ringed as an adult in the Lofoten Islands, Norway, in August 1974. Also, one found dead at Hartlepool on 6 February 1996 had been ringed at Grimsey in Northern Iceland as an adult on 27 July 1994.

BLACK GUILLEMOT *Cepphus grylle*

This is another of the relatively few species that are recorded less frequently now than they were in the past. Nelson, writing in 1907, records immatures seen sparingly between September and January, and an adult being captured at Redcar on 6 March 1883. There are no records between Nelson's time and 1953, although some birds must have occurred and have not been seen or recorded. Between 1953 and 1969, there are 11 records concerning 14 birds, an average of nearly a bird per year. Most of the sightings involving single birds passing South Gare and Hartlepool although two were recorded on 7 December 1967 and four passed South Gare on 16 November 1969. Additionally, singles were off Seaton Snook on 30 January 1954 and one was found dead at Saltburn on 20 February 1960.

Since 1969, there have been 14 records, an average of one bird every three years: an adult in breeding plumage found dead at Hartlepool on 25 May 1974; two off Hartlepool on 12 September 1976; one at the same place on 19 August 1979; one passing South Gare on 19 November 1988; one at South Gare on 13 October 1991; one passing Hartlepool on 27 June 1995; one passing Cowbar on 4 November 1995; singles passing Hartlepool on 10 July 2000, 2 and 3 September 2000, 9 November 2001, 20 September 2002, 7 September 2004 and 24 September 2005 and one at South Gare from 6 to 12 January 2007.

LITTLE AUK *Alle alle*

This is the smallest and most maritime of the auks recorded from the Cleveland coast, and is rarely seen except during strong onshore winds. The most likely weather conditions for Little Auk movements are north-westerly, northerly or north-easterly winds of least force 6 occurring between mid-October and late March. Under such conditions Little Auks can often be seen passing close inshore.

Since most sea-watching is done from Hartlepool, the highest counts of Little Auk are from this location: 344 passed over the two day period 9 and 10 March 1957, about 1,000 passed on 11 February 1983, 680 on 22 November 1987 followed by 1,700 the next day, 3,600 on 11 January 1995 followed by 5,000 next day, 1,850 on 12 November 1995, 2,008 on 9 November 2001 and 1,400 on 2 November 2006. One can only guess at the numbers which passed across Tees Bay in January 1895, when birds were seen continuously for a fortnight, and January-February 1912, when hundreds were washed ashore and birds found inland over most of northern and eastern England (Chislett 1952).

During onshore gales, it is not unusual for birds to appear inland, but February 1983 was exceptional with birds seen on Seal Sands, Coatham Marsh, Dormans Pool, Charlton's Pond, Wynyard Lake and Greatham Tank Farm. Birds were also found stranded at Teesport, Seaton Carew, ICI Billingham, Eston and just west of Cleveland in Darlington and Newton Aycliffe, Co Durham. Since 1945 Little Auks have also been noted at Lazenby, Normanby, on the Tees at Thornaby, on Redcar Boating Lake, Carlin How, Hutton Gate, Brotton, dead under wires at Elton and Reclamation Pond, and on New Marske Reservoir.

In most years around five to ten dead birds are found on the tide lines, including five in May (three in May 1950, one in May 1964 and one at South Gare on 30 May 1965). At least 166 Little Auks were found dead during the auk wreck of February 1983, and at least 65 between November 1987 and January 1988.

Also of interest: two passed Hartlepool on 22 September 2002, the earliest record; one landed in the quarry area of South Gare on 17 May 1997; one passed Hartlepool on 22

May 2004, the latest spring record; a bird that flew by Hartlepool on 19 November 1971 had white wings; and a bird caught in Hartlepool Harbour on 27 December 1981 was entangled in a piece of plastic used to hold drink cans. This specially designed item of plastic has been known to incapacitate or asphyxiate various species of gull on rubbish tips, so presumably rubbish dumped from ships at sea must create a similar hazard for seabirds. This particular Little Auk flew away strongly when released.

(ATLANTIC) PUFFIN *Fratercula arctica*

This auk has been seen offshore in every month of the year, but most sightings occur between April and September, particularly in June and July. The largest numbers have all been recorded off Hartlepool with 129 on 10 June 1972, 137 on 6 June 1986, 110 on 21 July 1994 and 115 on 4 October 2003. Such numbers invariably occur during quite strong onshore winds. It is quite unusual to see Puffins resting on the sea, whereas Razorbills and Guillemots regularly feed close inshore.

The Beached Bird Survey, operating since 1978, has reported very few dead Puffins on the tide line in the winter. No more than 20 have been noted each winter since 1978 with the exception of February 1983 when at least 95 Puffins were found dead on the tide lines of Cleveland, only seven of which were oiled (see Razorbill and Guillemot). Also 61 dead birds were found around Redcar and Teesmouth in May 1950.

Five of the February 1983 birds carried rings: three had been ringed as pulli on the Farne Islands, Northumberland, in 1970, 1981 and 1982; another was also ringed as a pullus at Runde, More and Romsdal, Norway in June 1982; and the fifth was ringed as an adult on the Isle of May, Fife, on 5 April 1974. In addition, two ringed as pulli on Fair Isle in July 1953 and July 1958 were found dead at Seaton Carew in January 1954 and December 1958 respectively; two ringed as pulli on Farne Islands in June 1982 and July 1984 were found dead at Redcar in May 1987 and Seaton Carew in February 1986 respectively; and one ringed as pullus on Isle of May in June 1991 was found dead at Hartlepool in April 1992.

There are three records of single Puffins inland; running along a road in Acklam on 1 November 1945 (Chislett 1952); dead under wires beside the Reclamation Pond in about 1976 and on Scaling Dam on 28 April 1977.

PALLAS'S SANDGROUSE *Syrrhaptes paradoxus*

This Asiatic species underwent several population irruptions between 1863 and 1909 though relatively few birds reached Britain, except in 1888. The records for Cleveland are: a party originally numbering 17 that arrived at Port Clarence on 13 May 1863 and remained for several weeks, other flocks being seen at Cowpen Marsh and

Seaton Carew up to July 1863; three were observed at Coatham Sands in late August 1876; three flocks of six, 30-40, and 20 were seen at Teesmouth, Marske and Ormesby respectively between mid-May and mid-June 1888; a single bird was near Guisborough on 23 October 1888; two were at Kirkleatham on 13 November 1888 and seven were at South Gare on 14 and 15 February 1889. This was the largest influx of Pallas's Sandgrouse ever known. It started in May 1988, involving about 800-900 birds in Yorkshire alone, and probably several thousand throughout Britain (Nelson 1907).

There have been a few other small influxes since then, resulting in two other records; three at Liverton on 1 June 1908 and nine at West Coatham on 17 May 1909.

FERAL PIGEON/ROCK DOVE (ROCK PIGEON) *Columba livia*

The 'true' Rock Dove has probably not bred in Cleveland since man domesticated various birds and animals for his own benefit thousands of years ago. However, the Rock Dove 'type' can be found in most of the populations of Feral Pigeons in Cleveland, substantial scattered colonies of which are present in all of the larger towns. Sizeable numbers also occur in many villages, as well as some farmyards, industrial complexes and along the cliffs from Saltburn to Cowbar.

Approximately 50% of the birds along the Boulby section of cliffs were regarded as having true Rock Dove plumage in 1948 and the percentage was very similar in 1987. Of the other half, most are quite close to the true Rock Dove plumage, but are darker and very few show white or red in the plumage. In the towns, less than 50% resemble true Rock Dove plumage with quite a high percentage of assorted colours being present. The breeding population of this bird in the county is difficult to assess but is probably 3,000-5,000 pairs.

Hundreds of birds can sometimes be seen flying in off the sea or over other areas, these birds being racing pigeons. The races generally take place on weekends and it is not unusual to find tired racing pigeons along the coastline and at Teesmouth. Some birds probably join their 'feral cousins' to breed in the wild, especially inexperienced young birds.

STOCK DOVE (STOCK PIGEON) *Columba oenas*

There are no historic records for this species in Cleveland prior to the 1860s. From the mid-19th century Stock Doves expanded their range from the south of England and the first Cleveland breeding record was near Elton in 1867 (Tristram 1905).

Within 20 years the species was fairly common in the area, and it was reported that 14 were killed with one shot at Redcar in 1888!

Holes of almost any description are utilised by this bird as nesting sites, mainly in old trees, including in witches brooms. It occurs in farmland and scattered woodland, but many industrial and derelict areas also hold considerable numbers, especially around the slag tips at the river mouth.

The breeding population seems to be around 200-250 pairs and was probably fairly stable for most of the 20th century, although there is evidence of a slight decline in recent years. Outside the breeding season, small flocks can be found in a few favoured areas, especially the fields around Cowpen and Saltholme Marshes. There is regularly a flock of 100-200 birds in this area from July to February (sometimes in June and March), though between 350 and 440 were in the fields between Saltholme and Cowpen Bewley from mid-October to late November 1995; and up to 680 in the Cowpen Marsh and Greenabella areas between November 2003 and February 2004. Flocks numbering 50-100 birds have been seen in recent years at Pinchinthorpe, Wynyard, Hart, Dalton Piercy, Elton and Poole Hospital and doubtless some birds are overlooked amongst the many Woodpigeons on most areas of farmland in winter.

There are odd records of birds being observed over the sea mainly in April, August and October, but whether these are local wanderers or true immigrants is unknown.

Over 400 birds have been ringed in Cleveland, almost all as pulli. One ringed as a juvenile at Guisborough on 9 August 1964 was at North Shields, Tyne & Wear, seven days later, one ringed at Blaydon, Tyne and Wear, in April 1945 was found dead at Hartlepool in December 1945 and one ringed at Knaresborough, North Yorkshire, on 8 July 1973 was killed in the Cleveland Hills in December 1973. The great majority of Cleveland birds probably remain in the local area throughout their lives unless a very severe cold spell affects the region in winter.

WOODPIGEON (COMMON WOOD PIGEON)
Columba palumbus

Every wood, park, copse and plantation in Cleveland holds some Woodpigeon and large trees in agricultural habitat, the bigger hedgerows and many of the more extensive mature gardens often support breeding pairs. In recent years the bird has also become increasingly common in urban areas. On farmland it is often regarded as a pest, eating very large quantities of greens and seed, and is a legitimate quarry species.

It can be found around Cleveland throughout the year. There are two records of birds ringed in Northumberland in summer and recovered in Cleveland during the following winter. One ringed as a pullus in Hampshire in August 1925 was in North Yorkshire in January 1926. In addition to these records, one ringed as a pullus in Nunthorpe in June 1969 was in Darlington in June 1973, another ringed as a first year bird at Marske in August 1980 was near Darlington in December 1987 and one ringed as a pullus in the nest on the

North Tees Marshes in June 1996 was shot on Cowpen Marsh in September 2003.

An accurate estimate of the breeding population in Cleveland is difficult due to the quite high densities of breeding pairs in some woodland, together with variable numbers of scattered pairs in agricultural and urban habitats. However, the best estimate at present is about 2,500 pairs.

Nelson (1907) records regular immigration of birds from across the North Sea, including an enormous influx in late October and November 1884. About 420 flew inland over Seal Sands on 4 November 1975, but were not actually seen to cross the coastline and at least 1,850 flew north-west along the coastline between Boulby and Skinningrove in four hours on 16 November 1994. Otherwise only single birds have been observed over the sea in recent years. Very large flocks are commonplace in winter, gathering of up to 3,500 having been recorded recently between November and February. Such flocks can usually be found on most agricultural tracts and it is likely that about 20,000 birds are present in Cleveland in fairly mild winters.

(EURASIAN) COLLARED DOVE *Streptopelia decaocto*

This species first bred in Cleveland at Linthorpe, Middlesbrough, in 1960, only five years after the first such event in Britain. The Collared Dove then spread rapidly, being seen in several places in Hartlepool in 1961, Kirkleatham in 1962, Redcar in 1963 and throughout most parts of Middlesbrough by 1965. The Hartlepool population was approximately 120 pairs by 1965, a flock of 201 having been noted in Burn Valley Gardens, Hartlepool, in October 1964. However, by 1971 the breeding population had declined to about 90 pairs. The population is now about 1,000-2,000 pairs.

Since 1967, a few birds have been seen annually passing along the coastline in spring and autumn, though whether these are wanderers from local breeding populations or long-distance migrants is open to debate.

The largest winter gatherings on record have been from the area around the grain silos in Hartlepool Docks where spilled grain was a regular food source until 1981. Regular counts revealed 135 in December 1973, 200 in December 1975, 520 on 8 February 1976, 460 in October 1976, 434 in January 1977, 330 in December 1979 and 62 in early 1982.

Since 1980, flocks of 20-80 have been observed in several areas, principally at night-time roosts. These include Locke Park, Charlton's Pond, Albert Park, Acklam, Kirklevington and Marske Fox Covert.

An adult ringed at Hartlepool on 6 November 1965 was found dead in Southend, Essex, in 1969. A full-grown bird, ringed at Twyford, Hampshire, on 23 July 1983 was killed at Egglescliffe on 9 May 1985 and an adult ringed at Grosmont, North Yorkshire, on 26 January 1991 was found dead at Linthorpe, Middlesbrough, on 26 June 2000.

(EUROPEAN) TURTLE DOVE *Streptopelia turtur*

Being at the extreme northern end of the British breeding range renders this summer visitor a fairly rare bird in Cleveland. It is quite particular in its choice of habitat preferring hawthorn scrubland. Such areas are scarce, but in the 1970s and 1980s a pair or two could be seen at the Wynyard Woodland Park, Loftus, Grinkle Park, Hutton Gate, Stillington, and near Kirklevington and in some years breeding was confirmed. In the past breeding records were more common. Seven nests were found within one mile of Nunthorpe in 1945 (Chislett 1952) and seven pairs were reported along the Castle Eden Walkway (now known as Wynyard Woodland Park) in 1986. However, there are no reports of breeding or even territorial birds since 1996.

In most years a few single birds are seen, but these are probably passage migrants and as such they can appear almost anywhere. The most observed in recent years were six flying south over Cowpen Marsh on 6 June 1972.

It is usually early to mid-May before any birds are seen, although the earliest date is 5 March (2000) and the last bird is noted in August or early September, but the latest date is 14 November (1992). Very occasionally a bird will appear on the coast during fall conditions, indicating a continental origin.

One was found freshly dead in Hartlepool town centre on 29 January 1972, but the observer could not rule out the possibility of an escaped cage-bird.

RING-NECKED PARAKEET
(ROSE-RINGED PARAKEET) *Psittacula krameri*

Since this exotic species was officially placed on the British list there have been five records for Cleveland up to 2004, all except one being of single birds. These are: Charlton's Pond from early October to 19 December 1990; over Haverton Hole on 3 August 1991; in the Norton area from 29 January to 7 April 1997; in Loftus from at least 22 April to mid-November 2001; at Kirklevington from 9 December 2002 to January 2003, a pair being seen on 11 February 2003.

From 2005, birds have been regularly seen at Acklam and Hartlepool, successful breeding occurring at Acklam in 2006, and six or seven birds have been seen in both areas in 2007. Birds have also been recorded less frequently at other places including Yarm, Nunthorpe, Greatham and Skelton.

Prior to this official acceptance, single birds were seen over Cowpen Marsh on 14 October 1972, at Crookfoot Reservoir on 13 February 1977 and over Coatham Marsh on 25 September 1986, all three birds being presumed to have escaped from captivity.

GREAT SPOTTED CUCKOO *Clamator glandarius*

A juvenile of this southern European species was present beside Dormans Pool and the Long Drag from 2 to 9 July 1995. Details of this record and field descriptions are given by Foster (1996).

COMMON CUCKOO *Cuculus canorus*

This regular summer visitor breeds very sparingly throughout Cleveland. In most years the first bird is seen, or heard, in the latter half of April, although the earliest is 3 April (1976) and the birds are on their territories from early May. This is usually the best time to assess the numbers, when there is a lot of activity and the Cuckoo's presence is frequently made apparent by the male's well-known call. The number of pairs in Cleveland is considered to be about 20-30 and there is evidence to indicate a continuous decline since the late 1980s.

There are few records of Cuckoo after July since it is known that juvenile birds are left with their foster parents, while the adults head south, so all the records of Cuckoos after early August concern birds of the year. The latest date is 15 October (1993). The largest number of birds seen together is eight on the Long Drag on 24 May 2000.

BLACK-BILLED CUCKOO *Coccyzus erythrophthalmus*

The only record for Cleveland of this North American bird concerns one trapped in Locke Park, Redcar, on the evening of 23 September 1975 and released there on the following morning. This was only the 7th record for Britain.

BARN OWL *Tyto alba*

This resident owl has been slowly declining in Cleveland for a number of years. As far as can be ascertained, there have probably never been more than about 30-40 pairs in the county during the 20th century. It is the replacement of old stone barns with steel and corrugated-roofed buildings that has been partly blamed for the national decline of this species, along with habitat destruction, human persecution, toxic chemicals and the relatively high number of birds that are killed on roads.

In the late 1950s and 1960s the Barn Owl was known to breed in at least 15 areas within the county including Pinchinthorpe, Wilton, Wolviston, Cowpen Bewley, Hartlepool, Hartburn, Graythorp, Port Clarence, Nunthorpe, Kirkleatham and Portrack. By the mid-1970s the breeding population was thought to be down to about eight pairs and by the mid-1980s to no more than three or four pairs. However, a similar number seems to be holding on in Cleveland, at least up to 2006.

Until the late 1970s, this bird could be seen in many areas throughout Cleveland in the autumn and winter as the birds dispersed from their nesting sites, but now so few remain that winter records have become extremely scarce. A relatively high number of records involve dead birds, mostly as road casualties. There are occasional records for the Tees Marshes, including at least three reports of the dark-breasted race *Tyto alba guttata*.

There are five known local recoveries of birds ringed elsewhere, all ringed as pulli at: Stocksfield in Northumberland; Barford near Coventry; Barnsley, South Yorkshire; Faugh, Cumbria, and Clacton, Essex. The first three were recovered in their first winter at Stockton, Wynyard and Middlesbrough respectively, the fourth being 16 months old and the last three years old.

Also, one ringed at Llanfenor, Gwent on 2 December 1997 was dead 'near Staithes' on 6 January 1998 and a pullus ringed at Rodding, Denmark, on 3 June 2003 was dead a few kilometres south of Cleveland on 1 December 2003. As is the case with many species, the young seem to disperse in all directions.

LITTLE OWL *Athene noctua*

The Little Owl is an introduced species in Britain. Several attempts at establishment were made in the late 19th and very early 20th centuries in Central and Southern England, eventually resulting in a gradual spread. The species reached the Cleveland area by the early 1930s, although it was recorded near Darlington, County Durham, in 1923.

Up to the 1960s, the Little Owl nested at several places in the Guisborough-Nunthorpe area, as well as Wynyard and a few other localities in the county. However, by the 1970s there seemed to have been a slight decline, although since then Little Owls have recovered. The destruction of hedgerows and other changes in the character of agricultural land, have affected the numbers. Since the 1980s, breeding has been proved, or thought likely at Moorsholm, Guisborough, Loftus, Boulby, Hilton, Longnewton, Greatham, Wynyard, Grindon, Cowpen Bewley, South Gare and the North Tees Brinefields and possibly other places. The present population estimate is about 60-70 pairs.

TAWNY OWL *Strix aluco*

With a breeding population of approximately 150 pairs spread throughout Cleveland, this owl outnumbers all of the other breeding owls combined and it seems likely to have been so for many years.

Tawny Owls regularly breed in large trees in the centre of the towns and villages and such pairs are probably more successful than those nesting in natural woodland. This owl is quite tolerant of human presence, though it will attack if provoked. Because of its

Birds of Cleveland

sedentary nature and nocturnal habits, the species is probably under-recorded. Very occasionally a wandering individual is seen around the coastal marshes.

The only ringing recoveries of any note concern pulli ringed at Wilton in May 1981 and found dead 15 km south-east at Castleton, North Yorkshire, in January 1982, and one ringed at Moorsholm in May 1983 and found dead 20 km north-west at Teesville, Middlesbrough, in July 1987. Over 300 Tawny Owls have been ringed in Cleveland.

LONG-EARED OWL *Asio otus*

This owl is a regular spring and autumn passage migrant along the coast, in small numbers and is recorded breeding in Cleveland in some years, though it probably does so every year.

Nelson (1907) recorded the species on the coast in autumn quite frequently, but between 1911 and 1962 there were no such sightings. Most recently between two to four birds have been seen annually in October and November at places such as Hartlepool, South Gare and Locke Park and one or two occasionally appear in April and early May. These are presumably birds heading for breeding areas in northern Europe.

During the winter months, between one and three birds are occasionally seen at inland sites. However, there has not been a regular roost site found in Cleveland since the 1930s when up to about 30 birds were known to spend the winter around Eston Nab. The highest number at winter roosts in recent years are up to 12-13 birds at one site in the Teesmouth area in December 1994 and December 1999, and a combined total of at least 26 birds at five locations north of the Tees in January 1995.

As a breeding species the Long-eared Owl nested near Marton in 1906, and Eston Nab, Nunthorpe and near Loftus in the 1940s. More recently, breeding has occurred near Loftus, Guisborough, Cowpen Bewley, Dormans Pool, Skelton, Urlay Nook and almost certainly in one of two other coniferous woods within the county. Also, one shot at Kirkleatham on 30 May 1892 may have been breeding.

There are three Cleveland recoveries, the first being a spectacular one of a bird ringed at Rybachiy, Kaliningrad, Russia, on 9 October 1979 and found dead 1,405 km to the west at Port Clarence on 10 January 1983. The second was a pullus ringed at Feldom Ranges, North Yorkshire, on 25 May 1995 and found dead at Loftus on 4 August 1995 and the third was ringed on Heligoland, Germany, on 7 April 2000 and found at Thorpe Thewles on 4 January 2002. Also, single pulli from Sweden and the Netherlands have been found in Yorkshire in the following autumn/winter.

SHORT-EARED OWL *Asio flammeus*

This owl is a regular winter visitor to the Teesmouth area, a spring and autumn passage migrant in small numbers along the coastline and a pair or two have bred on the moorland between Scaling Dam and Roseberry Topping.

Around Teesmouth, the favoured localities are Greatham Creek, Cowpen Marsh and the Dormans Pool - Saltholme Pools area and birds are generally seen from mid-August through to late April and occasionally during the summer months. Peak numbers are usually recorded in the period November-February. Since regular recording began in the 1950s, the peak count each winter has remained fairly constant between five and 14, although 21 were by Greatham Creek on 14 December 1980 and 20 were in the Hargreaves Quarry area in November 1992.

In most winters a bird or two is seen in the South Gare - Coatham Marsh area and sometimes further inland at such places as Longnewton, Durham Tees Valley Airport, Billingham Beck Valley and Eston Moor. Up to seven were present at Portrack Marsh in the early months of 1988 and up to nine were at Bowesfield in January 2003.

Passage birds sometimes arrive from the sea in late September to mid-November, although usually no more than five birds are recorded each autumn. Historic records include 10 on Redcar rocks in October 1876 and 20 around the mouth of the Tees in October 1895 (Nelson 1907).

The whole of the North York Moors supports about 5-15 pairs each summer and a pair or two is frequently seen in the Cleveland section of the National Park, but breeding is not proven every year. In the recent past Short-eared Owl has been known to nest in at least four areas of the moors and in 1976 a breeding pair was illegally shot near Lockwood Beck. A pair was reported to have bred near Thornaby in 1953.

No foreign-ringed birds have been recorded in Cleveland, though a pullus from Finland was present on the Yorkshire coast in the following autumn. Less than 20 birds have been ringed in Cleveland, one of which was released in June 1984 at Guisborough after having been injured. It was found long dead at Filey, North Yorkshire, in July 1984.

TENGMALM'S OWL *Aegolius funereus*

This owl from northern Europe is a rare vagrant to Britain, and there are only two Cleveland records, both of the birds being shot, in November 1861 near Cowpen Bewley and January 1872 near Loftus.

(EUROPEAN) NIGHTJAR *Caprimulgus europaeus*

This summer visitor to Britain is a rare passage migrant and an occasional breeder in Cleveland. Nelson writing in 1907 recorded it almost annually at Redcar in May and September, but there has been a substantial decline in numbers throughout Britain since about 1930 and it is now almost never recorded on passage within the county, even though Nightjars breed in a number of places to the north of Cleveland.

The species is known to have bred in Greatham Churchyard in 1862, and since the 1940s, Nightjars have probably bred near Eston Nab in 1947 and possibly for some years later: near Lockwood Beck in 1956; Guisborough from 1958 to 1964 (at least one, occasionally two males churring during the summer); at Wynyard from about 1960 to at least 1966 and maybe 1968 (one or two breeding pairs); Slapewath in the early 1960s; Grinkle Park between 1985 and 1987 (one pair); and Hutton Lowcross Woods since 2003.

Other sightings in this period are: one dead near Hart Station on 7 June 1954; one seen at North Gare on 8 September 1956; one at Birk Brow on 18 May 1969; one at South Gare in early August 1969; one in Wilton Woods on 11 May 1978; one flying over Marton on 27 May 1978; one displaying in Wynyard on 1 June 1982; a juvenile female found dying a few metres outside the Cleveland boundary at Scaling Dam on 16 August 1984; one near Saltholme Pools on 9 July 1987; a juvenile seen at Grinkle Park on 9 September 1990, but later found dead; one in Hargreaves Quarry on 6-7 June 1992; a female at Grinkle Park during at least 5-18 June 1993 and a female in Hutton Lowcross Woods on 25 May 1998.

(COMMON) SWIFT *Apus apus*

The Swift is a common summer visitor to Cleveland (with an estimated breeding population of 500-600 pairs and a predictable passage migrant in May and July-August.

The earliest date recorded for the county is 16 April (1996), but it is usually the first few days of May when the first Swifts are seen and within a week many birds are screaming over their nesting colonies and feeding over marshes and ponds.

Flocks of several hundred can be regularly observed over Teesmouth in the period late May to early August. These are presumably local breeding birds on feeding forays, although 1,800 were over Hargreaves Quarry on 16 June 1982. Their favourite breeding haunts are old buildings such as churches and large houses; places such as Hartlepool, Norton, Middlesbrough and Saltburn all have reasonable breeding colonies.

This is one of the earliest of summer visitors to leave Britain, many having left the area by early August, although there are always a few birds in September and sometimes in October. The latest date for the county is 8 November (1961).

Passage of birds over the sea and along the coastline in early autumn is usually quite marked with a few hundred heading south on some days, although 4,200 over Seaton Snook on 24 July 1961 was exceptional.

Over 800 Swifts have been ringed in Cleveland, but so far, there are no significant recoveries. One caught at Portrack Marsh in June 1987 had been ringed near Sutton Coldfield, Warwickshire, in May 1984. Another caught at Lovell Hill on 3 July 1996 had been ringed at Dronfield, Derbyshire, on 19 May 1996.

There are several recent records of individuals showing some white in their plumage, some of which superficially resembled Pallid or Alpine Swift. These include single birds in June 1989, June 1995 and July 1996 and two in May 1990.

PALLID SWIFT *Apus pallidus*

An influx of this southern European Swift into Britain in late October 1999 resulted in a single being recorded in Cleveland. It was present around Hartlepool Headland for about five hours on 25 October 1999. Details of the bird are given by Blick (2000). The second record was a single bird at Hummersea on 20 October 2004 and the third record was a single bird at South Gare on 2 November 2005.

ALPINE SWIFT *Apus melba*

There are five records for Cleveland, singles at South Gare on 16 October 1976, Kirklevington on 6 April 1985, Boulby Cliffs on 6 - 7 October 1985, Greenabella Marsh on 21 June 2000 and over Hartlepool Headland, Seaton Carew and Hartlepool Power Station on 9 June 2002.

LITTLE SWIFT *Apus affinis*

There is one Cleveland record of this African species; one flew north-west at Boulby on 10 May 1998. Details and field notes of this record are given by Blick (1999).

(COMMON) KINGFISHER *Alcedo atthis*

This specialised bird is one of the rarest breeding birds in Cleveland. Over the last decade, the population has remained about 10-15 pairs, though it was probably absent from the area in the mid-1960s after the severe winter of 1962-1963. It breeds in some years around Guisborough, Billingham, Wynyard, Leven Valley, and the River Tees from Portrack to Yarm, and occasionally in several other localities.

Young birds disperse in July and August and at this time there are usually sightings of birds around Teesmouth, at Lovell Hill and on other waters.

There are usually a few wintering birds in Cleveland, favourite areas recently being Billingham Beck, parts of the River Tees, Coulby Newham, Skelton Beck, Guisborough, North Tees Marshes and the Coatham Marsh - South Gare area. The highest count is of at least five at Lovell Hill on 18 September 1985. There are also a few records of birds flying over the open sea: singles on a boat off the mouth of the Tees on 14 November 1887; two miles off Redcar on 4 July 1905; and at Hartlepool Headland on 22 April 1975, 5 July 1975, 8 August 1985, 23 and 26 October 2002 and 21 December 2003. There are also at least five records of birds seen in Hartlepool Docks.

At least 60 Kingfishers have been ringed in Cleveland, but there are no significant recoveries. It is quite likely that birds from Durham and North Yorkshire move into or through Cleveland in autumn and winter.

(EUROPEAN) BEE-EATER
Merops apiaster

There are four records for Cleveland of this most colourful of birds; singles over Cowpen Marsh on 21 May 1981, at Margrove Ponds on 25-26 July 1987, at Boulby Cliffs on 24 May 1992 and South Gare on 7 August 1997.

(EUROPEAN) ROLLER *Coracias garrulus*

This colourful bird does not occur in Britain as often as it used to. The records for Cleveland are: a pair at Skelton in July 1847, the female of which, when killed, was found to be carrying eggs in the oviduct; one killed at Acklam, Middlesbrough, on 21 September 1901; and one shot in Grinkle Park on 11 June 1931.

Since then it has been recorded twice; at South Gare on 11 September 1993 and 18 August 2006.

HOOPOE *Upupa epops*

Date	Location
1950s	Crookfoot Reservoir
25 April 1956	Redcar
24 to 26 April 1959	Nunthorpe
17 May 1963	Seaton Carew
19 - 20 April 1964	North Gare
9 ~ 10 May 1964	North Gare
24 April 1971	South Gare
15 March 1972	Hartlepool
7 Jun 1976	Marton
25 September 1976	Hartlepool
20 September 1981	Hartlepool
6-7 May 1983	South Gare
10 to 12 Sept 1987	North Gare
6 October 1993	Coatham Marsh
28 Oct to 9 Nov 1993	North Gare
9 May 1994	South Gare
23 to 27 April 1996	Brotton
26 September 2001	Seaton Carew
10 to 12 May 2002	North Gare
26 April 2006	Norton Bottoms
Hoopoe Records	

The colourful plumage of this south European bird renders it conspicuous to even the non- bird-watcher, hence, it is likely that a high percentage of Hoopoes occurring in Cleveland have been recorded. The earliest dated record for the county is very unusual involving a flock at "Saltburn in 1836, several of which were obtained". Other historic records were single birds at Marske in September 1880, Redcar on 2 October 1881, Albert Park in the 1890s and Marton in September 1932. More recently single birds have been seen as shown in the table.

It will be noted that late April to mid-May and September are the most likely months for this bird to occur in the county.

(EURASIAN) WRYNECK *Jynx torquilla*

This unusual and beautifully marked relative of the woodpecker is now a regular passage migrant on the coast in small numbers, with most records in autumn, although it is occasionally seen in spring.

Wrynecks probably bred in the area quite regularly up to about 1845 and possibly a few times in the following 100 years. This is in line with the known decline of the species over England as a whole, the reason for which is not apparent. There are no breeding records for the county, although a bird seen in Stewart Park during the summer of 1935 gives a good indication and is the last record of a bird seen anywhere in Cleveland outside the months of passage i.e. April-May and August-October.

The first record for the 20th century of a coastal passage bird involved one near Graythorp on 28 and 29 August 1954, although the Wryneck can be very hard to see due to its camouflaged patterning and was undoubtedly overlooked in the past. Since 1954 it has been observed in September 1958 (four birds), September 1960 (two birds), September 1963 (two birds) and regularly, with an average of four birds per year since 1965, mainly during the autumn months.

The most seen in any one year is 13 in 1977, 10 of these occurring between Hartlepool, North Gare and South Gare during a fall of migrants on 18 and 19 August. One of the South Gare birds was caught on 20 August and had been ringed as a pullus at Grimstad, on the southern tip of Norway on 25 July 1977. A total of 10 Wrynecks were also seen on the coast between 20 and 25 August 1970.

Most of the spring records are of one or two birds, although five were seen between North Gare and South Gare during the first week of May 1969.

Since the 1935 Stewart Park record there have been nine inland records, two in spring on 15 May 1979 at Guisborough and on 6 May 2006 at Margrove Ponds, and seven in autumn at Hart Village, Hart Station, Pinchinthorpe, Kirklevington, Nunthorpe, Stewart Park (this bird being found dead) and Norton.

The earliest and latest spring records are 16 April (1976) and 17 May (1993) and the corresponding autumn dates are 10 August (2004) and 24 October (1971).

GREEN WOODPECKER *Picus viridis*

The impression given by the published reports of the late 19th and early 20th centuries is that the Green and Great Spotted Woodpeckers were roughly equal in numbers, i.e. a breeding resident in small numbers throughout the area in suitable woodland. Today the situation is very different. It can now be quite hard to find Green Woodpecker in Cleveland and probably no more than 20 pairs regularly nest. Great Spotted Woodpecker, however, can be located in many of the woodland and parkland habitats and even urban gardens, and has a much higher breeding population. -

Most of the records during the breeding season are of birds heard rather than seen, the favoured locations being Wynyard, Wilton Woods, Hutton Lowcross Woods, Leven Valley, Upleatham, Grinkle Park, Newton Woods, Skelton, Urlay Nook, Margrove Ponds and Eston Hills. After the breeding season wandering birds can be found almost anywhere; they have been occasionally recorded on Cowpen Marsh, Greenabella Marsh, Hargreaves Quarry and the Long Drag, and more regularly on the cliffs at Saltburn and Boulby.

The highest number recorded together is six on Eston Moor on 9 July 1995.

GREAT SPOTTED WOODPECKER
Dendrocopos major

This woodpecker is the commonest of the three species and is present in virtually any suitable woodland, including well-wooded suburban areas. It probably has not always been so widespread, as the records for the 19th century indicate that it was relatively scarce. This reflects the general spread northward of this species in England and into Scotland that began at the end of the 19th Century (Temperley 1952).

The Teesmouth Bird Club conducted a special survey of Great Spotted Woodpecker in 1979 although this was by no means comprehensive. However, it was concluded that the Cleveland population was at least 30 breeding pairs. Another survey in 1985 that covered all of the breeding species in woodland and farmland in Cleveland indicated at least 20 pairs in the area between Wilton, Ormesby, Nunthorpe, Roseberry Topping and Guisborough and a county population of 120-150 pairs. The reasons for this increase are not obvious. Perhaps its habit of frequenting bird-tables and nut feeders has resulted in a better overall survival rate. The first record of bird table feeding in Cleveland was in November 1974.

The birds described above are of the resident British race *Dendrocopos major anglicus*. The Scandinavian and east European race *Dendrocopos major major* is a migrant and reaches the east coast of Britain in some years, sometimes in quite good numbers and almost invariably in September. The earliest record of this race in Cleveland occurred on 14 September 1914, when one was found dead under wires by Coatham Sands. There are several more recent records of birds on the coast such as at South Gare, North Gare and Hartlepool Headland. These include: one ascending a flagpole at South Gare on 24 September 1949; three on the coast in September 1968; six on the coast between 18 September and 3 October 1972 (one of which was found dead at Teesmouth Field Centre and described as *D.m.major*); three between 30 August and 12 October 1974; seven or eight in the latter half of October 1990; and eight between 5 and 27 September 2003.

Not all birds seen near the coast are necessarily from northern Europe. It is not unusual to observe wandering birds outside the breeding season in quite open habitat with few trees, such as the Long Drag, Scaling Dam or Boulby Cliffs.

At least 100 birds have been ringed; the only significant movement reported concerns one ringed at Saltburn on 18 October 1997 that was at Scarborough, North Yorkshire, on 4 May 2002.

LESSER SPOTTED WOODPECKER
Dendrocopos minor

This is the smallest of the British woodpeckers, and whilst it occurs in the far north of Europe, Cleveland is at the northern extremity of its distribution in Britain. In the region it has declined in recent years to the point that it is not recorded every year. Up to the late 1980s there was likely to have been up to three pairs in Cleveland, but the last breeding record was in the Saltburn - Skelton area in 1992.

Past breeding records include Grinkle Woods in 1901 (Nelson 1907), in "a pinewood near Marske" in 1943 (Chislett 1952) and Saltburn Woods in 1956.

Since 1975, it has been seen fairly frequently in the Yarm - Kirklevington area with a male excavating a nest-hole in early May 1976 and successful breeding reported in 1983 and 1985. It has also occurred near Nunthorpe, where a drumming male was heard in May 1980 and breeding was thought 'likely' in 1984 and proven in 1985

Odd birds have also been seen recently at Grinkle Park, Leven Valley, Saltburn Woods, Wilton Woods, Wynyard, Pinchinthorpe and Hutton Gate, so more intensive bird-watching in these areas may yet reveal another pair or two of this unobtrusive bird.

(GREATER) SHORT-TOED LARK
Calandrella brachydactyla

This southern Palearctic lark is an annual visitor to southern Britain, but has only been recorded on nine occasions in Cleveland with all of the records being of single birds. The records are: between Redcar and Marske 14-16 September 1969; on Coatham Marsh 21 June to 14 August 1974; at Saltholme Pools 17 to 20 April 1983; South Gare on 5-6 November 1994, 30 April to 5 May 2000, 14 May 2000; Hartlepool on 20 May 1997; Cowbar from at least 4 to 12 January 2003 and South Gare 7-8 May 2006.

WOODLARK (WOOD LARK) *Lullula arborea*

There are only nine records of this bird, the first of which relates to a small flock on Redcar beach in January 1891, six of which were shot.

The remaining records, all of single birds, 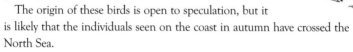 were at: Hartlepool on 16 November 1968; South Gare on 18 September 1969, 4 October 1973, 22 March 1986, 11 November 1989 and 24-25 October 1999; Upleatham on 6 January 1995; and Norton from 26 November 1996 to 21 February 1997. Details of the long-staying bird are given by Lawson (1997).

The origin of these birds is open to speculation, but it is likely that the individuals seen on the coast in autumn have crossed the North Sea.

SKYLARK (SKY LARK) *Alauda arvensis*

This common breeding bird is present throughout the year with an estimated 1,000 pairs breed in Cleveland. It is found in virtually all open habitats such as farmland, marshland, rough grassland and, to a lesser extent, on moorland. However, following the national trend there is evidence to suggest a decline in the number of pairs on farmland over the last 10-20 years.

The Skylark is also a passage migrant, its movements, however, being triggered more by weather conditions than by season. The largest counts in this respect were 400 passing Hartlepool Observatory on 29 December 1968, 170 passing Saltburn in 15 minutes on 24 February 1978, 170 passing Seaton Carew in 30 minutes on 2 February 1980 and 800 flying over the Long Drag on 23 December 2001.

During the winter large numbers resort to the coastal strip, flocks of a few hundred being normal around Teesmouth, although about 1,000 were recorded beside Seal Sands on 15 December 1976 and between Redcar and Marske on 9 January 1982. Approximately 1,000 were present in the same coastal fields in September 1969, but this gathering occurred at the same time as the arrival of a single Woodlark and Short-toed Lark, so perhaps a higher than normal number of continental birds were involved.

At least 500 Skylark have been ringed since 1967, but as yet there have been no significant recoveries, so it is probably true to say that the average Cleveland Skylark does not move more than a few miles each year. A pullus ringed at South Shields, Tyne & Wear, in June 1953 was present at Haverton Hole in December 1959.

During the three years 1969-1971 a pale coffee-coloured individual was seen regularly in the Reclamation Pond-Dormans Pool area of Teesmouth.

SHORE LARK (HORNED LARK) *Eremophila alpestris*

This lark is only recorded along the coastline, usually in winter and sometimes during spring or autumn passage. Prior to 1971, it had been quite regular, but in small numbers, the only recorded influx being mentioned by Nelson (1907) in *'Birds of Yorkshire'* when 200 were at South Gare on 22 December 1900.

Between October 1971 and April 1973, large numbers were seen in the winter months. A total of 153 were at South Gare with 17 at North Gare 23-25 October 1971, about 90 staying into December 1971. Up to 46 were on Seal Sands Peninsula in December 1971 and January 1972 and 63 were there on 8 April 1972. In the following winter up to 60 were around South Gare and up to 50 at or near Seal Sands.

Between 1973 and 1987, this winter visitor was remarkably constant in its occurrence, being seen in every year, but numbering no more than six birds per winter, with the exception of eight by Seal Sands on 12 December 1976. The favoured localities in this period were South Gare, North Gare, Seaton Carew seafront and Redcar Stray. Between 1987 and 1996 there were few records, three in mid-October 1991, three in March-April 1994, two-three from October 1994 to March 1995 and 12-16 at Cowbar in mid-April 1995.

Shore Larks have been seen every year since 1997, including four at South Gare on 9-10 May 1997, one of which had been ringed and was present at Gibraltar Point, Lincolnshire, from 21 December 1996 to 1 May 1997, and up to 29 at Cowbar between mid-March and mid-April 2003.

Favoured localities in recent years include Hartlepool , South Gare, North Gare, Boulby and Cowbar, but this probably shows the distribution of the birdwatchers as much as the birds. Shore Larks probably visit most coastal fields in Cleveland on occasion, and there are a few records of birds further inland, such as at the Long Drag and Coatham Marsh.

The earliest and latest dates are 18 September (1895 and 1971), and 17 May (1999) although the majority of records fall between mid-October and late February.

SAND MARTIN *Riparia riparia*

There had been a general decline in the numbers of breeding and migrating Sand Martins noted in Cleveland in the 20 years prior to 1993, but since then, the species appears to have increased considerably. The destruction of sand quarries certainly has not helped and many birds were reported to have perished in 1983 as they migrated south into Africa with relatively few being seen country-wide in the following spring.

In Cleveland, most birds probably nest in the banks of the Tees, especially around Portrack, Bowesfield and Preston Park, where about 80-100 pairs have been counted in recent years. Another colony was located in a sand quarry at Norton, with 33 occupied holes in 1979, and 24 in 1995. At least two other sand quarries existed in the valley between Norton and Wynyard estate in the 1970s, holding about 40-50 pairs combined, but both have since been destroyed. A new sand quarry was excavated in the same area in 1996, and Sand Martins certainly nested in it in 1996 and 1997, an estimated 200 pairs being present there in 1999. A very small seam of sand in the eroding cliffs at Redcar held 20-30 pairs from 2003 to 2007. Also one pair nested in a drainage pipe in Hartlepool in 2003. The Cleveland population was estimated to be about 200 pairs in 1997 and 300 pairs in 2000 and 2004.

Nelson (1907) mentioned a large colony on Boulby Cliffs and also a colony in the sand hills between Redcar and Saltburn, however this was deserted due to erosion about 1880.

Most birds arrive in mid-April and leave in August and early September, but the earliest and latest dates are 10 March (1977) and 25 October (1967). Large gatherings have included about 250 at Scaling Dam on 31 May 1965, 500 at Saltholme Pools on 13 July 1996, 600 at Dormans Pool on 13 August 1999 and 800 at Haverton Hole on 2 August 2001. Hundreds also regularly pass through the region at various migration watch-points, in spring and autumn.

At least 400 Sand Martins have been ringed in Cleveland, the significant recoveries being: one ringed at Earls Barton, Northamptonshire, in July 1987 and another ringed at Icklesham, East Sussex, in September 1987 were controlled at Portrack Marsh in May 1988; two ringed at Haverton Hole in July 1990 were controlled at Icklesham in September 1990; one ringed at Haverton Hole in July 1991 moved north and was controlled at Prudhoe, Northumberland, on 19 August 1991; another ringed at Haverton Hole in August 1991 was found dead on the roadside by Seal Sands on 1 May 1992; and one ringed at Inchture, Tayside, on 17 August 2000 was present at Seal Sands on 11 September 2000.

(BARN) SWALLOW *Hirundo rustica*

To many people, this is the bird that heralds the beginning of the summer, although it is not unheard of to have snow in Cleveland after the first swallow has returned.

It is a regular summer visitor and passage migrant, with a Cleveland breeding population estimated at about 900-1,000 pairs. There are approximately 240 farmhouses in

Cleveland and almost all, if not all, have some breeding Swallow, and small villages like Cowpen Bewley and Elwick support these birds in many different buildings. Around Teesmouth odd pairs are known to nest in former concrete blockhouses, old sheds and some bird-watching hides.

The main arrival of Swallows takes place from late April to mid-May and they normally begin to move south from mid-August onwards, although occasionally a bird is seen in November. The earliest and latest dates are 26 March (2005) and 5 December (2002). Hundreds of birds per day regularly pass along the coastline in spring and autumn, the recent highest counts being, 2,300 flying north-west at Boulby on 12 September 1995 and 1,455 flying north-west at the same place on 29 April 2003.

After the breeding season, some birds form a roost in the reeds at Haverton Hole, with up to 500 in the 1970s, but no more than about 200 in the 1980s. Other evening roosts noted include up to 3,000 at Dormans Pool in 1999 and 450 at Portrack in 2002. Whether these are local birds, staying at this locality for many nights, or Swallows moving from the areas to the north of Cleveland and using the reedbeds for one or two nights is not clear.

About 3,000 birds have been ringed locally, and interesting recoveries include: a nestling ringed in Yarm in August 1931 that was at Birmingham on 3 May 1934; an adult ringed on Teesside in August 1961 was controlled at the same place in June 1965; a juvenile ringed at Haverton Hole on 22 August 1974 was found dead at Halfway House, Transvaal, South Africa, on 16 January 1976; a nestling ringed at Knaresborough, North Yorkshire, in June 1980 was at Guisborough in the following May; a juvenile ringed at South Gare on 10 July 1981 was at Barnsley, South Yorkshire, 50 days later; and a nestling ringed at Cowpen Marsh on 17 August 1987 was reported from Aglou, Morocco, in January 1988. In addition: one ringed near Saltholme Pools in August 1987 was present at Spurn, Humberside, two days later, and another from the same locality was at Lower Halstow, Kent, seven weeks later; a bird ringed near Barnsley on 5 August 1990 had moved north to Haverton Hole by 25 August 1990, a pullus ringed at Cowpen Marsh on 11 July 1991 had moved south to Wintersett Reservoir near Wakefield, West Yorkshire, by 26 August 1991; another pullus ringed at New Marske on 19 July 1998 was at Icklesham, East Sussex, on 19 September 1998; a juvenile caught at Seal Sands on 23 August 2001 was found dead at Douglas, Lanarkshire, on 11 August 2002; and a pullus ringed at Nunthorpe on 20 June 1994 was at Bombale in the Central African Republic on 27 November 2000.

A completely white juvenile was ringed in the nest near Greatham Creek in late June 1990 and was seen around the North Tees Marshes throughout July and August 1990. Also a Swallow-House Martin hybrid was recorded at Hartlepool on 11 September 2002.

RED-RUMPED SWALLOW *Hirundo daurica*

There are four records for Cleveland: one flew south along the Long Drag on 10 September 1995, details of the 1995 bird are given by Little (1996); one flew north over Seaton Common on 29 April 2003; one flew over Ingleby Barwick on 6 May 2006; and one was at Boulby on 21 April 2007.

CLIFF SWALLOW *Hirundo pyrrhonota*

One seen at South Gare on 23 October 1988 is the only Cleveland record of this North American bird and the second record for Britain.

HOUSE MARTIN *Delichon urbica*

This regular summer visitor to Cleveland is present from late April until mid-October and breeds in small widely scattered colonies throughout all of the towns and some of the villages. The population is considered to be between 500 and 1,000 pairs.

In the 1800s it was recorded as nesting on the cliffs at Hunt Cliff and Boulby and probably has nested there for many years, before man provided the species with an ideal alternative in the form of brick and stone houses. House Martins still breed regularly along the cliffs with: 49 nests counted on Hunt Cliff in July 1963; at least 27 pairs noted on Boulby Cliffs in June 1987; 57 pairs nesting on Hunt Cliff in June 1988; and at least 34 pairs nesting on Boulby and Hunt Cliff combined in June 1991.

The normal first arrival date is about 20-25 April although occasionally none are seen before the first few days of May, with 31 March (2002) being the earliest recorded date for the county.

The departure of the species usually takes place in August and September, flocks of several hundred sometimes gathering over various places during these months. Sometimes considerable numbers remain into October. Approximately 1,000 birds were considered to be over Boulby Cliffs for several days in mid-September 1987 and about 1,800 flew north-west there on 12 September 1995. There are records of young being fed in the nest in late October and these are probably responsible for the occasional November record and the latest recent date of 2 December (1984); one very late bird was seen at Redcar from 14 to 20 December 1888.

Over 1,500 birds have been ringed in Cleveland since 1974, though the only significant recoveries to date are: one caught at Boulby Cliffs on 21 August 1986 was at Stokesley, North Yorkshire, on 7 June 1987; and one ringed in the nest at Hartlepool on 11 July 1990 was at Icklesham, East Sussex on 9 September 1990.

RICHARD'S PIPIT *Anthus novaeseelandiae*

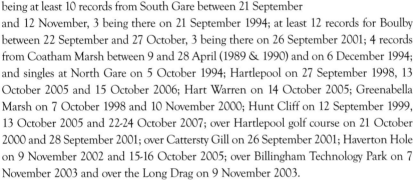

The first record of one in the Reclamation Pond area from 11 to 24 October 1970 was originally accepted as a Tawny Pipit, but a recent review of all Cleveland's Tawny and Richard's Pipits now considers this bird to have been a Richard's Pipit, making the single bird at South Gare on 1 and 2 May 1974 the second record for the county. No other Richard's Pipits were noted until one was present at South Gare on 4 October 1987.

Since then however, the species has occurred in every year except 1993, 1996 and 2004: there being at least 10 records from South Gare between 21 September and 12 November, 3 being there on 21 September 1994; at least 12 records for Boulby between 22 September and 27 October, 3 being there on 26 September 2001; 4 records from Coatham Marsh between 9 and 28 April (1989 & 1990) and on 6 December 1994; and singles at North Gare on 5 October 1994; Hartlepool on 27 September 1998, 13 October 2005 and 15 October 2006; Hart Warren on 14 October 2005; Greenabella Marsh on 7 October 1998 and 10 November 2000; Hunt Cliff on 12 September 1999, 13 October 2005 and 22-24 October 2007; over Hartlepool golf course on 21 October 2000 and 28 September 2001; over Cattersty Gill on 26 September 2001; Haverton Hole on 9 November 2002 and 15-16 October 2005; over Billingham Technology Park on 7 November 2003 and over the Long Drag on 9 November 2003.

No doubt this bird had been missed prior to the mid-1980s, but since then there has been a considerable increase in the number seen in Britain overall. The earliest and latest spring dates are 9 April and 2 May, and the corresponding autumn dates are 12 September and 6 December.

TAWNY PIPIT *Anthus campestris*

There are seven records of this large pipit for Cleveland: two on Cowpen Marsh on 12 April 1968 one of which was still there the next day; two at Saltholme Pools on 10 July 1974; one at Boulby on 3 October 1984 and 24 April 2000; one at South Gare on 14 May 1988 and 12-13 May 1999; and one at Hunt Cliff on 30 May 1997.

OLIVE-BACKED PIPIT
Anthus hodgsoni

There are three records of this rare pipit: one in Locke Park on 13 October 1982; one at Boulby Cliffs on 20 October 1990 and one in Hartlepool Docks on 26 November 2000.

TREE PIPIT *Anthus trivialis*

Special breeding surveys conducted in 1979 and 1985/86 showed this summer visitor to be commoner than was formerly supposed, with about 40-50 pairs. It appears to be almost totally limited to the Eston Hills and the northern edge of the North York Moors, between Roseberry Topping and Scaling Dam. There were considered to be 20 pairs in the Lockwood Beck - Birk Brow - Slapewath area and up to five pairs in Newton Woods, Bousdale Woods, Grinkle Park and Scaling Dam. Single pairs have also been noted near Kirklevington and Stillington in recent years.

Breeding Tree Pipits usually arrive in late April/early May and leave in August, although birds on passage are regularly seen on the coast outside this period. The earliest and latest dates are 28 March (1967 and 1968) and 29 October (1990).

In most years no more than 20-25 birds appear along the coast in spring or autumn. Slight passage can be seen along Boulby Cliffs in late April and May in some years, up to 12 birds in a day on occasion. The biggest numbers were in 1969 when 38 were at South Gare on 4 May, 30 at Hartlepool on 8 May and 30 again at Hartlepool on 17 September 1969.

Only 30 Tree Pipits have been ringed, all as full-grown birds, and there are no known recoveries.

MEADOW PIPIT *Anthus pratensis*

This common breeding bird can be seen in Cleveland throughout the year, especially around Teesmouth, but it is not a resident. It is a summer and winter visitor, and spring and autumn passage migrant.

From mid-March to early May, birds can be seen and heard moving north and west, several hundred per day being frequently observed at coastal localities, the heaviest recorded passages being 780 per hour flying over Redcar on 31 March 1961 and 850 per hour passing Boulby on 1 April 1991.

The birds that breed in Cleveland can be heard singing from late March to May, with quite high numbers breeding around the North Tees Marshes, South Gare - Coatham Marsh, Eston Moor and the moorland and upland fields between Scaling Dam and Roseberry Topping. Relatively few pairs breed in the agricultural areas. The total breeding population is about 700-1,000 pairs, with about 250 around Teesmouth and 200 on the moorland although, in common with many species, evidence of a decline has been noted in recent years.

From August to November birds can be seen heading south, but this is generally less evident than the spring passage. Flocks sometimes rest and feed along the coastal areas, temporarily giving high numbers at these places, but in December, January and February, relatively few birds remain in Cleveland.

A few birds are sometimes seen arriving from the sea, so it is likely that some of the passage and wintering birds originate in northern Europe, but the majority breed in northern England and Scotland.

Over 1,500 birds have been ringed, almost all as full-grown birds, rather than pulli, but so far only four have been known to move any distance. One ringed as a pullus at Graythorp Shipyard (adjacent to Seal Sands) in June 1930 and one ringed as a full-grown bird at Saltburn in September 1975 were both recovered in southern Spain the following January, another ringed as a full-grown bird at South Gare in September 1981 was dead at Heriot, just south of Edinburgh, Scotland, on 2 August 1983 and one ringed at Saltholme on 25 September 1999 was found dead in the Charente-Maritime region of France on 16 March 2000.

A pale brown bird with pale buff wings and tail was on Cowpen Marsh in May-June 1988 and April 1989.

RED-THROATED PIPIT *Anthus cervinus*

There are 5 records of single birds in Cleveland. They are: on Cowpen Marsh on 26 May 1963 and 24 May 1992; on Coatham Marsh from 15 to 17 May 1976 and 18 May 1976; and at South Gare on 25 September 1998, the only autumn record. Normally it would be assumed that the bird seen on 18 May 1976 was the same individual as that during the previous three days, however, that bird was ringed on Coatham Marsh during its stay whereas the bird seen on 18 May did not have a ring.

ROCK PIPIT *Anthus petrosus*

This pipit is similar to Meadow Pipit in that it can be seen in Cleveland throughout the year as a summer and winter visitor and passage migrant, but in much smaller numbers.

Approximately 12-15 pairs breed along the cliffs from Saltburn to Cowbar, and single pairs were known to have nested in the slag walls by Seal Sands in 1909, 1933 and 1940-44.

Slightly more birds are present in winter than in summer, approximately 5-10 being at Hartlepool Headland, North Gare - South Gare and on the saltings alongside Greatham Creek. About 20 can be seen frequently at Skinningrove. A few are present on the rocks below the cliffs from Saltburn to Cowbar in the winter months, but whether these are local breeding birds or migrants from the north and east is unknown.

Only about 10 Rock Pipits have been ringed in Cleveland, all as full-grown birds, but there are no known recoveries.

Unlike Meadow Pipit, the passage is more noticeable in autumn than spring, with counts of 11-22 in a day being recorded passing Redcar in October, but relatively few noted in March-April with no more than 5-10 on any one day. Coatham Marsh is a favoured spring passage locality and birds are occasionally seen at Scaling Dam.

The Scandinavian race *A.p. Littoralis* has been identified on several occasions, almost always during March-April.

WATER PIPIT *Anthus spinoletta*

The first record for Cleveland was one by Greatham Creek on 29 March 1956, but it is likely that this pipit has been overlooked more than most species; it is now an annual winter visitor.

Most records fall in the period early November to mid-April, birds occasionally being seen in full summer plumage in March and April. Most of these birds are on the marshes around the Tees, especially Coatham Marsh and the Dormans Pool – Saltholme Pools area. There are also numerous records from Haverton Hole, Cowpen Marsh and Scaling Dam, and occasional sightings from places like Seaton Common, Greenabella Marsh and Hart Reservoir.

Birds wintering in the region seem to be a more recent phenomenon, single birds having been noted since 1974, two in November-December 1984, up to five in December 1995, up to 17 in December 2000, 22 in February 2001 and 18 in January - February 2003.

YELLOW WAGTAIL *Motacilla flava*

The arrival of this annual summer visitor is quite predictable, the first usually being by Saltholme Pools or Dormans Pool, between 10 and 16 April each year. Departure probably takes place throughout August with a few seen in mid-September. The earliest and latest dates are 25 March (1966) and 3 November (1975).

After the first bird, many arrive within the next week or two, 30-50 regularly being counted on Coatham Marsh and between Saltholme Pools - Dormans Pool and Cowpen Marsh in the last few days of April and beginning of May, although 60-80 have been present on more than one occasion. However, since 1998, there has been a noticeable reduction in numbers in both spring and autumn. A trickle of migrants can be seen passing north-west along the cliff top at Boulby and Hunt Cliff at this time. Some of these birds continue northwards to their breeding grounds in Northumberland and around the Scottish border, but some remain in Cleveland, their stronghold being the North Tees Marshes, where about 20 pairs nested at least in the 1980s and 1990s. However, since about 2000, the numbers have declined to around 5-10 pairs. Also, up to three pairs have nested at Coatham Marsh, South Gare, Teesport, Wilton International, Longnewton, and occasionally other localities.

By mid-July numbers are beginning to build up at the autumn roosts, Haverton Hole and Hargreaves Quarry reedbeds being the usual roost sites. Over 100 birds are regularly recorded (and ringed) in August and early September, especially at the former locality, where at least 247 were counted coming in to roost on 3 August 1975 and about 300 were present on several dates in August 1981. It is likely that this roost draws birds from much further afield than Teesmouth. The regular use of North Tees Marshes during spring passage and the large late summer roosts makes the area very important for Yellow Wagtail.

In the summer of 1990, Longnewton Reservoir was completely drained and up to 30 Yellow Wagtails were seen there in August, a very high count for an inland location; the exposed mud undoubtedly attracted these birds and relatively large numbers of waders were also present at the same time.

Over 2,200 Yellow Wagtails have been ringed since 1977 (mostly at the two major roost sites) but few have been recovered or re-trapped. Recoveries include the following: one caught in September 1983 was present in Morocco as late as 8 May 1984; one caught by the Long Drag on 2 August 1987 was in South Wales on 1 September 1987; an adult at Saltholme on 7 September 1987, was found dead near Casablanca, Morocco, on 17 October 1990; a juvenile at Haverton Hole on 24 August 1985 was dead at Allenheads, Northumberland, on 10 May 1991; a juvenile at Haverton Hole on 5 August 1989 was present in Guadalajara, central Spain on 14 April 1991; and a juvenile at Haverton Hole on 11 August 1990 was recorded in The Gambia on 23 October 1992.

The history as detailed above concerns *Motacilla flava flavissima* but another seven sub-species have been reliably recorded at Teesmouth; the plumage and variants of this species are highly complex. All records refer to Teesmouth unless stated.

Blue-headed Wagtail M. f. *flava* is the commonest of the variants, having been seen in most springs since 1965. Virtually all records fall between mid-April and mid-June, although there are up to three records of birds in July, August and September, as late as 23 September (1965 and 1968). Three males were seen on 6 May 1900 and there were considered to be at least 10 around Teesmouth in the spring of 1979, four being observed together on Cowpen Marsh on 2 May. There is also a record of a single bird between Redcar and Marske on 29 March 1982 and one at Pinchinthorpe on 13 June 1988.

Sykes's Wagtail M. f. *beema* has been recorded in most years since three males were present around Saltholme Pools in spring 1970. At least one male bred in that year.

Ashy-headed Wagtail M. f. *cinereocapilla* was first recorded in May 1975 and has since been seen in June 1977, May 1979, May 1981 and April 1997. One was at Hartlepool on 12 May 2001.

Grey-headed Wagtail M. f. *thunbergi* was first recorded in May 1979 followed by singles in May 1982, May of most years since 1986, and 29 June 1982.

Spanish Wagtail M. f. *iberiae* has occurred twice; Dormans Pool on 21 June 1979 and Saltholme Pools from 19 to 23 April 1989.

White-headed Wagtail M. f. *leucocephala* is extremely rare in Britain, one being by Longnewton Reservoir on 4 May 1989.

Black-headed Wagtail M. f. *feldegg*: one was at South Gare on 9 June 2007.

Whilst the taxonomics may be subject to alteration and discussion, it cannot be denied that these Yellow Wagtails with various coloured heads are almost always beautiful birds and a delight to the eye.

CITRINE WAGTAIL *Motacilla citreola*

There are two records for Cleveland, an immature at Haverton Hole from 14 to 19 August 1994 (Blick 1995) and another immature by Dormans Pool from 4 to 7 September 1999.

GREY WAGTAIL *Motacilla cinerea*

This wagtail is very specialised in its breeding requirements, these being clean, undisturbed streams and rivers with mature trees in the immediate vicinity. Consequently breeding is restricted to no more than about 10 localities in Cleveland totalling 15-20 pairs. The stronghold seems to be Skelton Beck between Skelton and Saltburn, where up to six pairs have been recorded in recent years. Also up to three pairs have been noted on Easington Beck, Kilton Beck, River Leven, Wynyard and Crookfoot Reservoir.

By late July, a few birds can be seen moving around coastal areas and by early September there are numerous records of them flying over many places. As soon as cold weather reaches Cleveland, the birds feed by many streams and ponds, including parks and suburban gardens in towns such as Hartlepool, Middlesbrough, Redcar and Guisborough. Some birds can be found all winter in the breeding areas and nearby beaches at Saltburn, Skinningrove and Cowbar, so it is likely that those seen elsewhere include local young birds as well as birds from areas to the north of Cleveland.

Slight coastal passage in September-October and March-April sometimes involves up to 10 birds per day, principally over Boulby, but occasionally at Hartlepool and South Gare. Also 15 were seen at Guisborough Sewage Farm on 11 March 1985.

Approximately 150 birds have been ringed in Cleveland, but there are no significant recoveries.

WHITE/PIED WAGTAIL *Motacilla alba*

This is another example of a passerine that can be found in Cleveland all the year round, but at least in part it is a spring and autumn passage migrant as well as a summer and winter visitor.

A fair percentage of birds stay in Cleveland throughout the year, but there is a small passage of birds south in autumn and north in spring, the highest counts being 120 flying north at Boulby on 14 March 1991 and 50 per hour passing on 31 March 1997. One of three known ringing recoveries concerns a first-year bird ringed at Dingwall in Scotland on 15 August 1979 and controlled at a roost at Lackenby on 16 March 1981. This would indicate that some of the birds roosting in Cleveland in winter come from breeding grounds to the north. Another recovery concerns one ringed on Fair Isle, Scotland, on 22 April 1963 and found dead at Loftus on 8 May 1963.

At various times in recent years, roosts of Pied Wagtails have been noted at places such as Billingham Bottoms, Haverton Hole, Redcar Ore Terminal, South Gare and Teesport, involving up to a few hundred birds. Also, about 1,500 were seen to roost in the pipework of the Tar Distillation Plant at Port Clarence in December 1980. Such numbers are likely to be quite normal at winter roosts in Cleveland and obviously include birds from outside the area, since the breeding population is considered to be about 400 pairs.

Most pairs nest around farms and villages, though a few can be found in town centres. Pied Wagtails feed in virtually all open habitats and especially in urban, industrial and agricultural areas. Up to 100 birds could regularly be seen in the Guisborough Sewage Farm area in the winter months, but this site is now much less attractive.

At least 550 birds have been ringed in Cleveland, many at roosts, but the ringing recoveries mentioned earlier are the only long distance movements known.

The race known as White Wagtail, *Motacilla alba alba*, which breeds in Continental Europe, is a regular spring passage migrant around Teesmouth. Most birds occur in April and early May, although the earliest and latest dates are 16 March (2003) and 11 June (1975 and 1977), and in most years about 10-20 birds are seen. A bird or two is sometimes noted at inland localities, and occasionally, flocks drop in for a few hours, the highest counts being 23 at Teesmouth on 29 April 1946 and 17 on Coatham Marsh on 19 April 1975.

(BOHEMIAN) WAXWING *Bombycilla garrulus*

Numbers of this winter visitor tend to fluctuate dramatically over a period of years, only one or two being recorded in some winters and flocks of 200-400 in others. The Waxwing is well-known as an irruptive species, large numbers moving south and west from Scandinavia and Russia when good breeding seasons are followed by harsh winter conditions and/or failure of the food supply.

An invasion of this bird is usually anticipated by a few birds seen crossing the coastline in October and November, the biggest numbers building up by the end of the year, although a large invasion occurred in January of 2001.

Since the mid-1940s, over 100 Waxwing have been recorded at the end of 1946, 1949, 1959, 1965, 1970, 1988, 1990, 1991, 1996, and 2003 at places as diverse as Carlin How, Albert Park in Middlesbrough, Billingham, Portrack, Saltburn and Guisborough. During the last two months of 1959, 1965 and 1988 at least 400 birds were in Cleveland and probably a hundred or two more. Over 300 were in Albert Park on 10 November 1965 and about 600 were in central Middlesbrough on 27 November 1988, these being the biggest flocks ever recorded in Cleveland. In an 'average' winter about 35-40 birds are seen, yet for 10 consecutive winters from 1976 no more than five were noted, with the exception of 35 in the 1979/80 winter.

During the 1980s, the favourite locality has undoubtedly been Guisborough, especially along the disused railway line and in adjacent estates, although some birds occasionally appear in most towns and villages, depending on the supply of berries.

The earliest and latest dates are 2 October (1966) and 16 May (1997).

There are six recoveries, all ringed as full-grown birds: at Helsinki, Finland, on 2 October 1966 and found in Guisborough on 7 December 1966; ringed at Jossingham, Rogaland, Norway, on 12 November 1973 and found in South Bank on 3 December 1973, two out of six ringed at Hartlepool on 3 November 1974 were recovered, one near Helmsley, North Yorkshire, on 15 March 1975 and one at Toombridge, Co Antrim,

Northern Ireland, on 16 April 1975; one ringed at Acklam on 19 November 1988 was present at Monkwearmouth, Tyne & Wear, on 1 May 1989; and one ringed at Middlesbrough on 28 December 1996 was at Immingham, Humberside, a month later.

Four colour-ringed birds were seen in Guisborough in the 1990/91 winter. All had been ringed in the Grampian region of Scotland in November 1990, one being seen in Edinburgh in December 1990 before reaching Hemlington in February 1991 and Guisborough in March 1991.

A dead bird found in Albert Park, Middlesbrough, in December 1953 was considered to belong to the race *Bombycilla garrulus centralasiae* which occurs east of the Urals.

(WHITE-THROATED) DIPPER *Cinclus cinclus*

This bird is one of the rarest of Cleveland's residents, with a breeding population of about eight to twelve pairs: this is unlikely to increase because of a lack of suitable habitat. It is known to breed regularly on the stream through Saltburn Woods, on Easington Beck, Kilton Beck, the River Leven and occasionally on Marton West Beck.

It is not unusual for a bird or two to be seen in the Guisborough Sewage Farm area and on Billingham Beck during the winter months; it is possible that a pair nests upstream of both places, but possibly outside the Cleveland boundary.

There are also records of birds, mostly during winter months, at Cowbar, Hutton Gate, Hutton Village, Scaling Dam, Lockwood Beck, Skelton Castle and in Burn Valley Gardens, Hartlepool. A bird was seen to fly in from the sea and into the Fox Covert at Marske on 23 September 1972.

Nelson (1907) stated that birds had been seen on the rocks on the shoreline during severe weather, but there are no recent records of this habit.

A pullus ringed in the nest at Saltburn on 26 April 1988 was found dead 95 km to the south-west at Baildon, Yorkshire, on 29 November 1989, one of only 50 or so Dippers ringed in Cleveland. Also, a Norwegian-ringed pullus, ringed on 31 May 1993 was found dead in North Yorkshire in October 1993

One in Saltburn Woods in December 1988 and January 1989 showed the characteristics of the Continental race, known as Black-bellied Dipper (*Cinclus cinclus cinclus*).

(WINTER) WREN *Troglodytes troglodytes*

This little bird is very common in Britain and throughout Cleveland, being familiar in gardens and recorded breeding virtually in every habitat except open moorland and the cliffs and beaches of the coastline. The breeding population is estimated at about 3,000 pairs. Being widespread, virtually concolourous and resident renders the Wren extremely uninteresting in the eyes of some birdwatchers; consequently there are very few records available.

Small numbers are seen at the coastal watch points in autumn, but they could have flown from the nearby urban/agricultural areas, rather than from crossing the North Sea.

One bird ringed at South Gare on 9 October 1974 was controlled at Spurn, Humberside, five days later. One ringed as a juvenile at Wilton in July 1978 was controlled near Retford, Nottinghamshire, in October 1978 and one ringed at Elwick on 11 October 1986 was near Saltholme Pools 15 days later. A bird ringed near Loftus on 8 July 1989 had flown 383 km west to Castleblaney, Eire, by 5 November 1989. These are the only known recoveries/controls out of more than 3,200 full-grown birds ringed in Cleveland. Also, a bird ringed in the Netherlands on 19 October 1999 was in Durham 4 days later.

DUNNOCK (HEDGE ACCENTOR) Prunella modularis

This is another 'small brown bird' with an estimated breeding population in Cleveland of about 4,000-5,000 pairs..

It can be found throughout the year in a variety of habitats, especially on farmland and in parks and gardens around the urban areas. It is also a spring and autumn passage migrant, quite reasonable numbers sometimes being seen along the coastline. The highest counts are 50 between South Gare and Hartlepool on 22 March 1964, 36 at South Gare on 17 September 1969 and 100 at Hartlepool on 1 October 1998.

It is not unusual to see a small, loose flock of birds in August-October, at places where they do not breed and obviously 'on the move'. These birds have probably not come from very far away and, whilst continental birds may occasionally be involved, there is no proof of this in Cleveland.

Out of 5,000 birds ringed, the only interesting recoveries concern an adult ringed at Poole Hospital in October 1965 that was still there on the 1 January 1969, one ringed at South Gare on 25 October 1988 that was at Knaresborough, North Yorkshire, on 26 March 1989 and one ringed at Hartlepool on 5 November 2000 that was at Stannington, Northumberland, on 30 March 2001.

(EUROPEAN) ROBIN Erithacus rubecula

To most non-birdwatchers, this is the bird associated with Christmas and snow-scenes. Indeed there is an influx of birds in the winter, especially to the urban habitat, but it is also a common breeding resident and a regular passage migrant along the coast.

It is frequently seen in the gardens and parks of Cleveland and is widespread throughout the deciduous woodland as a breeding bird with an estimated population of about 3,000-4,000 pairs.

As a passage migrant it is regularly observed at the coastal watch points in April and September-October, usually in very small numbers, but occasionally in much greater numbers. Such falls always involve other species such as Black Redstart, Bluethroat, thrushes and warblers, generally indicating that Scandinavian birds are involved. Falls involving over 100 Robins have occurred in: very late March 1958; mid-April 1966, 1973 and 1986; mid-September 1969 and 2001; and early to mid-October 1951, 1965, 1979, 1982, 1988 and 2004. At least 400-600 birds were involved in spectacular falls in October 1965, April 1986 and September 1998.

The origin of the Robins that appear in suburban gardens in autumn is not clear, but Scandinavian individuals may well make up a proportion.

Over 5,500 Robins have been ringed in Cleveland, and this has resulted in several notable recoveries. Relatively few pulli have been ringed and there are no records of significant movements, but first-year birds ringed at Lovell Hill in July 1981, 1982 and 1988 had moved to Heysham, Lancashire, by late August 1981; Withernsea, Humberside, by October 1982, and Little Preston, West Yorkshire, by mid-December 1988 respectively. This indicates a slow southern or western movement of British-bred birds in autumn. However, another first-year bird ringed at Saltholme in September 1999 was at Penrith, Cumbria, in September 2000.

Birds ringed on the coast have shown some interesting movements. One at Hartlepool on 25 April 1973 was controlled in Jutland, Denmark, three days later and one ringed at Graythorp on 24 April 1973 was found dead in the Netherlands in October 1973. In autumn, birds ringed in October-November on the coast have been recovered in Algeria in the following October and Denmark in the following April. One bird ringed on an October morning in Marske Fox Covert had reached Seaton Carew by the same afternoon. One ringed at Falsterbo, Sweden, on 2 October 1990 was at South Gare 19 days later, and another, ringed at Sappi, Finland, on 20 September 1998 was present at Hartlepool 14 days later. An adult ringed at Guisborough on 6 April 1985 was found dead at Shelford, Nottinghamshire, on 12 March 1986 and one ringed at Boulby on 3 September 1988 was present in Birmingham, West Midlands, on 15 November 1989.

An individual with a white head was at Norton in January-February 1997.

THRUSH NIGHTINGALE *Luscinia luscinia*

There are five records of this bird, which has been increasing in numbers in Scandinavia during the last 20 years. The first was seen in Locke Park, Redcar, on 16 May 1967, being found dead next day, and the remaining four were all on Hartlepool

Headland, from 13 to 15 May 1985, 23 May 1989, 13 May 1996 and 18-19 May 1997.

There are also three other records, concerning four different birds, that were either Thrush Nightingale or Nightingale. They all occurred at South Gare, 10 to 12 May 1970 (a second being seen on 12 May), 25 April 1971 and 30 August 1986. All four of these birds occurred during falls of typically Scandinavian birds, such as Bluethroat, Wryneck, Red-backed Shrike, Greenish Warbler and Ortolan Bunting, but there were doubts about the specific identification.

(COMMON) NIGHTINGALE *Luscinia megarhynchos*

During the 20th century, there have been five records in Cleveland, whereas in the 19th Century Nightingales certainly bred around Normanby (in the 1840s) and may well have done so in other suitable areas in the 1700s and early 1800s (Nelson 1907).

The 20th century records are: a pair by Flatts Lane, Normanby, from 15 to 28 May 1932; one singing at Dalehouse, just south of Cowbar, on three nights from 24 April 1959; one on Hartlepool Headland on 7 October 1984; one at South Gare on 8 May 1988 and one singing at Ingleby Barwick from 26 April to 11 May 1995.

Four Nightingales that were not specifically identified have been seen at South Gare (see Thrush Nightingale).

BLUETHROAT *Luscinia svecica*

Since 1974, this passage migrant has been seen in 65% of the springs and 20% of the autumns. No more than 5 birds have been recorded in any one year, with the exception of May 1985, when at least 35 were seen along the coastline and May 1987 and 1994, when about 10 were present between Hartlepool, South Gare and Locke Park. These three localities are the best places to observe this bird, though one or two have been noted at Seaton Carew, North Gare, Coatham Marsh and Boulby in recent years.

Prior to 1974, most birds were present in autumn and the largest fall was in mid-September 1960, when at least 20 birds were recorded. Only four individuals were seen in spring before 1974, the first being in May 1967.

The appearance of Bluethroats is fairly predictable; misty or rainy conditions combined with an easterly wind between late April and late May and again in September and early October frequently produces this species as well as other migrants. The earliest and latest spring records are 24 April (1971) and 25 May (1995) and the corresponding autumn records are 16 August (1929) and 26 October (2004). All of the above are considered to refer to the red-spotted race *Luscinia svecica svecica* which breeds in northern Europe and is the commoner of the two races seen in Britain. However, the race of some of the autumn birds cannot be safely established.

There is one definite record of a male White-spotted Bluethroat *Luscinia svecica cyanecula* beside Dormans Pool on 7 and 8 April 1983.Three birds of the White-spotted race were released from captivity near Yarm in the spring of 1970.

Most birds stay no more than a day or two, although a few have been known to remain for 7-8 days in recent springs.

RED-FLANKED BLUETAIL *Tarsiger cyanurus*

The sole Cleveland record of this beautiful bird concerns one at Cattersty Gill on 25 September 2001. Details are given by Money (2002).

BLACK REDSTART *Phoenicurus ochruros*

About 90% of the records of this species concern birds along the coastline during spring and autumn passage, most of these falling between early April and mid-May and between early October and mid-November.

In most recent years, more have been seen in spring than autumn, South Gare, Hartlepool Headland, Boulby Cliffs and Skinningrove being favourite places, but no more than about 10 birds are usually involved. The highest counts at one site are six at South Gare on 12 April 1974, six at Boulby on 21 October 1987 and seven at Hartlepool on 23 October 2004. Occasionally none is seen in autumn, although up to 15 have been noted spread along the coastline in a single day.

Birds have also been seen in December, January and February, occasionally in July and in August 1976 at Skinningrove. A pair reared young in the Redcar area in the summer of 1986; breeding may have occurred in the Boulby area in 1990, fledged young being seen in August and in the Saltburn area in 1997, young birds being fed by a female in June.

Away from the coast, singles were at: Guisborough in October 1961, December 1965 and November 1978; Fairfield, Stockton-on-Tees, in April 1963; New Marske Reservoir in November 1967; Skelton in November 1978, April 1997 and April 2001; Billingham in May 1984 and April 1989; Crookfoot Reservoir on 10 April 1993; Scaling Dam on 30 March 2000 and 7 April 2005; Dunsdale in April 2003; and Margrove Ponds on 18 April 2003.

Almost all of the birds are in immature/female plumage, although adult males are noted occasionally.

(COMMON) REDSTART *Phoenicurus phoenicurus*

This summer visitor is one of the scarcest breeding birds in Cleveland. It requires reasonably secluded mature deciduous woodland, which is now a scarce habitat.

A few migrant birds are noted moving through Cleveland in late April and May, being seen in virtually any wooded area, such as Flatts Lane and Wynyard, but in some years more birds are recorded as spring and/or autumn passage migrants along the coast other than inland. Falls of passerines in these seasons generally involve Redstarts, especially during September. About 300-400 birds were noted in the usual Hartlepool-South Gare areas on 17 September 1960 and 17 September 1969, and at least 190 were seen between Hartlepool and Boulby in mid-September 1993. In most springs, no more than about 10 individuals are noted and in most autumns a total of about 20-40 birds are seen from Hartlepool to Boulby.

Newton Woods is the main area for breeding Redstarts in Cleveland; generally three to five pairs are present, with one or two pairs in some years at Loftus Woods, Eston Hills, Wilton Woods, Wynyard, Dimmingdale, Bousdale Woods and Birk Brow.

The earliest and latest birds each year are almost always seen on the coast, the first birds usually appearing in mid to late April and the latest in early October. The actual earliest and latest dates are 23 March (1986) and 15 November (1968).

Over 230 birds have been ringed. This has resulted in one long-distance recovery: a bird ringed at South Gare on 17 September 1969 during a big 'fall' of Redstarts was found dead one month later at Melilla on the north coast of Morocco. Two other birds have been ringed elsewhere and controlled in Cleveland: a full-grown bird ringed at Neustrelitz, northern Germany, on 13 October 1969 was controlled in Hartlepool 12 days later and a pullus ringed at Helmsley, North Yorkshire, on 24 June 1984, was controlled at Lovell Hill, due north of its birth place, on 18 August 1984.

WHINCHAT *Saxicola rubetra*

This summer visitor breeds in small numbers in suitable habitat in Cleveland and is a regular passage migrant on the coast in autumn and to a lesser extent in spring.

The principal breeding sites are Scaling Dam, Eston Moor and one or two areas of the North Tees Marshes. Also, one or two pairs are seen in most years at Lockwood Beck, Newton-under-Roseberry, Margrove Ponds, Guisborough, Haverton Hole, Teesport, Coatham Marsh, Billingham Bottoms, Birk Brow and Stillington.

While it is likely that there are scattered pairs of Whinchat in less well-watched parts of Cleveland, especially the moorland edges, the overall population is probably only about 20-30 pairs and seems to be declining.

The first birds of the spring are usually seen in the last week of April or first few days of May and are regularly present at the breeding sites before being noted on the coast. Since regular recording began, the earliest date is 19 April (1964), but there is a record of two at 'Redcar sandhills' on 28 March 1906. The latest date is 19 November (1989), although the majority have left by late September.

Autumn passage on the coast can be quite substantial when the weather conditions produce falls of migrants. The largest of such falls occurred on 17 September 1960, when about 100 were present between Crimdon Dene and Marske, and between 8 and 10 September 1995, when about 115 were seen along the coastline.

There is a regular post-breeding gathering in the vicinity of the North Tees Marshes in August and early September usually totalling about 15-20 birds, although 49 were counted on 8 September 1974.

Over 100 Whinchats have been ringed, but there has not been a significant recovery to date.

STONECHAT *Saxicola torquata*

In England, the Stonechat is quite a rare breeding bird along the east coast, habitat destruction being partly responsible for the decline reported in recent decades.

It has probably never been common in the Cleveland area. The known historic breeding or summering records include: the Elwick and Hartlepool district in the early 1800s; Eston Nab in at least 1900 and 1925; Cowpen Bewley up to 1949; between Dormans Pool and Port Clarence from 1969 to 1977; South Gare in 1971; Scaling Dam in 1975; Eston Moor in May 1984; and Boulby in 1998 and 1999. Stonechats probably bred quite frequently along the moorland edge between Scaling Dam and Guisborough in the past.

From 2002, Stonechats have bred at a number of sites including Hart Warren, Greenabella Marsh, Seaton Common, Hartlepool Power Station site, Dormans Pool, Haverton Hole, South Gare, Saltburn, Boulby and Scaling Dam. There were considered to be three pairs in Cleveland in 2002, 2003 and 2004, five pairs in 2005 and 2006 and seven pairs in 2007.

In the 1990s, it was solely a scarce winter visitor and passage migrant, (early October to mid-April), most sightings being around the Greenabella Marsh - Teesmouth Field Centre area, Port Clarence - Dormans Pool - Long Drag area and South Gare - Coatham Marsh with fewer records from Saltburn, Boulby, Redcar, Upleatham, Haverton Hill, Billingham Bottoms, Portrack Marsh and Scaling Dam. Only three birds were recorded in the whole of 1997.

At the time of its breeding near Dormans Pool in the 1970s, there were regularly six to eight birds during the winter and 12 in November 1975. Similarly, the breeding records since 2002 have occurred at the same time as increased numbers of birds in winter and on passage; 14 were at Haverton Hole on 26 November 2001 and at least 52 were along the Cleveland coastline on 17 March 2004, including 28 at South Gare and 17 at Hummersea.

The status described above refers to the British race *Saxicola torquata hibernans*, but there are eight records of single continental Stonechats of the races *Saxicola torquata maura* or *Saxicola torquata stejnegeri*. The first was at Hartlepool on 26 October 1960 and was only the second record for Britain, although nationally there are now about five or six birds each autumn. The second was a male, also at Hartlepool, from 13 to 15 May 1985, which was subsequently found dead. This constituted only the fourth record of a spring male in Britain. The records since then are single juveniles at: Seaton Cemetery from 9 to 13 October 1991; South Gare on 23 and 24 October 1993; Hunt Cliff on 16 and 17 October 1999; Boulby on 26 October 2001; and South Gare on 20 October 2004 and 24 October - 2 November 2004.

(NORTHERN) WHEATEAR *Oenanthe oenanthe*

This summer visitor is one of the few to be regularly seen in March and is frequently the first summer migrant to arrive in the spring. The vast majority pass through the area *en route* to breeding grounds to the north and west of Cleveland, but one or two pairs usually stay to breed. The return passage is under way by August with a few late birds usually being seen in October.

The earliest date is 11 March (1957 and 1977), although it is usually the first week of April before Wheatears appear in any numbers, the passage extending through to late May. The highest spring count occurred on 7 May 1976 when at least 320 were on the coast between Hartlepool and Marske, although it is likely that several hundred birds pass through Cleveland every spring to their breeding grounds.

Autumn passage is frequently less noticeable, numbers usually being less than 10, unless winds from the south or east prevail. The highest counts in autumn are 100 around Teesmouth on 1 September 1963 and at least 310 between Hartlepool and South Gare on 17 September 1969. Apart from odd birds seen at Hartlepool and North Gare in December 1959 and January 1960, and South Gare from 18 December 1999 to 4 January 2000, the latest date is 20 November (1978).

The breeding population is probably about three to five pairs, nesting being reported from South Gare, Teesport and the Seal Sands slag walls in some years, as well as parts of the moorland to the south and east of Guisborough. Historic breeding records include nests in rabbit burrows at Seaton Snook prior to 1829 and nests in the slag walls at Redcar about 1900.

Birds of the large Greenland race *Oenanthe oenanthe leucorrhoa* are frequently recorded in spring, generally in late April and early May.

Over 600 Wheatears have been ringed to date and there are two significant recoveries from this total: an adult male ringed at South Gare on 18 April 1975 that was killed near Knouribga, Morocco, on 14 October 1977; and another ringed at South Gare on 25 April 1998 that was in Morocco, on 27 September 1998. A male ringed on Fair Isle, Shetland on 1 May 1977 had flown 535 km south to Hartlepool by 21 May 1977 and an adult ringed at Kvisker, Iceland, 9 May 1996 was at South Gare on 20 April 1997, this being the first Iceland-ringed Wheatear to be found in Britain.

PIED WHEATEAR *Oenanthe pleschanka*

The only record for Cleveland concerns an immature male by Hartlepool Power Station on 6 November 1994. Details of this bird are given by Joynt (1995).

DESERT WHEATEAR *Oenanthe deserti*

There are two records: the first concerns a male at Boulby from 12 to 14 November 2000. Details of this bird are given by Mitchell (2001). The second was at South Gare on 29 November 2005.

RING OUZEL *Turdus torquatus*

A regular spring and autumn migrant on the coast, usually in very small numbers, although up to 30 have been recorded on days in April and May and 50 in October.

In spring, the first migrants are generally seen in the first week of April and the last usually in early May, although there are three records of birds in January or February and many sightings of birds in March. The latest date for a spring migrant is 31 May (1999). Ring Ouzels are occasionally seen away from the coast in April and May at such localities as Scaling Dam, Lovell Hill, Stanghow, Eston Moor, Hutton Gate and Roseberry Topping where at least 15 were present on 10 April 1961 and 30 on 23 April 1968. Presumably such birds are *en route* to their upland breeding grounds. Single birds have been noted several times in June in south Cleveland and a pair bred in the Guisborough-

Lockwood Beck area in the 1960s, 1975-77 and 1986 and probably in several other years. Additionally, singles were at Wilton on 10 July 1976 and Scaling Dam on 21 July 1994.

Autumn passage is dependent on the weather conditions and probably involves a reasonable percentage of Scandinavian birds blown off course. It can occur between mid-September and late October, although birds have been seen as early as 5 September and as late as 12 November (1994). Virtually all birds observed in autumn are along the coastline, although a few have been recorded in September-November in places like Guisborough Moor, Cowpen Bewley, Portrack Marsh, Charlton's Pond and Norton. The largest count was made on 1 October 1965 when about 50 were at South Gare and others were seen at several other localities in the area.

The only two ringing recoveries to date concern birds caught at Graythorp on 2 October 1965 during a fall of continental migrants. Later in the month one of these birds was identified in France. The other was recorded in Spain in October 1968. In total about 30 birds have been ringed in Cleveland.

The three mid-winter records concern singles at Stewart Park on 25 February 1900, Skelton from 3 to 10 January 1996 and Kirkleatham Reservoir from 17 to 24 February 1996.

One ringed in Hargreaves Quarry on 17 October 1987 showed characteristics of the Alpine race *Turdus torquatus alpestris*.

(COMMON) BLACKBIRD *Turdus merula*

This species is a common breeding resident in woodland, gardens and hedgerows, nests being reported from March to October. In autumn large numbers arrive from Northern Europe to winter in Britain, return passage in spring being much less noticeable.

In 1984, the total Cleveland breeding population was assessed at over 5,000 pairs, making it one of the county's commonest breeding birds. Some interesting records include: nests with eggs at Loftus on 24 December 1865; and in Stockton in January 1988; and single pairs using the same nest to rear four broods in Stockton in 1977 and New Marske in 1987.

The arrival of north European birds is recorded from mid-September to late November and in most years no more than 100 are seen on the coast on any one day, although it is certain many more arrive unseen. The maximum number recorded is 1,055 arriving at Hartlepool on 15 November 1969, while 1,000 were observed arriving at Graythorp on 24 October 1965.

Rarely are more than 10 birds noted on the coast in spring, although up to 50 were at South Gare in mid-April 1974 and 70 were at Graythorp plus 24 at South Gare on 7 April 1984.

At least 17,000 Blackbirds have been ringed in Cleveland in the last 40 years, resulting in many recoveries and consequently an insight into the movements of the species. It would appear that most local Blackbirds remain in the vicinity of their birthplace throughout their lives and many birds are recovered no more than a few kilometres from where they were ringed, the oldest ringed bird to date being 7 years. The birds that arrive in autumn and depart in spring are mainly Scandinavian Blackbirds, and would appear to pass through Germany and the Netherlands as well as south Scandinavia to and from Britain. At least one ringed bird was recovered in Russia the following spring. They do not always stay throughout the winter in Cleveland, although some probably do, as recoveries from Ireland and the west coast of Britain have been reported, including one ringed at Marske on 26 October 1985 that was on Bardsey Island, Gwynedd two days later. There is also a recovery of a bird ringed at Graythorp in October 1965 which was in the The Gironde area of France one month later.

DUSKY THRUSH *Turdus naumanni (eunomus)*

This species is one of the rarest British vagrants on the Cleveland list. It was only the second record for Britain at the time of its occurrence on Hartlepool Headland from 12 December 1959 to 24 February 1960 (Coates 1960).

FIELDFARE *Turdus pilaris*

While this large thrush is a winter visitor to Britain, more are seen in Cleveland during autumn passage (in October and November) than at any other time.

Hundreds are frequently recorded in favourable conditions, arriving from the sea on late autumn days, and many thousands probably pass over between early October and mid-November. An estimated 20,000 arrived at Hartlepool on 18 October 2001, 2,600 birds were seen to arrive at South Gare on 23 October 1971, 2,500 were at Hartlepool on 15 November 1969 and 1,600 were at Hummersea on 20 October 2004. The birds spread out as soon as they arrive, to feed mainly on agricultural land, but many continue to move south and west into other areas. Relatively few remain locally throughout the winter, though flocks of 100-200 can be seen in some areas. Some birds move into gardens in the towns, especially in freezing conditions.

The return in spring is less noticeable than the autumn arrival, although flocks of several hundred are sometimes evident in late March and April. If onshore winds combined with rain or mists prevail in April, small flocks of Fieldfares sometimes appear on the coast, as if they have arrived from the sea. This they may well have done, but after leaving Britain somewhere near Cleveland, only to be forced back to land by adverse weath-

---

er. The latest birds are usually seen in early to mid May, although they have been reported in June and July on more than one occasion.

A male was observed at Charlton's Pond on 19 April 1990 attempting to mate with a Song Thrush, a pair with three full-grown young was reported in Wynyard in July 1967 and one bird was heard and seen in a birchwood in the south of Cleveland in June 1974. There are several records of birds in August, usually involved with falls of Scandinavian migrants, but it is generally mid to late September before any Fieldfares are seen.

Over 150 birds have been ringed in Cleveland, but the only recoveries concern birds ringed elsewhere. One ringed near Bergen in Norway as a pullus in June 1944 was dead in Yarm in February 1945 and one ringed as a first-year bird at Kivach Reserve, Karelia, in north east Russia in June 1980 was found dead at Norton in January 1984. Another ringed in central Norway as a pullus in June 1953 was located just to the south of Cleveland in May 1954.

SONG THRUSH *Turdus philomelos*

U rban and parkland habitats hold the majority of Cleveland's breeding Song Thrushes, though deciduous and, to lesser extent, coniferous woodland also have some birds. Overall, the breeding population is thought to be about 1,500-2,000 pairs, being outnumbered by the Blackbird by about 3:1, but in turn outnumbering the Mistle Thrush by about 6:1. Breeding usually starts in April, however a nest with four eggs was found at Yearby on 18 February 1904 and two full-grown young were being fed by an adult in central Middlesbrough on 21 February 1990. The majority of Song Thrushes nesting in Cleveland probably stay throughout the year; none of the birds ringed as pulli have been known to move very far.

Many birds reach our coastline in autumn, principally between late September and early November. Over this period thousands probably arrive annually, but rarely more than 100-200 on any one day. However, over 1,000 were recorded at Hartlepool on 18 October 2001 and about 2,000 at South Gare on 20 October 2004. These birds are considered to be mainly of Scandinavian origin. One bird ringed as a pullus in Hordaland, Norway, in May 1974 was at Marske on 2 October 1976 and another ringed at South Gare on 7 October 1977 was controlled at Ameland, the Netherlands, on 5 October 1980.

There are several recoveries of birds ringed in September or October in Cleveland that have moved south or west including individuals to: the Calf of Man in November; the Algarve in Portugal in January; Co Down in Ireland; Bath in Somerset; Seville in Spain in February; and Amares, Portugal, in March.

However, there are other recoveries that do not seem to follow this pattern; one ringed at Thornaby in September 1955 was in East Lothian, Scotland, by 2 February 1956 whilst another ringed at Haverton Hole in August 1977 was recorded near Perth, Tayside, Scotland, on 7 March 1979. Another bird ringed at Redcar in December 1981 was found dead in Norfolk in April 1984 and one ringed at Graythorp in October 1968, which would be expected to be a Scandinavian or perhaps Scottish bird, was killed by a model aircraft at Nunthorpe in June 1969.

Over 3,000 birds have been ringed, nearly 20% as young in the nest (pullus) but as mentioned earlier, the Cleveland-bred birds seem to be quite sedentary.

REDWING *Turdus iliacus*

The penetrating 'seee' call of this winter visitor is a frequent night-time sound over Cleveland from early October to mid-November as thousands of Redwings arrive from northern Europe. Influxes of Redwings often include Song Thrushes, Blackbirds and Fieldfares at the same time, but the Redwing is generally the commonest of the four.

Although the main arrivals start in October a few birds are sometimes seen during falls of passerines on the coast in mid to late September, the earliest date being 27 August (1968). Normally, a few hundred is the maximum count for any particular day in autumn, although many thousands probably pass through the county during the stated period. If onshore winds and rain prevail, large numbers of tired and exhausted birds sometimes arrive, the maximum count being about 11,000 at Hartlepool alone on 7 October 1977. On the same day, 2,000 were at Lovell Hill and presumably a few thousand along the coast from Redcar to Boulby. It does not follow that more birds arrived in the autumn of 1977, just that the arrival was much more concentrated and visible than usual.

Very nearly all of the Redwings that arrive in Cleveland pass through, heading for wintering areas to the south and west, although flocks of up to 100-200 are sometimes reported in well-wooded urban areas, parks etc, the numbers usually depending on the severity of the winter.

The return in spring is much less conspicuous, though flocks of birds sometimes appear in April along the coast and a few occasionally stay into May. The latest date is 28 May (1984) although one Redwing was seen in Locke Park, Redcar, from 9 to 13 June 1967 and 14 July 1967.

Considering that many birds are seen in Cleveland in winter and that more than 100 pairs are thought to be breeding in northern Scotland, it is rather surprising that a bird or two does not summer in Cleveland more frequently. Birds have regularly been heard giving a subdued song on warm March and April days.

Over 2,000 Redwings have been ringed in Cleveland. Ringed birds have been found dead in the same winter as ringing at Minho and near Lisbon in Portugal, and at Oakley near Bedford. Birds found dead in the year following ringing include records from: Chelm, Poland; Newark, Nottinghamshire; and Cley, Norfolk, and one was controlled in the autumn following ringing at Gibraltar Point in Lincolnshire. Birds ringed elsewhere include: a pullus from Alava (Vaasa) Finland, ringed in June 1962 that was dead in Middlesbrough in January 1963; a first-year bird ringed at Epse in central Netherlands in October 1962 and found dead at Hartlepool in December 1962; one ringed at Kippax, near Leeds, Yorkshire, in November 1969 and found dead near Wolviston in January 1973 and one ringed at Pinezhskily Reserve, Arkhangelsk, Russia, on 14 July 1988 was in Nunthorpe on 4 December 1988.

A leucistic bird was at Margrove Park on 22 February 1993.

MISTLE THRUSH *Turdus viscivorus*

This thrush is a resident in Cleveland with a breeding population estimated at about 400-500 pairs. They nest mainly in the well-wooded parts of the towns and parks and in deciduous woodland, though a few pairs have recently taken to nesting inside the various industrial complexes such as Wilton, Billingham and the Hartlepool Power Station. In autumn, wandering birds can sometimes be found near to the coast on the Tees Marshes and occasionally at South Gare and Hartlepool Headland. It is also an autumn and winter visitor to gardens, principally to feed on rowan berries.

Nelson (1907) and Stead (1964) mentioned continental immigrants on the coast, the former recording large numbers arriving on 4 October 1884 and 11 October 1885 and the latter regarding "a few on the coast in spring and autumn" as likely continental birds.

Small flocks of 10-20 are quite normal in autumn in the vicinity of the nesting areas, although about 50 were known to roost regularly in Wilton Woods during the autumn of 1973, 55 were at Lockwood Beck on 26 August 1990, approximately 60 were at Skelton Castle on 22 September 1998 and about 70 were at Scaling Dam on 4 August 2001.

About 100 Mistle Thrushes have been ringed in Cleveland. A first-year bird ringed in Locke Park on 17 December 1977 was found dead 18km to the south-east at Castleton, North Yorkshire, on 16 July 1983. Also, one ringed at Ramsgate, Kent in February 1979 was dead one kilometre south of Cleveland at Great Ayton in December 1981.

CETTI'S WARBLER *Cettia cetti*

The only Cleveland record involves a single bird at Dormans Pool from 2 November 2005 to 11 April 2006. Details of this bird are given by Blick (2006).

(COMMON) GRASSHOPPER WARBLER
Locustella naevia

This summer visitor can be very secretive and about 90% of the records are of birds heard rather than seen. Consequently the first arrival date each year is relatively easy to determine with the earliest record being 11 April (1999). The males continue 'reeling' for long periods from the moment they reach Cleveland, through May and into June. Very few sing from July onwards, so departure dates are more difficult to determine; however, a bird was seen at South Gare on 21 October 1987.

In most years, a bird or two is seen at the coastal migration points in spring, but less so in autumn, the highest counts being four at Hartlepool Headland on 3 May 1969 and four at South Gare next day.

Whilst it can be very difficult to prove, it seems likely that the breeding population numbers about 50-60 pairs in most years, the favourite areas being along the Eston Hills from Lovell Hill to Ormesby, Kirklevington, several localities around the North Tees Marshes and Guisborough. 'Reeling' birds are sometimes heard at other possible breeding sites, such as Charlton's Pond and Coatham Marsh. Numbers have decreased markedly since about 1970.

Less than 100 birds have been ringed in Cleveland, but there are no significant recoveries.

SAVI'S WARBLER *Locustella luscinioides*

There are five records for Cleveland of this bird, singles at Haverton Hole from 23 to 29 May 1982 and 23 to 26 April 1994; Coatham Marsh from 24 May to 2 June 1986; and the Long Drag from 1 to 4 May 1995, all of which were single males. Also, a pair was by the Long Drag in late July 1994.

AQUATIC WARBLER *Acrocephalus paludicola*

A bird caught and ringed in the reedbeds beside the Long Drag on 12 August 1986 constitutes the only Cleveland record.

SEDGE WARBLER *Acrocephalus schoenobaenus*

This warbler is rather predictable in its appearance each spring. The first birds are generally singing by Dormans Pool or Coatham Marsh in the period 15-25 April and within two weeks many, if not all, of Cleveland's breeding males are delivering their characteristic song from prominent perches.

The Cleveland breeding population can be assessed with a reasonable degree of accuracy because of the relative scarcity of the species' favoured habitat, though occasional pairs breed away from wet habitats. The North Tees Marshes are undoubtedly the stronghold, with an estimated 30 pairs in 1980 and 50 pairs in 1986. Coatham Marsh held 11 pairs in 1975 and these had increased to at least 20 pairs in 1987. Other areas that hold a reasonable number of breeding pairs include Stockton Racecourse, now Teesside Park (about 12 pairs up to 1989, but now probably 6-8 pairs), Margrove Ponds (8-10 pairs), and Billingham Beck Valley (5-8 pairs). Charlton's Pond held about 5-10 pairs in the early 1980s, but none since about 1983-1984. Up to 10 pairs have been recorded in recent years at Coatham Stob, Bowesfield, Portrack Marsh, Upsall Carr, South Gare, Eston Moor, Preston-on-Tees and several other small  marshy areas. Singing birds have also been noted in agricultural habitat in recent years, though in relatively few places. The present estimate of breeding pairs is about 250, about half being around the Tees Marshes.

Apart from being a summer visitor, it is also a passage migrant in very small numbers. Up to four or five birds are seen at the coastal watch points in spring. Similar numbers appear in autumn on the coast, although it is quite likely that some of the birds that breed further north move through the North Tees marshes during their migrations rather than along the coastline. The earliest and latest dates are 29 March (2003) and 5 October (2001).

Teesmouth birds migrate south in autumn through marshland, as indicated by those ringed at Teesmouth: one was at Sandwich Bay, Kent, five days after ringing; another was at Goole, Humberside, seven days after ringing; one was at Radipole, Dorset, nine days after ringing; one was at Chichester; West Sussex, 12 days after ringing; four others were at Icklesham, East Sussex, 13-16 days after ringing; and one was at Thurlstone, Devon, also 16 days after ringing. Ten others ringed at Teesmouth (in August 1977, 1987, 1990, 1991, 1996 and 2003, and July 1993, 1996 and 2000) were on the west coast of France between seven and 31 days later. One ringed as a pullus in June 1994 was trapped in France in August 2000, six years old and at least six birds have been ringed in France in autumn, and then re-trapped in Cleveland in the following spring or summer. Some Teesmouth-ringed birds have returned to their natal site; one ringed in May 1972 was there again in July 1977 in at least its sixth year.

Over 4,000 birds have been ringed in Cleveland.

Status when ringed	Date and location of ringing	Subsequent sightings
Juvenile	Topsham, Devon 5 September 1971	Lovell Hill, 6 May 1973
Juvenile	Warrington, Cheshire 9 September 1981	Lovell Hill, July 1982
First-year bird	Belgium, 11 August 1992	Hargreaves Quarry, 13 May 1993
Juvenile	Inchture, Tayside, Scotland, 20 August 1992	Haverton Hole, 5 September 1992
Adult	Senegal, January 1993	North Tees Marshes, May 1993
Adult	South Gare, May 1994	Heysham, Lancashire, May 1995
Adult	North Tees Marshes, May 1994	Gosforth Park, Tyne & Wear, June 1995
Juvenile	St. Abbs Head, Borders, 1 August 1999	Billingham, 28 August 1999
Juvenile	Billingham, 28 August 2003	Kings Lynn, Norfolk 29 August 2003
Juvenile	Loch Spynie, Grampian 27 July 2003	Haverton Hole, 6 August 2003

A selection of the Ringing Recoveries for Sedge Warbler

PADDYFIELD WARBLER *Acrocephalus agricola*

Despite being an extremely rare bird in mainland Britain, it has occurred five times in Cleveland, singles being at the bowling green on Hartlepool Headland from 18 to 21 September 1969 and 27-28 October 1984, followed by one on Seaton Tip 17-18 September 1994, one trapped in Redcar Fox Covert on 18 September 1994 and one beside Redcar Golf Course on 31 October 1996.

MARSH WARBLER *Acrocephalus palustris*

This warbler is a rare breeding bird in southern Britain, and it is likely that those seen in Cleveland are wanderers from the European mainland. There are records from three principal sites: Haverton Hole (singing males) 27 to 30 June 1987, 13 June - 18 July 1993, and 11 to 15 July 2006; South Gare, singles on 28 October 1991, 22 to 28 May 1994 (with a second bird on 22 May 1994), 29-30 May 1998, 8 June 2002; and Hartlepool Headland, singles on 29-30 May 1992, 6, 8 and 10 June 1992, 29 May 1998 and two on 6 June 2002.

Singles have also been seen at Locke Park, Redcar, on 30 October 1991, Seaton Carew on 30 May 1998, and Hartlepool Docks on 31 May 1998. One was ringed at Saltburn on 5 June 2000. One was at Lovell Hill 6-27 June 2005.

All the coastal birds since 1991 have occurred in the period 22 May to 10 June.

(EURASIAN) REED WARBLER *Acrocephalus scirpaceus*

This warbler is now a regular summer visitor and nesting species in the Tees Marshes and other ponds and wet areas where there are Phragmites reedbeds, and an occasional migrant on the coast.

Historically a pair was noted annually up to 1907 at Linthorpe Brick Pond (eggs from there being in the Nelson collection, Dorman Museum), but the pond was filled in shortly after this date. The next indication of possible breeding came from Billingham Bottoms where birds were seen in May 1969 and August 1970, but there was no definite proof of nesting there until about 1984. A bird singing at Haverton Hole on 25 June 1972 was the next, but nothing more was noted until one bird was seen in August 1974. Breeding was suspected at Haverton Hole in 1975 and confirmed in 1976. A total of 10 adults was caught and ringed at Haverton Hole between late June and early August 1976, and four or five birds were heard singing. Since 1976, the breeding population at Haverton Hole has increased, albeit slowly to about 45-50 pairs, apparently being quite successful, judging by the number of young birds ringed each summer.

Since 1979, singing birds have been recorded in the Dormans Pool area, in the stands of Common Reed *Phragmites australis*, on the reclaimed part of Seal Sands alongside the Long Drag, Greenabella Marsh, Cowpen Marsh, Portrack, Bowesfield, Teesside Park, Coatham Marsh, South Gare and Margrove Ponds.

One or two birds also occasionally sing on passage at places such as Scaling Dam, which are not included amongst their known breeding sites. A survey in the summer of 1987 revealed 27 singing birds at eight localities, a survey in 1997 showed about 40 pairs at 10 localities, in 2004 there were at least 60 pairs and by 2007 there were about 200 pairs. Most singing males arrive in the first half of May, though the earliest date is 16 April (2003).

Coastal migrants have been recorded in 1965, 1966, and 1969 and annually since 1971. The typical number is four to five birds per year, although at least nine were seen in the autumn of 1976, and about 30 in September-October 1998. Spring passage birds are quite unusual, but the autumn records can occur any time between mid August and mid-October. However, there are two November records; singles at Graythorp on 15 November 1975 and Locke Park on 4 November 1984.

Regular ringing at Haverton Hole by D. Clayton in most summers since 1976, (and more recently by the Tees Ringing Group by the Long Drag) has resulted in over 2,500 Reed Warblers being ringed. This has shown that birds in this particular population at the northern edge of its British range are reasonably site-faithful, the oldest known bird being caught in August 1991 when it was at least 11 years old, having been ringed as a full-grown bird in July 1980 and re-caught in seven other years between 1980 and 1991.

Status when ringed	Date on location of ringing	Subsequent sightings
Adult	Lovell Hill, 12 August 1972	Ross Carr, Selby, 28-31 August 1975
Juvenile	Corsham Lake, Chippenham, Wiltshire, 9 August 1976	Haverton Hole, 3 June 1977
Pullus	Rostherne Mere, Cheshire 26 June 1975	Haverton Hole, June 1976 and Rostherne Mere in August 1977
Juvenile	Haverton Hole 28 August 1981	found dead in an army barracks in the Sahara at Tan-Tan, Morocco, 19 October 1982
Juvenile	Haverton Hole 16 August 1986	Stodmarsh, Kent 16 August 1988
Juvenile	Morocco on 11 April 1989	Haverton Hole on 14 July 1990 and August 1991
Juvenile	Chelmarsh Reservoir, Shropshire July 1997	Long Drag in July 1998
Juvenile	Long Drag, 2 August 1998	Slimbridge, Gloucestershire 27 August 1998
Juvenile	Isle of Grain, Kent, 23 May 2000	Long Drag 11 June 2000
Juvenile	Haverton Hole, 26 August 2004	Portugal 22 September 2004
Interesting recoveries for Reed Warbler		

GREAT REED WARBLER *Acrocephalus arundinaceus*

This southern European warbler is recorded annually in south-eastern Britain, but there are only four Cleveland records: a male that was caught and ringed at Lovell Hill on 19 May 1973, a singing male at Haverton Hole from at least 22 June to 4 July 1995, a singing male on Coatham Marsh on 15 - 16 May 2001 and one in a crop field at Hummersea on 19 May 2002.

BOOTED WARBLER *Hippolais caligata*

One at Hartlepool Headland on 7 - 8 June 1992 was the first Cleveland record and the first spring record in Britain. This was quickly followed by one at Marske on 18 - 19 September 1993, one at Hartlepool on 20-21 September 1999 and one at Hartlepool Old Cemetery on 10 August 2004.

ICTERINE WARBLER *Hippolais icterina*

Rather surprisingly this regular autumn passage migrant was not recorded in the area covered by this publication before 1965, although it is possible that some birds were overlooked.

From 1965, occurrences have averaged two birds per year, though varying from none to 10 birds in any one year. Almost invariably this species is recorded during falls of Scandinavian migrants, which, as has been mentioned in earlier species accounts, depends largely on easterly winds, often coupled with mist or rain, in the appropriate months.

More than half of the birds have been seen on Hartlepool Headland, with most of the remainder at South Gare. A few have also been recorded at coastal places like North Gare, Seaton Carew, Coatham Marsh, Locke Park, Boulby, Cattersty Gill and Marske Fox Covert.

About 50% of the records have occurred in the latter half of August, a total of nine birds being observed on 30 August in various years. With the exception of spring birds at South Gare on 8 June 1992 and 2003, at least seven, spread between Hartlepool and South Gare from 22 to 25 May 1994, and three at the same sites from 28 to 30 May 1998, the earliest and latest dates are 3 August (2002) and 29 September (1983).

MELODIOUS WARBLER *Hippolais polyglotta*

The only Cleveland record of this warbler concerns one at South Gare on 31 May 2003.

SUBALPINE WARBLER *Sylvia cantillans*

This southern European warbler is now an annual visitor to Britain, albeit in extremely small numbers, the six records for Cleveland are: a male on Hartlepool Headland on 8 May 1975; a female at Lovell Hill on 28 May 1978; a male at South Gare on 30 September 1983 and 22 May 1994; a male at Hartlepool on 7 May 1999; and a male at South Gare on 8-9 June 2002

BARRED WARBLER *Sylvia nisoria*

Since the first record in September 1959 at South Gare, this autumn vagrant has been seen in most years. Single birds were observed in 1960, 1962-1967, with three to five every year from 1968 to 1976. A total of seven was present in 1977, but since then up to four have been recorded in 1978, 1980, 1981, 1988, 1989 and 1991-2006. None was seen in the years 1979, 1982-1987 and 1990.

The vast majority of records are from the coast, 80% being from Hartlepool and South Gare. A few have been recorded at North Gare, Locke Park, Marske Fox Covert, Graythorp (the only record of an adult bird being seen here on 17 September 1967), Dormans Pool, Lovell Hill, Hargreaves Quarry, Marske sewage farm, Hartlepool power station and Cattersty Gill.

Most of the records fall within the period late August to late September, with the earliest and latest dates 8 August (1992) and 9 November (2000). The most seen on any one day was three at Hartlepool on 2 October 1974.

LESSER WHITETHROAT *Sylvia curruca*

This summer visitor breeds sparingly in Cleveland with a population of about 50 pairs, although there is evidence to suggest that there was a general increase in the 1960s. This is illustrated by the fact that prior to 1962 the only breeding records for the Teesside coastal plain area were from Normanby in 1955 and Stockton some time about 1900.

In the early 1960s birds were recorded holding territories at Wynyard, Lazenby, Pinchinthorpe and Wilton, this last area holding five pairs by 1972. By the late 1970s, birds were regularly recorded from up to 10 localities, quite a large percentage being in the Eston Hills area between Wilton Woods and Ormesby Brick Works, at least 13 territories being located there in 1985. In the 1990s singing males could be heard at the above localities, as well as Port Clarence, Wynyard Woodland Park, Lovell Hill, Guisborough, Thornaby, Yarm, Kirklevington and a few other places.

Small numbers are seen on the coast in spring and autumn, the earliest being 10 April, and in some years singing males on their breeding territory are noted before coastal migrants. The highest numbers seen on the coast have been 14 at South Gare on 9 May 1970 and 15 at Hartlepool on 29 May 1998.

The occasional October - early November birds are sometimes thought to be of the Siberian race *Sylvia curruca blythi*, and a bird trapped in Redcar Fox Covert on 23 September 1972 showed the characteristics of this race. One at South Gare from 9 November to 9 December 2000 was trapped and identified as being of the race *Sylvia curruca minula*, known as Desert Lesser Whitethroat (Money 2001). However, one trapped at Teesdale, Thornaby on 18 January to 24 January 2005 was considered to be of the race *S. c. curruca*, the 'normal' Lesser Whitethroat that breeds in Britain.

Over 700 Lesser Whitethroats have been ringed in Cleveland. The only significant records concerns one ringed at Theddlethorpe, Lincolnshire, on 30 April 1995 and controlled at Lovell Hill 8 days later; a juvenile ringed at Bootle, Cumbria, on 2 August 1998 that was breeding at Lovell Hill in May 1999; and one ringed at Dungeness, Kent, on 17 September 1990 that was also breeding at Lovell Hill, in June 1991.

(COMMON) WHITETHROAT *Sylvia communis*

Prior to the population crash in the 1968/69 winter, this summer visitor was reasonably common in Cleveland. An estimated 77% of breeding pairs did not return to Britain in the spring of 1969, this extremely high level of mortality being attributed to the continuing drought in the Sahel region of the Sahara Desert, the species' principal wintering area.

A Common Bird Census has been conducted on one area of farmland near Pinchinthorpe since 1962 and while the 1969 breeding season saw a reduction in numbers from the 1968 level, it was not as dramatic as indicated on the national scale. However, the decline continued locally through the 1970s and into the 1980s, but appears to have been reversed since about 2000. Quite large numbers of singing males have been counted throughout Cleveland in recent years, and the areas that hold the highest densities of breeding pairs are places like Cowpen Bewley Pond, Lovell Hill, Flatts Lane - Ormesby, Guisborough Branch Walkway, disused parts of Teesport and the Skinningrove valley-Hummersea area. The current breeding population is estimated at about 1,000 pairs.

Small numbers of birds are regularly seen on the coast in spring and autumn, although it is not unusual for them to be recorded at their breeding grounds before any are noted on the coast. Large falls of migrants in both spring and autumn never produce many Whitethroats, no more than about 15-25 being recorded at any one time.

It is usually the last few days of April or the first week of May when the birds are first seen and most have left Cleveland by early September. The earliest and latest dates are 10 April (1964) and 6 December (1950) although this last bird could have been over-wintering as there are no other records after late October.

Over 1,800 Whitethroats have been ringed in Cleveland. The only significant recoveries are: a juvenile ringed at Lovell Hill on 28 July 1980 was controlled near Santander, northern Spain, on 13 September 1980, a juvenile ringed at Guisborough on 16 August 1981 was dead at Morpeth, Northumberland, on 3 July 1982 and one ringed at Lovell Hill on 13 May 1989 was controlled at Titchfield Haven, Hampshire, on 9 September 1990.

GARDEN WARBLER *Sylvia borin*

This, the plainest of the warblers that breed in Cleveland, is quite widespread as a summer visitor, but fairly thinly distributed. It is also a spring and autumn passage migrant and in some years it is recorded on its breeding grounds before any are seen on the coast, usually in very late April or the first week in May.

The highest numbers are almost always observed on passage in autumn and falls of passerines along the coast between mid-August and early October generally include small numbers of Garden Warblers. Up to 30-40 per autumn is quite normal, although 70 were counted at South Gare alone on 17 September 1969, with perhaps as many at the other coastal sites on the same day. A fall of migrants along the coastline between 9 and 13 September 2002 produced about 60 at South Gare, 40 at Hartlepool, 35 at Saltburn and 20 at Skinningrove. No counts were received for several other areas on the coast such as Seaton Carew and Boulby, so it is likely that 350-400 birds arrived in Cleveland during these few days.

The earliest and latest dates are 10 April (1968) and 11 November (2000). Breeding is regularly recorded at many areas of woodland, including Flatts Lane, Wilton Woods, Newton Woods, Poole Hospital, Wynyard, Loftus Woods, Guisborough Woods, Birk Brow and Leven Valley. The majority of these localities are south of the River Tees, which holds most of the deciduous woodland within the county. The total Cleveland population is estimated at about 150 pairs.

Over 800 birds have been ringed in Cleveland, one at Redcar in September 1965 being found at Ushant in France 12 days later, one ringed as a juvenile at Wilton in August 1974 was controlled at Walberswick, Suffolk, in July 1977 and one ringed at Hunt Cliff on 8 September 1995 was in Norway on 9 July 1999.

BLACKCAP *Sylvia atricapilla*

Whilst this warbler is mainly a summer visitor, it is regularly recorded in small numbers during the months November-March, usually in suburban gardens. In some years, it has been recorded in every month.

The first of the summer visitors arrive in mid-April, singing males on their breeding territories usually being found before any are noted on the coast and occasionally none are reported along the coast in spring. By mid to late May, Blackcaps can be seen and heard at many places, their favourite habitat being mature woodland with some undergrowth. Reasonable numbers breed in Wynyard, Newton Woods, Ormesby Woods-Wilton Woods area and the Leven Valley. The present Cleveland population is estimated at about 500 pairs. This renders the Blackcap about three times more numerous than the Garden Warbler; this is very similar to the ratio given by the annual ringing totals since 1974.

As a passage migrant it is more numerous in autumn than spring, sometimes being the commonest warbler in fall conditions. It is also seen a little later than most warblers, being noted on occasions through October and into November. These late birds are thought to originate from northern Europe since they often arrive here with the northern thrushes. In falls of passerines in early to mid October, up to 50 Blackcaps have been seen at South Gare and Hartlepool and probably a few hundred of them arrive along the Cleveland coastline at such times.

The occasional birds that are seen during the winter months seem to favour suburban gardens, presumably because of the relative warmth around buildings and they are frequently noted eating apples, cake and other food, specifically put out for birds. Usually only single Blackcaps are recorded. However, up to five were reported at Hartburn in the first three months of 1983, 10 birds were ringed at Skelton Castle between 24 November and 31 December 1995, and nine were ringed there between 14 November and 20 December 2000. Extensive studies have shown that the majority of Blackcaps wintering in the British Isles come from southern Germany and Austria. (Benthole 1958)

Overwintering seems to be a relatively recent phenomenon, the earliest winter record being 1959. Nelson (1907) mentions no winter records but Chislett (1952) records the occasional bird wintering in Yorkshire since 1943.

Date and location of ringing	Subsequent records	Notes
Marske, 21 October 1967	Portugal, 17 November 1967	Shot
South Gare 16 September 1977	Nicosia, Cyprus, 21 May 1978	Dead
Minsterworth nr Gloucester 29 April 1978	Nunthorpe, 4 June 1978	
Seaton Carew, 12 October 1982	Belgium, 16 October 1982	
Bourne, Lincolnshire 19 June 1993	Skelton, 24 June 1993	dead
Errington Woods, August 1983	Spain, April 1985	
Monkseaton, Tyne & Wear 27 March 1986	Middlesbrough 23 December 1987	
Saltholme , 3 September 1989	St Albans Head, Dorset 25 September 1989	
Lovell Hill , 5 September 1992	Gibraltar, 15 October 1993	controlled
Lovell Hill , 30 June 1995	Wintersett Reservoir, Yorkshire 9 September 1995	Juvenile when ringed
Skelton Castle, 21 August 1998	Beachy Head, East Sussex 4 October 1998	Juvenile when ringed
Saltholme, 28 September 1999	Gosforth Park, Tyne & Wear 16 July 2000	
Vest-Agder, Norway 12 September 2001	Hartlepool, 27 September 2001	
Errington Woods , 21 July 2002	Gibraltar Point, Lincolnshire 25 August 2002	
The Long Drag 21 September 2002	Worplesdon, Surrey 3 October 2003	
Blackcap Ringing Recoveries		

GREENISH WARBLER *Phylloscopus trochiloides*

There are currently sixteen accepted records of this central and eastern Palaearctic vagrant.

Three additional records were accepted, but are now considered to be unproven. It is known that some subspecies of Chiffchaff can show a distinctive wing-bar, especially northern birds which pass through Britain in September, October and November and this fact had not been taken into account at the time. The records originally accepted, but now rejected are: 20 October 1961 at Redcar, 6 to 13 November 1966 in Locke Park and 16-17 September 1967 at Hartlepool. There was also a bird in Locke Park from 31 October to 2 November 1973 which was thought to be a Greenish Warbler for some considerable time but was finally identified as a Chiffchaff.

Date	Location
16 May 1970	Hartlepool
22 to 24 August 1973	Locke Park, Redcar
28 to 30 August 1986	Locke Park, Redcar
25 August 1987	Hartlepool
27 to 31 August 1987	Boulby Cliffs
7 September 1988	Hartlepool
31 August 1989	Hartlepool
13-14 September 1989	Hartlepool
18 September 1995	Hartlepool
9 September 2002 (2 birds)	South Gare
10 September 2002	Hartlepool
11 to 17 September 2002 (2 birds)	Hartlepool
10 September 2005 (2 birds)	South Gare
10-11 September 2005	Seaton Common
11 September 2005	nr Hartlepool Golf course
Greenish Warbler records (all singles except were shown)	

ARCTIC WARBLER
Phylloscopus borealis

The breeding range of this species extends further north in Europe than the preceding species and birds generally occur in Britain several weeks later.

The four records for Cleveland are of singles, in West View Cemetery, Hartlepool, on 4-5 October 1979 and on Hartlepool Headland on 6 September 1984, 31 August to 2 September 1991 and 19 to 23 September 1996.

PALLAS'S WARBLER
(PALLAS'S LEAF WARBLER) *Phylloscopus proregulus*

This Asiatic warbler, described as a "flying fairy light", is a rare, but increasingly regular visitor to Cleveland.

Prior to 1982, this bird had only been recorded three times in Cleveland at Hartlepool Headland on 12 October 1962, 9 October 1974 and 19-20 October 1981. Six were seen in 1982, the first one appearing on Hartlepool Headland on 9 October, being joined by a second bird next day. Also on 10 October, one was caught at Boulby Cliffs and on 11 October one was at South Gare. Finally, two were in Locke Park on 14 - 15 October 1982. The six Pallas's Warblers in Cleveland that year were part of an influx of at least 130 in Britain which is rendered all the more incredible by the fact that only three had occurred in Britain prior to 1958 and they breed more than 5,000 km to the east of our shoreline. The next were singles at: Redcar Lane Cemetery on 23 October 1988; North Gare on 12 October 1991; Hartlepool on 13 October 1991, 14 to 17 October 1993, 17 October 1994, 4-5 November 1994, 10-11 November 1995, 27 October 1997, 19-20 October 1999, 8 November 2000; Hazel Grove, Saltburn on 29 and 30 October 1992; Marske on 6 November 2000; Zinc Works bushes on 7 November 2000, West View Cemetery, Hartlepool on 8 - 9 November 2000; and South Gare on 19 October 1994, 17 October 1999, 7-8 November 2000, 21 October 2001 and 12 to 14 October 2002. Another influx in 2003 brought at least 13 birds to Cleveland: singles at South Gare on 13 October, 16 to 19 October (two on 17 October) and 21 October; one at Brotton Golf Course on 15 October; two at Boulby on 15 October; two at Hartlepool on 19 and 22 October; one at North Gare on 26 October; and one at the Zinc Works bushes from 1 to 3 November. At least nine occurred in 2004: one at Saltburn on 12-13 October; two at Hartlepool, two at Hummersea and one at South Gare, all on 20 October; one at Boulby on 21 October; one at Hazel Grove on 23 October; and one at Hunt Cliff on 30-31 October. The only birds since then are singles at Saltburn from 15 to 17 October 2005 and South Gare on 16 and 17 October 2005.

This magical bird has been seen in 14 years since 1988, and has averaged more than two birds per year. There are undoubtedly more observers in the field in the 1990s and 2000s, than in the 1960s and 1970s, but this increase in records must reflect greater numbers of these birds arriving in Britain.

YELLOW-BROWED WARBLER *Phylloscopus inornatus*

This warbler has been recorded every year since 1962, with the exception of 1970 and 1978 and is usually seen between late September and late October though it has occurred as early as 16 September and as late as 11 November. The only record prior to 1962 is also the earliest date, one at Boulby Cliffs on 9 September 1959.

The majority of the 300 or so records concern birds seen along the coastline, including Hartlepool Headland, Seaton Cemetery, North Gare, South Gare, Saltburn, Skinningrove and Boulby, though in part this may reflect observer coverage as much as species preference. In most years three to six birds are recorded, but eight were seen on 22 September 1985, 14 between 5 and 8 October 1986, 18 between 17 September and 6 November 1994 and about 30 between 30 September and 25 October 2003. Up to six were at Hartlepool in September 1967, October 1987 and October 2003, four were at Redcar in October 1967 and three or four were in Locke Park in October 1979, October 1988 and October 1990. However, these records are overshadowed by the occurrence of an estimated 76 birds along the Cleveland coastline in October 2005.

Single birds have been recorded away from the coast as follows: Norton on 25 September 1977; Charlton's Pond on 13-14 October 1981 and 30 September to 2 October 1991; Errington Woods on 1 October 1983 and Eston Cemetery from 2 to 5 October 1991.

As will be apparent from the above-mentioned records, most of the birds move away from the area within a day or two, although the first to be seen in the Teesside area in 1962 stayed in West View Cemetery, Hartlepool, for 24 days from 14 October to 6 November.

HUME'S YELLOW-BROWED WARBLER
Phylloscopus humei

This bird was formerly regarded as a sub-species of Yellow-browed Warbler, but has recently been given full species status. The three Cleveland records concern singles at Hartlepool on 11 November 1994, (details are given by Beck 1999), North Gare from 10 to 12 November 2000 and Skinningrove on 15 October 2003.

RADDE'S WARBLER *Phylloscopus schwarzi*

There are six records of this warbler, the first being a single at Hartlepool on 12 October 1988. The remaining records are all singles and at South Gare; from 12 to 14 October 1991, 3 October 1992, 27-28 September 2001, 16 October 2005 and 16 October 2006.

DUSKY WARBLER *Phylloscopus fuscatus*

This warbler has been recorded seven times, all singles and all except one, in October: Seaton Carew Cemetery on 24-25 October 1981; Hartlepool Headland on 11 October 1982; South Gare on 26 October 1985; Locke Park, Redcar, from 26 to 28 October 1999; Cattersty Gill on 25-26 September 2001; Brotton Golf Course from 28 to 30 October 2003; and Boulby from 19 to 21 October 2005.

WOOD WARBLER *Phylloscopus sibilatrix*

This summer visitor is the rarest of the breeding warblers in Cleveland. Up to 1995 the breeding population was thought to be about two to five pairs, singing males being regularly noted in the Wilton Woods - Eston Hills area, Newton Woods and Bousdale Woods and less frequently at Saltburn - Skelton Woods, Saltergill Woods and Wynyard. However, after 1995 it has not been proved to breed every year, and since 2000 there has only been one known nesting record, a pair with young in Newton Woods in June 2002.

The occurrence of singing males in April and May in suitable woodland does not necessarily indicate breeding, as these birds could still be moving north to their actual breeding sites; such birds have been recorded at many places, including Norton, Crookfoot Reservoir, Errington Woods, Newham Hall, Locke Park and Hutton Gate.

Most of the spring passage records fall between late April and mid-May, the earliest record being 11 April (1963), although in recent years no more than two or three spring passage birds are seen or heard.

Autumn passage is equally unusual, only one or two birds being noted in most years, generally at the usual coastal migration points between early August and early September. However, three were at Hartlepool on 14 August 1969. The latest record is 30 September (1991).

(COMMON) CHIFFCHAFF *Phylloscopus collybita*

When not singing, this species can be difficult to distinguish from Willow Warbler; these two warblers generally arrive each spring in the first half of April, occasionally being reported on the same day, but usually the Chiffchaff precedes the Willow Warbler by several days.

It is not unusual for one or two Chiffchaffs to be recorded in the last 10 days of March with the earliest date of 8 March (2003). These birds may have wintered in southern Britain or northern France.

By mid to late April Chiffchaffs can be heard in many wooded areas of Cleveland, the places with most breeding pairs being the Lovell Hill-Wilton Woods and Flatts Lane - Ormesby areas. A few are also regularly heard at Hutton Lowcross Woods, Grinkle Park, Newton Woods, Saltburn Woods, Leven Valley and Wynyard, and smaller areas of woodland doubtless hold a pair or two. Singing birds in April do not necessarily stay to breed locally, but overall the Cleveland population is estimated at 80-100 pairs.

By August-September, small gatherings of warblers are not unusual, as adults and young congregate before heading south. At such times parties of up to 30-40 Chiffchaffs have been recorded from places such as Lovell Hill and Errington Woods.

In mild autumns singing Chiffchaffs can occasionally still be heard and a few birds frequently linger into November. It is possible that some of these November birds originate from north of the county and occur after the Cleveland birds have already left the area for wintering grounds to the south.

As a passage migrant, very few are seen on the coast in spring, but reasonable numbers sometimes occur in autumn, generally arriving later than Willow Warblers. In autumn, perhaps 10-30 individuals are noted in September and October and sometimes into November. Birds of the Scandinavian and western Russian race *Phylloscopus collybita abietinus* are occasionally reported and, since November 1990, a very few individuals of the Siberian race *Phylloscopus collybita tristis* have been observed, principally in late November - early December.

Over-wintering birds are not recorded every year, although they are easily overlooked, and they can be found in urban gardens along with wintering Blackcaps. In some years, Guisborough Sewage Farm has held a number of birds. Up to three individuals have been seen here in late November and December, and other places with more than one record are Saltburn Woods, Charlton's Pond, Lovell Hill, Haverton Hole and Hartlepool. No more than three individuals have been known to be present in Cleveland in January or February

Locally over 1,200 Chiffchaffs have been ringed, and five controls have been noted for Cleveland. The first was ringed on Sark, Channel Isles, on 1 May 1976 and controlled near Port Clarence seven days later. The second was ringed at Marske on 2 October 1976 and controlled on Orkney on 5 May 1977. The third was ringed near Madrid, Spain, on 26 November 1976 and found at Lovell Hill on 23 April 1978. The fourth was ringed in southern Sweden on 28 September 1996 and controlled in Hargreaves Quarry on 13 April 1997. Finally, the fifth was ringed in Pori, Finland, on 27 Jun 2004 and controlled at Hartlepool on 20 October 2004.

WILLOW WARBLER *Phylloscopus trochilus*

With a probable breeding population of about 1,000 pairs, this warbler is the commonest of the summer visitors. It can be heard singing in virtually any area of woodland, low scrub and young conifer plantations, but not as much in mature or dense stands of conifers.

The mean arrival date over the last ten years is 8 April, although it has been seen as early as 31 March and is frequently first seen on the breeding grounds before appearing at the coastal migration points.

Work conducted specifically on Willow Warblers in Guisborough Forest in the four years 1980-1983 by T G Dewdney showed that most males arrive in April and most females in May. Also, both juveniles and adults have vacated the breeding site by mid-August.

An idea of the mortality rate of this warbler is given by the fact that 9% of adults returned the year after ringing and only 2.5% returned 2 years after ringing, although some birds will undoubtedly have moved to other breeding sites.

While the Willow Warbler is mainly a summer visitor to Cleveland, it is also a regular passage migrant, occurring in reasonable numbers on the coast in spring and autumn, in some years. It is likely that most of the birds seen on spring passage are British birds moving further north to their breeding grounds, but it is likely that the majority of the birds seen in autumn originate in north Europe.

The only recoveries of ringed birds to support this hypothesis are one bird ringed at South Gare on 14 August 1969 that was found dead at Wangerooke, East Frisian Islands, Germany, on 7 June 1970, and one ringed in Rogaland, Norway, on 4 August 2001 that was controlled at Hartlepool 15 days later.

Although over 12,000 Willow Warblers have been ringed in Cleveland, there are few significant recoveries. There are single occurrences of birds ringed as juveniles moving from Lovell Hill to the Guisborough Forest area in the following year, moving from Guisborough Forest to Ingleby Greenhow in North Yorkshire, in the next year, and being trapped at Beachy Head, Sussex, on 27 August 1979 and re-trapped at Guisborough Forest on 25 May 1980. Juveniles ringed in the summer at Lovell Hill have been controlled at: Retford, Nottinghamshire, one month later; Gibraltar Point, Lincolnshire, one month later; Naseby Reservoir, East Sussex, 21 days later; Blunham, Bedfordshire, 24 days later; in south-west France six weeks later; and Scout Dyke Reservoir, South Yorkshire, and West Burton, Nottinghamshire, two months later. Other records include: a juvenile ringed at Nunthorpe in July was at Beachy Head six weeks later; a juvenile ringed at Guisborough Sewage Farm in July 1986 was in the central Netherlands three weeks later; an adult ringed at Lovell Hill in May 1974 was recovered in the Seine Maritime region of France in April 1975; a juvenile ringed at Lovell Hill in July 1988 was dead at Texel, Netherlands, in the following April; a first-year bird ringed at Lovell Hill in July 1988 was dead on the Isle of Skye, Western Isles, in the following May; a juvenile ringed at Moorsholm in July 1988 was at Dungeness, Kent, in the following April; a juvenile ringed at Eigersund, Norway, on 4 August 2001 was at Hartlepool 15 days later; a first-year bird ringed at Glencaple, Dumfries & Galloway, on 4 September 2002 was at Billingham Beck four days later; a first-year bird ringed at Lovell Hill on 9 July 1997 was at Errington Woods on 16 June 2002, having reached the age of five years, a first year bird ringed at Ripon, North Yorks on 24 July 2004 had moved north to Lovell Hill by 8 August 2004 and one adult ringed at Hartlepool on 16 May 2006 was 148kms north at St. Abbs Head, Borders next day.

In spring, the highest recorded numbers seen on the coast are 80 in Locke Park on 20 April 1968 and 70 between Hartlepool and Redcar on 7 May 1976 and 9 May 1981.

The autumn maxima are at least 200 between Crimdon Dene and Redcar on 17 September 1960, 'hundreds' at South Gare on 10 October 1965, 100 at South Gare on 13 August 1969, 140 between Hartlepool and South Gare on 19 August 1979 and about 300 along the Cleveland coastline between 8 and 11 September 1995. In some years the peak count of passage birds is less than 10.

The earliest and latest dates are 31 March (1963) and 13 November (1993) although it is not normally recorded after the beginning of October and, unlike the Chiffchaff, has never been noted in winter. One was seen and heard singing at Ormesby on 6 November 1946.

GOLDCREST *Regulus regulus*

Quite a common resident in suitable woodland throughout the area, this little bird is also a regular passage migrant on the coast between late March and late April and again from early September to mid-November.

Goldcrests were probably less common in Cleveland before large areas of conifers were planted, though it may have been more of a garden bird than it is today. Certainly it nested in a Norton garden in several years around 1812. Its strongholds at present are Guisborough Forest, Grinkle Park, Wynyard and the plantations around Eston Nab. It probably breeds in many smaller woods holding scattered conifers, especially old ornamental gardens such as are found at Poole Hospital and Stewart Park. The total breeding population is probably quite stable at 500 pairs, though it is probably affected by severe winters.

As a passage bird, it is not always recorded in spring and even when it is, rarely are more than 10 birds involved, these usually being seen at Hartlepool, North Gare and South Gare, although 40 were recorded on 9-10 April 1987. It is always reported in the autumn on the coast, usually involving between 30 and 60 birds in total. The largest falls include: about 500 between Hartlepool and South Gare on 1 October 1965; at least 220 between Hartlepool, Seaton Carew and South Gare on 2-3 October 1983; about 200 between Hartlepool Headland and West View Cemetery on 23 October 1990 and 5-6 October 1998; and about 200 at Hartlepool on 7 to 9 November 2000 and 21-22 October 2001.

Despite the fact that at least 2,400 Goldcrests have been ringed in Cleveland, there are few significant recoveries. An adult ringed at Pitsea in Essex on 26 September 1971 was found dead in the spring of 1972 at Cargo Fleet, Middlesbrough; a first-year bird ringed at Bornholm, southern Denmark, on 8 October 1990 was at Graythorp 14 days later; and a first-year bird ringed at Falsterbo, Sweden, on 17 October 2001 was at Hartlepool five days later. One ringed at South Gare on 4 October 1992 was controlled at Leicester on 3 November 1992; one ringed at South Gare on 23 October 1993 was in Lancashire on 7 November 1993; and one ringed at Hargreaves Quarry on 12 September 1998 was in Leicestershire on 15 October 1998.

An interesting historic, but unconfirmed record, concerns a workman involved in the construction of the South Gare breakwater on 16 October 1881 who saw a Short-eared Owl land very close to him, then observed a Goldcrest rise from the owl's back and fly off (Nelson 1907).

FIRECREST *Regulus ignicapillus*

This beautiful little bird was not definitely recorded in Cleveland until 1966, although there are two earlier records described as 'probable' Firecrests: Marske on 22 November 1959 and Hartlepool on 23 October 1960.

The first accepted record was one at South Gare on 9 October 1966; the next one was in Locke Park from 14 to 22 November 1970 and the bird is now almost an annual passage migrant on the coast, with up to seven birds per year. Between 1970 and 1992 there was an average of three birds every two years, but since 1993, it has averaged over four per year, 60% being between late September and mid-November, and most of the remainder from late March to late April. Single birds have been noted inland at such places as Saltburn Woods, Wilton Castle, Skelton Castle and Cowpen Bewley Pond, principally in November or December.

The earliest and latest spring dates are 28 March (1981) and 12 May (2001) and the corresponding autumn dates are 18 September (1996) and 24 November (2002). There are also a few records of wintering birds: 25 November 1995 - 24 February 1996 (two birds

28 November-2 December 1995) in Hargreaves Quarry; 17 December 1995 - January 1996 in Locke Park; and 8 November 2003 - 15 January 2004 at South Gare. Perhaps a few birds regularly winter in the area and are simply overlooked.

On passage, Firecrests have been seen at many places on the coast, such as Hartlepool, South Gare, North Gare, Locke Park, Saltburn and Boulby. The most observed on any one day is five on 3 October 1972, when three were on Hartlepool Headland and two at South Gare.

The relatively recent increase in Firecrest records corresponds well with the northern expansion of its range through Europe. It is known to have bred in Denmark since 1961 and in Britain from 1962.

SPOTTED FLYCATCHER *Muscicapa striata*

Numbers of this summer visitor have declined quite markedly since the early 1990s. There was an estimated breeding population of about 150 pairs in the 1970s and 1980s, but is now thought to have declined to about 30 pairs.

Spotted Flycatchers prefer more secluded, mature gardens with parkland or deciduous woodland nearby, but may be induced to nest in less suitable areas by the provision of open-fronted nest boxes. Favoured locations are Upleatham, Lockwood Beck and Dimmingdale. The species used to nest in places such as the Stewart Park - Marton area, the Albert Park - Linthorpe area, Stockton parks, the wooded habitats in Norton, Yarm, Hartlepool and the woodland areas such as Wynyard, Newton Woods, Grinkle Park and Flatts Lane. No doubt a few pairs are still to be found away from the regular birdwatching sites, but if the present decline continues, the bird may soon be lost as a breeding species in Cleveland.

As a passage migrant, it is seen at coastal migration points in spring and autumn in very small numbers, birds usually occurring between early May and early June and between mid-August and early October. In most years no more than five are noted in spring and 10-20 in autumn, although in falls of passerines in late August to mid-September up to 20 have been noted on a single day. The earliest and latest dates are 12 April (1966) and 1 November (1981).

About 200 Spotted Flycatchers have been ringed in Cleveland, but only one bird has been recovered; this was ringed at Hartlepool on 31 July 1969 and recovered in Bordeaux, France, in October 1969. Another ringed at Ushant, France, on 2 September 1961 was in Middlesbrough in June 1962 and one ringed at Knaresborough on 5 August 1967 was at Wynyard on 30 June 1968.

RED-BREASTED FLYCATCHER *Ficedula parva*

This rare passage migrant has been noted in about five out of every six years since the first record in 1959. Most occurrences fall in the period mid-September to late October, although there are a few recent spring records.

The earliest and latest autumn dates are 19 August (1979) and 11 November (1983). The spring records are: singles at South Gare 1-3 June 1983, 16 May 1985 and 5 June 2000; in Locke Park on 4 June 1985; and Hartlepool on 11 May 2001. Over 80% of the records have been of single birds although two have been seen on a few occasions, three birds were at South Gare on 1 October 1965, at least four birds were involved in a fall of migrants from 14 to 17 September 1967 between Hartlepool and Redcar, and five were seen at Hartlepool on 25 September 2001.

As is normal with most scarce, but regular, passage migrants, the vast majority (over 90% in the case of Red-breasted Flycatcher) are noted at the coastal watch points, such as Hartlepool Headland, West View Cemetery, Seaton Carew Cemetery, Hummersea Farm, South Gare and Locke Park.

Only three have been known to move more than a few hundred metres inland. These were birds at Acklam on 12 October 1961, Graythorp on 23 October 1965 and in a Norton garden on 4 October 1985. Most autumn birds are immatures; only five or six of the 70 or so birds seen have been adult males showing the orange throat patch.

PIED FLYCATCHER *Ficedula hypoleuca*

This bird is a regular passage migrant on the coast in autumn when the weather conditions produce 'falls' of migrants, usually about 15-25 birds being recorded between early August and early October. Birds are also seen in spring on the coast, albeit in very small numbers and not every year; again their occurrence is dependant on the weather conditions.

Breeding has been proved in Newton Woods in 1983 and may have occurred in 1982 when a male was singing in June. Three singing males were seen there in 1984 and 1996 but only two in 1985 and 1986. Nelson (1907) records breeding in the vicinity of Loftus regularly prior to 1906. The only other suggestions of breeding concern a female found dead in a nest box containing a clutch of Great Tit eggs at Crookfoot Reservoir in May 1985, a male present around the nest boxes at Lockwood Beck for three weeks in May 1990 and a male singing by a nest box at Hutton Gate from 3 to 31 May 2003.

The highest count of migrant Pied Flycatchers was at least 150 between Hartlepool and Redcar on 17 and 18 September 1969. Smaller 'falls' have been recorded as follows: at least 50 in Marske Fox Covert on 2 September 1959; about 30 at Hartlepool and South Gare combined on 4 September 1965; at least 44 between Hartlepool and Redcar on 30

August 1974; about 100 along the coastline on 8 September 1995; and at least 73 along the coastline between 9 and 13 September 2002. The most seen in spring was between 18 and 21 along the coastline in mid-May 1993.

Inland records have come from a variety of localities, 70% of these being in spring and including Grinkle Park, Normanby Hall, Marton, Charlton's Pond, Lovell Hill, Leven Valley, Kirklevington and the Hutton Gate - Hutton Village area, where singles have been seen in six years between 1962 and 1982. Several of the inland spring records involve singing males, although virtually all seem to be on passage and are rarely seen for more than a day or two.

The earliest and latest dates are 16 April (2007) and 24 October (1986).

The origin of the birds observed on the coast is not known, though it is likely that many cross the North Sea from Scandinavia when appropriate weather conditions prevail although some birds may be moving to or from their British breeding areas to the north of Cleveland.

About 150 have been ringed. One ringed at South Gare on 16 September 1973 was killed four days later at Retuerto Baracaldo on the north coast of Spain and another bird ringed in June 1985 at Barnard Castle, Durham, was controlled near Loftus on 5 May 1986.

BEARDED TIT
(BEARDED REEDLING) *Panurus biarmicus*

Historic records include one of a male at Kirkleatham in 1841 or 1842 (Booth 1845). The first authenticated record concerned two males and a female at Ingleby Barwick on 6 and 7 December 1948, but it was 1966 before it was again reported in the county with two males near Dormans Pool on 3 December and four birds, at least one of which was a male, at the same place on 18 December.

Despite a general increase in breeding pairs in south-east England in the 1960s and 1970s, it was nearly 16 years before the species was seen in Cleveland again; three males which passed along the eastern edge of Locke Park and on to Coatham Marsh on 19 October 1982. The next record came quickly; a female on Dormans Pool from at least 1 April to 7 July 1983 that was caught and ringed during its stay. A male joined the female on 25 April 1983 and was last seen in the area on 2 October of that year. It is possible that the pair attempted to breed on Dormans Pool as they were always to be found in the same small area during May and June although no young birds were seen. The 1983 male had been ringed as a juvenile at Ousefleet, Goole, Humberside, on 25 July 1982 and had flown 104 km north north-west to Teesmouth.

The next was one at Charlton's Pond on 13 January 1988, followed by three records at South Gare, two on 22 October 1988, one from 17 to 30 April 1989, and a pair from

5 to 7 November 1993, the male being caught and ringed on the last date. A male was seen around the North Tees Marshes between 2 and 15 May 1995, and was trapped at Haverton Hole on 6 May 1995, when it was found to have been ringed in the nest at Leighton Moss, Lancashire, on 9 May 1994 and had remained at Leighton Moss until at least 19 September 1994. Also, one was on the Boulby cliff-top path on 24 October 1996.

Bearded Reedling is now an annual visitor to Cleveland in very small numbers, principally between October and April (and occasionally May), there being: three by the Long Drag from 25 October 1997 to 15 March 1998; up to five around the North Tees Marshes from October 1998 to March 1999; up to five in the 1999/2000 winter, up to three in the 2000/2001 winter; one in the 2001/2002 winter; up to eight in the 2002/2003 winter; two in the 2003/2004 winter; up to 11 in the 2004/2005 winter; up to 8 in the 2005/06 winter, but none in the 2006/07 winter.

The Phragmites beds alongside the Long Drag have been the favoured site in recent winters, although one was on Portrack Marsh on 15 October 1998 and up to three have been seen at Coatham Marsh in recent years, but rarely staying for more than a few days.

LONG-TAILED TIT *Aegithalos caudatus*

Whilst this tit is widespread in Cleveland, it is not particularly numerous, but can be found in many areas throughout the year.

Breeding pairs are usually in their territories by March, favoured areas in recent years including Lovell Hill - Wilton Woods, Flatts Lane - Ormesby, Errington Woods, Skelton Castle - Upleatham, Hutton Lowcross Woods, Slapewath, Leven Valley, Wynyard Woodland Park and Wynyard.

Small copses and overgrown, disused railway lines also hold scattered pairs and the Cleveland population is considered to be about 500-600 pairs. Breeding birds can be rather difficult to locate, but as soon as the young have fledged, noisy family parties are quite easy to find. Such parties are apparent from June-July onwards with individual family parties tending to join up with others, up to 50 birds being seen together on occasion.

In September and October, wandering birds can be observed anywhere, including along the coastline. Small parties have been seen on Hartlepool Headland, at Seaton Carew, North Gare bushes, Long Drag, South Gare, Locke Park, Marske Fox Covert and Boulby Cliffs. It is almost certain that these coastal records involve local wanderers rather than continental birds. However, a bird was seen to arrive from the sea at Hartlepool on 25 October 1989. The biggest flocks reported close to the coast are 31 in Locke Park on 23 October 1983 and at least 50 on Hartlepool Headland on 8 October 2000. Birds are also seen in the well-wooded parts of towns and gardens in autumn and occasionally flying over towns such as Middlesbrough and Guisborough.

Towards winter this bird is inclined to mix with other tits as well as species such as Treecreeper and Goldcrest. It is less frequently recorded in gardens taking food in the manner of Great and Blue Tit, although Long-tailed Tit has been noted feeding on bird-tables at places like Hartburn, Skelton Castle and Hutton Gate during the winter months. Long-tailed Tits tend to suffer more in severe winters than those species that regularly visit bird-tables.

At least 2,700 Long-tailed Tits have been ringed in Cleveland, but the only birds known to have moved any distance are: one ringed at Redcar on 30 June 1973 was at Spurn, Humberside, on 23 October 1973; one ringed at Ebchester, Co Durham, on 27 September 1989 was at Cattersty Pond on 29 October 1990; and one ringed at Skelton Castle on 17 January 2000 was at Bridlington, North Yorkshire, on 15 January 2001.

The above details relate to the British race *Aegithalos caudatus rosaceus*, but a white-headed bird that may have been an individual of the north European race *Aegithalos caudatus caudatus* was reported at Skinningrove on 13 October 2002.

MARSH TIT *Poecile palustris*

Separation of Marsh Tit and Willow Tit can be quite difficult, however, both are quite localised in Cleveland and are rarely seen together.

The Marsh Tit prefers drier habitats than the Willow Tit in the summer but in winter roving tit flocks can be seen almost anywhere, and Marsh Tits are more often seen in such flocks than are Willow Tits.

The Cleveland population is estimated at about 80-90 pairs, breeding being regular in many scattered small areas of woodland, including Wynyard, Elton, Kirklevington, Yarm, Newton Woods, Skelton Woods, Upleatham, Saltburn Woods, Flatts Lane, Leven Valley, Grinkle Park, Errington Woods, Dalton Piercy, Hart Station and Wolviston.

Wherever flocks of tits wander in winter, one or two Marsh Tits may be found, though 10 were counted in Saltburn Woods on 9 December 1984. Also, two were on Hartlepool Headland on 11 October 1985.

At least 150 Marsh Tits have been ringed in Cleveland but none has been known to move very far from the ringing site.

WILLOW TIT *Poecile montanus*

Like the very similar Marsh Tit, this bird is rather scarce in Cleveland but is probably under-recorded. It prefers damp areas of woodland, a fairly scarce habitat. However, it does occasionally visit bird tables and feeders in urban gardens.

The breeding population is probably quite similar to that of Marsh Tit, about 50-70 pairs, but nearly three times as many Willow Tits have been ringed in Cleveland. The reason for this is not apparent, though Willow Tits are more likely to frequent dense hawthorn scrub such as that found at Graythorp and Lovell Hill in which it is relatively easy to catch birds for ringing. One ringed at Guisborough in August 1986 was controlled 7 km away at Errington Woods in March 1987, and another ringed at Lovell Hill in June 1989 was found 8 km away at Great Ayton in July 1990.

The largest number seen together is eight at Lovell Hill on 2 August 1969. This no doubt represented a family party, or perhaps two.

Breeding probably occurs annually at Yearby Bank, Lovell Hill, Wilton Woods, Poole Hospital, Flatts Lane, Margrove Ponds, Court Green Woods, Marton, Wynyard Woodland Park, Wynyard, Crookfoot Reservoir, Kilton Woods and Wolviston.

COAL TIT *Periparus ater*

With an estimated breeding population of about 500-600 pairs, this bird is one of very few that seem to have benefited from the planting of large areas of conifers. In some areas it is one of the commonest breeding birds, Guisborough Forest, Westworth Woods, Grinkle Park, Eston Nab and parts of Wynyard being favoured.

Areas of mixed deciduous/conifer woodland also hold some birds, especially Errington Woods, Poole Hospital, etc. and it is likely that, wherever a few mature conifers are present in parkland or deciduous woodland, Coal Tits will breed.

Birds begin to disperse from late August onwards, frequently being seen in towns and gardens away from the breeding areas. In most years a bird or two is noted along the coast between mid-September and early November, although four were at South Gare on 3 April 2004. Favoured coastal locations are Locke Park and Marske Fox Covert although birds have been seen at Hartlepool Headland, North Gare, Seaton Carew Cemetery and Boulby Cliffs. Rarely are more than one or two birds involved though 15 were around Redcar on 18 October 1957, six were at Boulby on 4 October 2001 and six were on Hartlepool Headland on 4 October 2003. Most, if not all, are likely to have wandered from nearby breeding sites rather than crossed the North Sea from northern Europe.

Approximately 2,500 birds have been ringed in Cleveland; the only bird known to have travelled any distance was ringed at Fairfield, Stockton, on 25 October 1985 and found dead 107 km south at Almondsbury, near Huddersfield, West Yorkshire, on 30 April 1986. Another, ringed in Stockton in October 1986, had moved 41 km east south east to Grosmont, North Yorkshire, by April 1987 and one ringed at Skelton Castle in February 1998 was 58 km west at Redford, Co. Durham, in January 1999.

BLUE TIT *Cyanistes caeruleus*

This is one of relatively few birds that can be readily attracted to almost any garden by the provision of a string bag containing nuts.

The provision of a suitable box will frequently induce Blue Tits to nest, especially if placed close to trees. Indeed, a fairly high proportion of Cleveland Blue Tits nest in garden nest boxes, with most of the remainder in deciduous woodland. A few breed in coniferous woodland and in isolated large trees on farmland. The usual clutch is 7-12, but a nest at Kirkleatham in 1902 contained 24 eggs (Nelson 1907). The Cleveland breeding population is estimated at about 4,000 pairs.

After the breeding season, the dispersal of the birds generally includes some seen along the coastline, although birds of the continental race are also occasionally reported. Up to 40 Blue Tits are quite regularly observed on Hartlepool Headland with similar numbers at Seaton Carew, Locke Park and Boulby. However, all of these places are close to breeding areas so the birds are probably local in origin. Only South Gare is sufficiently distant from the nearest breeding Blue Tits to show real migration and relatively few birds are noted here.

Wandering tit flocks seen in autumn and winter can be found in almost every area of woodland and Blue Tits generally outnumber all of the other tit species. A leucistic bird was ringed at Skelton Castle on 7 November 1996.

Over 24,000 Blue Tits have been ringed in Cleveland, more than any other bird on the Cleveland list. Consequently, there are a good number of recoveries, although a high percentage of these have not moved far. No pullus ringed in Cleveland has been known to move very far, but first year birds ringed in autumn have been found four months later in Northumberland, in the following spring at Houghton-le-Spring, and Hamsterley Forest, Durham, Hutton Rudby and Grosmont, North Yorkshire, and Leeds, West Yorkshire, and within Cleveland up to three years after ringing. Blue Tits ringed in winter in Cleveland have been found at: Eastbourne, East Sussex; Swarland and Hexham, Northumberland, in the following winter; and in a nest box at Ripley, North Yorkshire, in the following spring. Also, individuals ringed in March are known to have flown up to 26km in four days.

Birds ringed as pulli at Easby, Grosmont and Kildale, North Yorkshire, and Gosforth, Tyne & Wear, have been found in Cleveland in the following autumn and winter. Also, one ringed at Spurn in October 1985 was at Guisborough on 2 April 1986, one ringed at Bilton-in-Ainsty, North Yorkshire, on 11 March 1986 was at Guisborough on 2 April 1986, one ringed at Brierley, South Yorkshire, in September 1985 was at Wilton on 15 December 1986 and one ringed at Prudhoe, Northumberland, on 24 September 1994 was at Hart on 23 January 1996.

As can be seen from the above recoveries and controls, the movements of this species are quite complex, birds not always moving south in autumn and north in spring as one might expect.

GREAT TIT *Parus major*

In habits and habitat, this tit is similar to the Blue Tit, but is generally numerically scarcer. It breeds in the same places as the Blue Tit but for every 2 pairs of Great Tit there are 4 pairs of Blue Tits giving a breeding population of about 2,000 pairs. It can be attracted to gardens by the provision of peanuts, but in lesser numbers.

It also nests in boxes in gardens and parks, but is equally inclined to nest in natural holes in deciduous and mixed woodland. After the breeding season, the appearance of one or two birds on the coast is predictable, but never in the numbers that Blue Tits attain. Seaton Carew Cemetery and Locke Park are favoured localities, both of which are close enough to local breeding sites to be visited by wandering birds in autumn. However, it is quite scarce at South Gare, and two seen on the Seal Sands peninsula in March 1986 were in a very unusual habitat.

Winter flocks of tits almost always include some Great Tits, up to 40-50 having been recorded as maxima in recent years, though a flock of 85 in Wynyard on 1 January 1986 was probably exceptional.

About 10,000 Great Tits have been ringed in Cleveland and the significant recoveries to date include birds ringed in Hartlepool in January 1987 that were controlled at Dunsdale in late January and early February 1988; ringed at Saltburn in January 1987 that had reached Grosmont, North Yorkshire, 3 weeks later; ringed at Marton in December 1985 and controlled at Old Malton, North Yorkshire, in March 1986; ringed in Newton Woods in June 1987 and controlled at Scarborough, North Yorkshire, in April 1988; ringed at Saltburn in November 1993 and controlled at Grosmont, North Yorkshire, in February 1994; and ringed at Pickering, North Yorkshire, in December 1999 and controlled at Skelton Castle in February 2000.

The prize for furthest distance travelled goes to one caught at Skelton Castle on 25 February 2000 that had been ringed in Kaliningrad, Russia, on 24 September 1999, 1,380 km to the east, and 154 days earlier. This is the first Russian-ringed Great Tit to be caught in Britain, and assuming it travelled in a straight line, averaged 9kms per day, quite fast compared to the Yorkshire recoveries, some of which managed 1km per day.

(WOOD) NUTHATCH *Sitta europaea*

This bird is a breeding resident in Cleveland, albeit in very small numbers. It has a tendency to breed in one area for a few years only to disappear completely and then re-appear in the same area some years later.

In the first few years of the 20th century, it was known to nest in Wynyard, Grinkle Park, Wilton and Saltburn and had been shot at Elton in about 1895. More recently, it has certainly nested in Wynyard from about 1970 and possibly since 1961; Stockton in 1976; Kirklevington from 1977; Stewart Park from 1979 to 1983 and again from 2001; Normanby Hall from 1979; Eaglescliffe from 1985; Hartburn in 1986 and from 2002; Saltburn Woods from 1990; Hutton Village from about 1992; Skelton Castle from 1994; Wilton Village from about 1995 and possibly since 1985; and Upleatham from 1999.

Wandering birds are occasionally seen at a few other places such as Yarm, Poole Hospital, Guisborough, Ward Jackson Park in Hartlepool, Lockwood Beck, and Grinkle Park, where it may occasionally breed.

In total, the population is about 25 pairs, a significant increase from about 10 pairs in the 1980s.

Migrating birds have been noted at Boulby Cliffs on 20 April 1996 and 24 June 1997 and on Hartlepool Headland on 9 August 2004 and 5 May 2007.

At least 60 birds have been ringed in Cleveland, but none has been known to move any distance.

(EURASIAN) TREECREEPER *Certhia familiaris*

A resident in Cleveland, this bird is widespread, breeding in deciduous and mixed woodland as well as in parkland and some of the more arboreal suburban gardens. The overall population is estimated at about 250 pairs though very cold winters probably reduce the population from time to time.

Single birds are occasionally seen along the coastline in spring and autumn, especially in Marske Fox Covert, Locke Park and Graythorp bushes, though they are almost certainly no more than wandering local birds. Singles at Hartlepool Headland in September 1961 and three times in autumn 1990, and South Gare in October 1961, April 1964 and October 1998 might have been continental birds.

A wandering flock of tits sometimes includes a Treecreeper or two in the autumn and winter months, though up to eight have been observed in Saltburn Woods and up to 14 in Wynyard in recent years.

About 350 birds have been ringed in Cleveland, almost all as full-grown birds, but there are no known recoveries.

(EURASIAN) PENDULINE TIT *Remiz pendulinus*

This southern and eastern European bird is now recorded annually in Britain and has been recorded three times in Cleveland. The first two were singles trapped, at Haverton Hole on 17 July 1992 and Hargreaves Quarry on 8 May 1993, this second bird still being present next day. The third record concerns two males at Portrack Marsh between 23 March and 6 April 2006 and also seen again at Dormans Pool on 9 April 2006.

(EURASIAN) GOLDEN ORIOLE *Oriolus oriolus*

There are 13 records for Cleveland of this European bird. It breeds in quite small numbers in south-east England and in recent years has been seen slightly more frequently in the northern half of England.

The first record was of a male in the Greatham - Newton Bewley area on 17 May 1929, followed by one singing near Guisborough on 23 May 1971. More recent records are: a male found several days dead by North Gare on 19 May 1984; a male at South Gare on 15 May 1985; a female near the Long Drag on 27 May 1985; two at Boulby on 24 May 1992; one at Nunthorpe on 8 June 1992; one at Flatts Lane on 9 June 1992; a male on the Long Drag on 30 April 1994; two on the Long Drag on 29 May 1995; one on the Brinefields on 19 June 1995; a male in Hargreaves Quarry from 14 to 16 May 1999; and one at South Gare on 24 - 25 May 2001.

All records fall between 30 April and 19 June with most birds seen in the second half of May.

RED-BACKED SHRIKE *Lanius collurio*

This bird used to breed in the area encompassed by Cleveland, but it is now only an almost annual spring and autumn migrant.

There has been a steady decline throughout England, due in part to habitat destruction, and this bird may have bred in various places locally prior to the 19th century, the only known breeding records being nests found near Redcar on two occasions about 1870 and at Marton in June 1898 (Nelson 1907).

Since 1966, at least one bird has been noted in Cleveland every year, apart from 1975 and 1989, and there has been an average of four birds per year over this 40-year period. The great majority are seen at the well-watched localities of Hartlepool and South Gare, but others have also been recorded at North Gare, Seaton Carew, Lockwood Beck, Seaton Snook, Stanghow, Scaling Dam, Saltburn, Locke Park, Coatham Marsh,

Graythorp, Lovell Hill, Marske Fox Covert, Marske, Hunt Cliff, Boulby, Hummersea, Margrove Ponds, the Reclamation Pond, Kirkleatham Reservoir, Eston Moor, Charlton's Pond, Flatts Lane, South Bank, and Skinningrove.

The records since 1966 are split almost equally between spring and autumn with most being in the periods 8 to 22 May and 18 August to 25 September, although the earliest and latest dates are 6 May (1972) and 9 June (1987) in spring and 3 August (2002) and 29 October (2000) in autumn. There is also a late record of a male at South Gare on 21 November 1954. Most are of single birds, however 13 were observed in Cleveland between 7 and 20 May 1985, all but two being on the coast.

LESSER GREY SHRIKE *Lanius minor*

There is only one record of this southern and eastern European shrike, a bird in the Hargreaves Quarry area from 29 June to 3 July 1974.

GREAT GREY SHRIKE *Lanius excubitor*

This is probably one of the few species whose status in Cleveland has not changed over the last hundred years. It is an almost annual visitor in very small numbers between late October and mid-April with an average of two birds per year since 1960, although five were seen in 1966, 1972, 1974 and 1976, and six in 1990.

It can turn up almost anywhere; however over 60% of the records have been on the coastal strip between Hartlepool, South Gare and Redcar. Away from this coastal concentration, birds have been seen more than once at Boulby Cliffs, Lockwood Beck, Scaling Dam, Charlton's Pond and Flatts Lane.

The earliest record is 16 September (1972) and nearly half of the sightings are for October with a few lingering into November and, even fewer being seen in December, January and February. More are observed in March and April, presumably as wintering birds start to move east to cross the North Sea and the latest date is 7 May (1978).

A bird ringed at South Gare on 2 April 1974 was recovered at Schagen, Noord-Holland, the Netherlands, on 29 October 1974, and is one of the few foreign recoveries of Great Grey Shrike. This bird gives an indication of the route used by the species between wintering and breeding areas and is one of only five ringed in Cleveland.

WOODCHAT SHRIKE *Lanius senator*

There are two records for Cleveland. Single adults were at Billingham Bottoms on 24 - 25 April 1971 and South Gare on 10 May 1999.

(EURASIAN) JAY *Garrulus glandarius*

Compared to other members of the crow family found in the county, this bird is remarkably colourful, though surprisingly well camouflaged in woodland. Whilst it certainly takes the eggs and young of small birds, it almost certainly has no effect on 'game' species such as Pheasant, Partridge and grouse.

In Cleveland, it can be found breeding in coniferous and mixed woodland as well as parkland, but not as much in deciduous woodland. Overall, the Cleveland population is estimated at approximately 150 pairs, about 75% of which are south of the Tees; this probably represents quite a major increase during this century due to the afforestation of parts of Cleveland, notably around Guisborough and Wynyard.

As with many woodland species, there is a general dispersal in autumn, though the Jay very rarely appears near the coastline in the same way as other woodland birds. The exceptions to this concern one flying north over Hartlepool Headland on 25 April 1962 and five singles flying south-west over Hartlepool town between 26 October and 12 November 1983. Relatively large numbers were seen elsewhere during the autumn that year including about 35 in Wynyard on 19 October. Very large numbers occurred in southern Britain in the autumn of 1983 and birds were seen in places where Jays are normally absent, indicating a large emigration from northern Britain. Also, one was at Boulby Cliffs on 15 October 1989, one was at Hunt Cliff on 17 October 1994 and one flew over the Long Drag and Dormans Pool on 22 September 2005.

No more than nine together have been reported locally since 1983; up to three birds have been noted feeding on bird tables and wire peanut holders in the Guisborough area and Normanby in recent years.

Only about 60 Jays have been ringed in Cleveland, but there are no recoveries.

(BLACK-BILLED) MAGPIE *Pica pica*

Several factors may be responsible for a steady increase in the number of Magpies in Britain over the last few decades including the reduction in gamekeeping and a decline in egg-collecting. In recent years it has been suggested by some that there are now too many Magpies and that they are having an adverse effect on the number of smaller passerines, by virtue of their habit of eating eggs and nestlings of other birds., though this is not supported by some dedicated studies.

As a resident it is seemingly capable of withstanding the coldest of winter weather, though there may well be a slight movement of birds in a southerly and /or westerly direction in harsh winters.

The Magpie used to be a scarce bird at Hartlepool Headland and South Gare, but it is now seen quite regularly in both places. An unusual record involved two arriving from the sea at South Gare on 1 February 1958.

The Cleveland population is estimated at about 900 pairs, birds nesting in woodland, hedgerows, parks, and recently in large well-wooded gardens, and more recently still in scattered bushes around the marshes of Teesmouth.

In winter small roosts of Magpies form in many places, usually in clumps of hawthorn and similar bushes, and usually numbering 30-50 as a maximum. The biggest known roost was near Nunthorpe in February-March 1947 when an estimated 200-300 Magpies were seen each evening, but the highest counts recently are from Flatts Lane, where 113 were seen in March 1999 and 115 in January 2001.

(RED-BILLED) CHOUGH Pyrrhocorax pyrrhocorax

This member of the crow family is restricted in Britain to a few localities on the west coast but historically was more widespread. In the early 1800s,'red-legged daws' were said to be on the cliffs at Boulby and they certainly bred on cliffs in Yorkshire up to the beginning of the 19th century.

The recent records are: one at Hunt Cliff from 27 April to 22 May 1957; two at Hartlepool in late March 1969; one by Seal Sands on 18 September 1969; and one on a chimney in Marske on 16 January 1978. It is possible that only the 1957 record concerns a genuine wild bird, the other three perhaps being escaped caged birds.

(EURASIAN) JACKDAW Corvus monedula

Of the three common 'black' corvids, this is the smallest and probably the most wide-spread in Cleveland. It breeds in most habitats, including the centres of towns, cliffs, industrial areas and deciduous woodland. Small colonies exist in towns and on cliffs, whereas in woodland, parkland and agricultural areas pairs tend to be spread out as a result of there being relatively few trees with suitable nesting holes.

Overall the Cleveland population is close to 1,500 pairs and after the breeding season mixed flocks of Rooks and Jackdaws can be seen feeding in many agricultural areas, a few hundred Jackdaws being quite regular in these gatherings. The largest gatherings recorded include 800 near Guisborough in February 1983 and 750 at Marton West Beck in January 1995.

Individuals showing the characters of the continental race, *Corvus monedula monedula*, have been noted at Guisborough in October 1969 and January 1970 and the occasional migrant may well pass along the coast in spring and autumn.

A bird in Locke Park in October 1972 was mostly white, with only some small areas of black on its body, one at Graythorp on 8 March 1993 was about one third white, one in

Nunthorpe in October 2000 was shades of brown and cream and one at Port Clarence in August 2001 was covered in white spots.

About 100 Jackdaws have been ringed in Cleveland, but none is known to have moved very far. One found dead at Cowpen Marsh in August 1994 and one shot (to protect a bean crop) in Wynyard on 27 March 2000 had both been ringed in the nest at Crookfoot Reservoir, the first in May 1985 and the second in May 1995.

ROOK *Corvus frugilegus*

This, the most numerous of the crow family in Cleveland, is largely sedentary. There were close to 70 Rookeries in Cleveland, with a total breeding population of 4,000 pairs in the 1980's, it has now declined to 1841 pairs (Joynt et al 2008), many birds staying near their rookery throughout the year. It is not unusual to see gatherings of Rooks in fields in autumn and winter, over 3,000 being present on occasions, often accompanied by smaller numbers of Jackdaws.

The biggest rookery in Cleveland is at Skelton with about 350 pairs in the 1970s and 1980s. A leucistic bird was present there in 2001.

A bird or two is occasionally seen coasting or arriving from the sea during times of passage, these birds probably being from northern Britain.

The only bird to be recovered in Cleveland was at Guisborough on 21 March 1981; it had been ringed at Consett, Co. Durham, on 5 February 1981. Also, one found in Yorkshire in December 1930 had been ringed in Germany on 31 October 1927.

CARRION CROW *Corvus corone*

The BTO Atlas Survey conducted between 1968 and 1972 throughout Britain gave an average of about three pairs per occupied square kilometre, whereas the surveying of Cleveland in the mid-1980s produced an average of just over one pair per occupied square kilometre. This low density may be due to the close proximity of the coastline and industrial areas to the species' favoured habitat of farmland and woodland. Also, there are relatively few large trees in Cleveland compared to similar areas in other parts of England. The Cleveland population is estimated at about 500-700 pairs, spread evenly throughout the area.

Unlike Rooks, this corvid does not usually form flocks, but groups of 30-60 have been recorded on occasions at places such as Cowpen Marsh, Preston Park, Wilton and Stanghow. However, Eston Moor held about 220 in December 1989, 370 in November 1995 and 300 in April 1997, and Stewart Park regularly holds 100 birds.

It is not unusual to see individuals and small groups coasting or arriving from the sea, predominantly in late March and April, 21 arriving at Redcar on 29 June 1966, 22 at

Hartlepool on 8 April 1972, 13 per hour passed Boulby on 20 and 21 April 1994 and 54 passed Cowbar in 5.5 hours on 5 May 1996.

Oddly-coloured birds have been recorded, including one around Saltholme in 1979 that had pale grey wings and one at Stillington in December 1981 that was dark brown with fawn wings.

HOODED CROW *Corvus cornix*

Until 2000, this bird was regarded as a race of Carrion Crow, but is now accepted as a full species. It used to be recorded each winter, usually about three to ten individuals, but occasionally considerably more than this. However, Hooded Crow has declined locally in recent years with none being seen in the years 2000-2002.

Influxes occurred during the winters of 1947/48, 1960/61, 1969/70 and 1976/77. About 40-60 birds were the maximum counts, although it is likely that over 100 birds passed through Cleveland in some of these winters. Large gatherings have been seen on Marske beach, Dunsdale Tip, Stanghow-Lockwood Beck area, Liverton Moor and Eston Moor, but all are eclipsed by the passage recorded on 25 October 1881 when 200 passed Redcar in 4 hours.

Since 1994, all records have occurred in the months September - April, but prior to then there were occasional birds seen in May and June. In some years, passage can be observed along the coastline in October-November and more noticeably in March-April. In late March-early April 1987 at least 20 individuals flew north-west over Boulby in the space of two weeks.

There are no Cleveland ringing recoveries, but one in North Yorkshire on 2 January 1926 had been ringed in a Danish nest and another shot in North Yorkshire in the mid-1950s had been ringed in a Norwegian nest.

(COMMON) RAVEN *Corvus corax*

This, the biggest of the crow family in Britain, has been reported eleven times in the last 100 years, but single pairs nested at Hunt Cliff up to 1845, Boulby Cliffs up to about 1860 and Highcliff and Cass Rock, near Guisborough up to 1866. The shooting of Ravens, practised in many parts of Britain in the 19th century, was probably the main cause of its disappearance from this area.

The recent records are: three at Eston Nab in the summer of 1936; one over Hartburn on 14 April 1973; two over Wilton on 26 July 1984; one over Thornaby on 12 June 1989; one over Guisborough on 3 November 1990; one over High Moor, south of Lockwood Beck, on 31 October 1998; two over New Marske on 27 September 2001; one over Scaling Dam on 21 October 2003; one at Sleddale on 27 February 2006, up to three were seen in the Sleddale, Lockwood Beck and Hutton Village areas between 1 and 6 April 2006 and one was at Scaling Dam on 5 June 2006.

(COMMON) STARLING *Sturnus vulgaris*

It is difficult to bird-watch anywhere in Cleveland in daylight hours and not see Starlings, although there has been a decline since the 1980s. In the summer, pairs breed in many habitats, wherever there are suitable holes either in trees or the walls and roof cavities of buildings, but not on the coastal cliffs. In winter large flocks feed on farmland and just about every garden in Cleveland will be visited by small groups during any one day. Many people put out household scraps and bird food in the winter months which undoubtedly help many Starlings to survive the cold.

In autumn flocks regularly arrive from over the sea, occasionally thousands being counted on any one day between mid-October and late November. In spring, however, very few are seen returning to the north and east.

Enormous night-time roosts of Starlings form in the winter months, usually on industrial structures at Billingham, Wilton, South Bank and Hartlepool, sometimes numbering up to 50,000 or more birds. Smaller roosts are also used in winter in several places, such as parks and occasionally, reed beds. Overall, probably around one million Starlings roost in Cleveland on winter nights, the large roosts at warm industrial sites probably drawing birds from feeding areas in Durham and North Yorkshire.

Ringing by the late P.A.Rayfield in Thornaby throughout the 1950s showed that a good number of our wintering Starlings come from Scandinavia and northern Russia. At least 40 birds ringed between late November and early March have been recovered or controlled in these areas in the following summers, including Finland, Denmark, Sweden, Norway, Germany, Poland, Lithuania and near Leningrad (St. Petersburg), Russia. However, other birds ringed in Cleveland in winter have been reported in Leicestershire, Yorkshire, Lincolnshire, Buckinghamshire, Essex, Herefordshire, Newcastle-upon-Tyne and Fair Isle in following summers.

Birds ringed in Cleveland in one winter have been reported in the following winters in Cleveland, at Scarborough and Great Broughton in North Yorkshire, Cumbria, Northumberland, Lancashire, West Midlands, Hereford, Worcester and Dundee. One ringed in Guisborough in February 1984 was in Vest-Agder, on the southern tip of Norway on 22 March 1987, another ringed in Stockton in November 1992 was in Norway on 25 February 1995, and one ringed in Guisborough in March 1986 was in Poland on 1 January 1988. Another ringed as a juvenile in Cleveland in August had reached Scunthorpe, Humberside, by 1 December in the same year.

Individuals ringed elsewhere in Britain include: one ringed in Liverpool in February

---

1953 and found in Thornaby in February 1955; two ringed in Beal, Northumberland, in November-December 1958 and noted in Norton and Middlesbrough, both in June 1963; and one ringed in Aberdeen in January 1984 and found at Billingham in July 1985. Over 6,500 Starlings have been ringed in Cleveland since 1974 and a few thousand prior to the formation of the county.

Completely white birds have been seen around the North Tees Marshes in 1974, 1977, 1978 and 1995, at Elwick and Hartlepool in 2000 and Hartlepool in May 2003. An individual with a white body but dark wings, tail and head was in Billingham in 1980, a bird with a lot of pink and white feathers was in Redcar in 2000 and very pale grey or brown individuals were on the North Tees Marshes in 2003.

Approximately 8,000 pairs of Starling breed in Cleveland.

ROSE-COLOURED STARLING
(ROSY STARLING) *Sturnus roseus*

There are at least six historic records, all adults: at Coatham Marsh on 28 August 1851; Middlesbrough on 12 August 1855; 'several' at Skinningrove in 1862-1863 and one before 1844; and at Redcar on 23 November 1889 (Nelson 1907).

The next record was over 80 years later when a single bird was at Billingham from at least 27 to 30 June 1973. In 2002 there was an influx into Britain involving over 100 birds that brought three Rose-coloured Starlings to Cleveland. Singles were at South Gare on 8 June 2002, Marske on 11 June 2002 and Dormans Pool on 17 June 2002. These were quickly followed by one at Redcar on 20 April 2003 and one at South Gare on 10 June 2003.

HOUSE SPARROW *Passer domesticus*

A detailed study conducted in the 1950's by Dr J.D. Summers-Smith, partly in Stockton and partly in Hampshire, concluded that the vast majority of House Sparrows never move more than a kilometre or two from their birthplace and that approximately two birds per acre could be found in typical urban habitat and 0.1 bird per acre in the agricultural habitat (Summers-Smith 1963). The BTO Atlas 1968-1972 gave a spread of 10-20 pairs/km^2 throughout Britain, though it could be much higher in specific areas. Surveying of all habitats in Cleveland in the 1980s produced figures of about 150 pairs/km^2 in the urban habitat and four pairs/km^2 in the agricultural habitat. Given that there are about 80 km^2 of built-up areas and over 300km^2 of fields in Cleveland, the population is estimated at about 11,000 pairs although there is evidence of a decrease in recent years. A small number of pairs also nest in woodland and parkland, generally in holes in trees.

The urban House Sparrow regularly rears two, three or even four, broods of young in one summer, and the resulting flocks of birds resort to stubble fields in autumn. Flocks of over a thousand birds used to be seen quite frequently in many parts of Cleveland at this time, this being the only time period when birds moved away from their breeding areas. In recent years flocks generally number no more than 100-200 birds, and there are fewer flocks to be seen.

Ringing recoveries have shown that some birds can reach five or six years of age and occasionally 9-10. One ringed in Linthorpe in November 1961 was found dead at the same place 10 years later in June 1971. The only bird known to move far was ringed at Spurn in October 1964 and found at Newton-under-Roseberry in April 1965, though Nelson (1907) regularly recorded numbers of migrants on the coastline. There are no recent observations of such coastal movements.

Well over 1,000 birds were ringed in the area in the 1950s and 1960s but less than 1,000 have been ringed in Cleveland since 1974.

(EURASIAN) TREE SPARROW *Passer montanus*

This bird is quite widespread in Cleveland, but nowhere is it very numerous. It breeds throughout the agricultural areas, given suitable breeding sites, but is known to fluctuate quite dramatically in numbers over a period of years. In the 1960s the population had reached a peak countrywide and was quite numerous as a spring and autumn passage migrant along the coast. Reasonably-sized flocks could be found in the winter months, the maximum being about 400 on Coatham Marsh on 27 November 1971, and over 100 birds were reported at many places.

Coastal counts include "hundreds" passing Redcar on 1 November 1959, 130 flying north-west at the same place in 90 minutes on 16 October 1960 and 46 passing Hartlepool on 8 October 1970. Smaller numbers were regularly seen in April and May in this period, but in the late 1970s and 1980s very few were recorded moving along the coastline, and since about 1994 there have been years when no birds were seen at the coastal migration points.

As a breeding bird, the Cleveland population was probably around 500-700 pairs in the 1980s. A study by Dr J D Summers-Smith in 1993 revealed between 130 and 150 pairs during the summer and about 330 wintering birds. One area of farmland near Pinchinthorpe has been monitored for the Common Bird Census from 1962 to 2000 and the number of Tree Sparrows has varied from none to five pairs over this period, with a peak in the late 1960s and trough in the 1970s and early 1980s. There is some evidence of a recent increase in numbers as Tree Sparrows take over farm buildings abandoned by House Sparrows.

Since the 1980s, flocks of 60-100 have been seen in the winter months at several areas including Saltburn, Brotton, Wynyard Woodland Park, Durham Tees Valley Airport, Aislaby, Ingleby Barwick, Hart and Greatham.

Over 1,500 birds have been ringed in Cleveland, but none has been known to move very far.

RED-EYED VIREO *Vireo olivaceus*

One at North Gare on 12 and 13 October 1991 is the only Cleveland record of this North American passerine. It was first seen on the same day as a Pallas's Warbler and Radde's Warbler, birds from Siberia, so the route it took to arrive in Cleveland is open to speculation.

CHAFFINCH *Fringilla coelebs*

Apart from being a common resident in Cleveland, this colourful bird is also a spring and autumn migrant, and winter visitor in fairly small numbers.

Breeding Chaffinches can be found in all habitats except industrial and coastal tracts, and in the woodland habitat it is frequently the commonest breeding bird. Many pairs nest in parks and larger gardens and these Chaffinches frequently become quite tame.

The total Cleveland population is estimated at about 4,000 pairs making it one of the commonest breeding birds. After the breeding season, sizeable flocks build up in woods and parks, sometimes numbering 100 or more.

In autumn small numbers arrive from northern Europe, usually between late September and early November. Occasionally up to 100 birds are seen in a day at Hartlepool, South Gare and passing Boulby. However, at least 1,200 flew north-west at Boulby on the morning of 24 October 1994, but only 28 in the same period next day.

Very small numbers appear in the Hartlepool and South Gare areas in spring but there is a steady trickle of birds heading north-west at Boulby Cliffs in April, tens being seen on some days. These may be birds that breed in northern Britain that have wintered further south, either in Britain or continental Europe, rather than Scandinavian birds.

Winter flocks of over 100 birds can be found in many areas, especially parks and around farmyards often, but not always, associating with other finches and buntings. The largest single flock recorded in Cleveland is 380 in Wynyard on 6 March 1982, though there were probably thousands spread over Cleveland at this time.

Something in the region of 5,500 Chaffinches have been ringed in Cleveland, but very few have been known to travel any distance. The recoveries are: ringed Thornaby in December 1950 - found Acklam April 1956; ringed Heligoland, Germany, on 23 September 1969 - found dead Hartlepool about two weeks later, ringed Ormesby on 10

February 1980 - found dead Hyllestad, southern Norway, on 16 May 1983; ringed near Moorsholm on 25 March 1990 - controlled Loop Head, Clare, Eire, on 4 November 1990; ringed near Moorsholm on 24 June 1990 - controlled Hardwick, South Yorkshire, on 26 January 1991; ringed at Nunthorpe on 17 March 1993 - found dead at Olst, Netherlands, on 31 January 1996; and ringed at Hartlepool on 10 September 2002 - controlled Froggat, Derbyshire, on 14 February 2003.

BRAMBLING *Fringilla montifringilla*

This northern European finch is a regular winter visitor, sometimes in quite large numbers, usually arriving in October and November and leaving in March and April. However, there are records as early as 19 August (1976) and as late as 28 May (1996).

The first birds of the autumn are almost invariably noted on the coast, a few spending a day or two around the gardens and open areas at sites such at Hartlepool or South Gare before moving inland. The largest immigration noted was in early October 1966 when 773 were seen arriving at South Gare on 6 October and 394 a week later. The normal autumn count is usually around 100-200 birds between early October and early November; in some winters virtually all the autumn birds have moved out of Cleveland, fewer than 10 sometimes being noted in December-February.

Wintering areas depend on the beech mast crop, stubble fields and the severity of the winter weather. Their favourite localities at various times have been: Stewart Park - Marton area, where up to 350 were seen in February 1980 and 200 in January 1981; Acklam Hall, where up to 150 were seen in December 1976 and 180 in February 1981; Billingham Bottoms where 160 were seen in February 1976; Hartburn Beck with 190 seen in December 1981; and Poole Hospital, which was used as a roost by many finches, but appears to have been deserted in recent years. Several hundred Brambling were ringed there during the 1960s, the highest count being 250 in March 1968. More recently, up to 400 were at Brotton from December 1993 to February 1994, up to 200 were at Hutton Gate between December 1994 and February 1995, up to 210 at Lockwood Beck from November 2004 to February 2005.

If the weather becomes very severe, Bramblings sometimes move nearer to the coast. Up to 1,000 were seen at Graythorp in December 1965, 200 were feeding on the roadside verges at Cowpen Bewley in January 1972, 100 were feeding along the edge of the A66 near Thornaby in December 1981 and up to 350 frequented Seaton Carew tip in January 1982 and January 1984. Also, up to 250 were in Hartlepool Docks in January 1984. Since the 1981/82 winter, birds have been observed in suburban gardens and at feeding stations eating foods such as peanuts and sunflower seeds.

Other localities where Brambling are sometimes reported include Upleatham, Wynyard, Elton, Albert Park, Saltburn, Skelton Castle and Norton Green, though it is likely that some birds also frequent places such as farmyards and open fields away from the usual birdwatching areas.

Ringing of the birds at their roosts between December and February has resulted in birds being reported from France in November and December, Holland and Belgium in November and January, Germany in January, Gibraltar Point, Lincolnshire, in January, (one year later), and Shropshire in November, (one year later). Also, a bird ringed in Germany on 29 March 1976 was at South Gare on 5 October 1976, one ringed at Manchester on 19 March 1993 was at South Gare on 21 October 1994, one ringed at Brotton on 22 January 1994 was at Swarland, Northumberland, on 7 April 1994 and one ringed in Rogaland, Norway, on 9 October 1997 was at Guisborough on 12 April 1998.

(EUROPEAN) SERIN *Serinus serinus*

There are seven records for Cleveland of this southern European finch, which is an annual summer visitor to the south of England and has bred in several places in recent years.

The records are: singles at Hartlepool Headland on 14 September 1968 and 5 May 1969; a female in Locke Park and nearby gardens of Redcar from 24 December 1985 to 14 April 1986; a singing male at Yarm on 10 April 1990; one in Locke Park on 16 September 1993; a singing male at Skelton Castle on 17 April 1996; and one over the Zinc Works road on 29 June 2002.

(EUROPEAN) GREENFINCH *Carduelis chloris*

This finch is a frequent visitor to garden bird tables and nut feeders, and one might imagine that it is resident in Cleveland, birds being present in all months of the year. However, the many ringing recoveries indicate that there is considerable movement north and south through Cleveland.

As a breeding species, the vast majority of the birds are confined to the urban and parkland habitats with relatively few in deciduous woodland and farmland. In the two principal types of habitat it has a density of around 25-30 pairs/km^2 though there will be 'prime' areas in most of the towns, where the figure will be higher. Given this density, the total Cleveland population is reckoned to be approximately 2,500 pairs.

After the breeding season, reasonably-sized flocks can be found in suitable areas, usually on weedy waste ground and in winter in the reed beds around Teesmouth. Normally no more than 200-300 are seen together, but on Coatham Marsh on 10 January 1971 about 1,000 were recorded and on the large reclaimed section of Seal Sands about 800 were noted on 16 December 1972 and 1,400 on 27 November 1976.

Night-time roosts regularly form in the winter months; Poole Hospital was a favourite site in the 1960s, over 2,500 being ringed there between 1962 and 1972 and over 9,000 have been ringed in Cleveland since 1972. "Hundreds" were regularly present at the Poole Hospital roost and up to 400 were seen at a roost near Saltburn in January 1966.

Nelson (1907) recorded this finch as a regular passage migrant on the coast "many" being seen arriving in October 1883, 1887 and 1901 and on 1 May 1901. In recent years, few birds have been observed at the coastal watch points such as Hartlepool Headland and South Gare, although there is sometimes significant movement of Greenfinches (in company with other finches) along the cliff top at Boulby.

Date and location of ringing	Subsequent records	Notes
Hertfordshire, 25 February 1948	Loftus, 6 March 1948	
Spurn, Humberside, October 1949	Loftus, June 1951	
Monks House Observatory, Northumberland, February 1953	Hartlepool May and July 1953	two birds
Costock, Nottinghamshire March 1975	Hartlepool August 1975	
Teesport, 6 December 1975	Overijssel, the Netherlands January 1977	
Dundrum, Co Down, Northern Ireland, December 1976	Guisborough, 1978	
Kettleness, North Yorks October 1985	Guisborough, 5 March 1986	
Bradford, West Yorks, 25 April 1987	Stockton, 25 April 1987	same day
Spurn, Humberside, 7 July 1991	Hartlepool, 1 December 1991	ringed as a pullus
southern Norway 10 November 1991	Saltburn, 23 November 1991	
Preston, Lancashire 19 October 1993	Saltburn, 5 May 1994	
Normanby, June 2000	Sinnington, North Yorkshire 28 December 2000	juvenile
Hartlepool, 15 October 2000	Thornton-le-Clay, North Yorkshire 16 December 2000	
Hargreaves Quarry, October 1999	Bedale, North Yorkshire, 4 May 2003	found dead
A selection of Greenfinch Ringing Recoveries		

There are at least 40 recoveries of birds moving significant distances. Birds ringed in Cleveland in the months November-March have been recovered or controlled later in the same winter at Mansfield and Retford, in Nottinghamshire, and in the following spring at Scarborough in North Yorkshire, Brocklesbury in Lincolnshire and Ellesmere in Shropshire. In the following summer birds have been recovered at Stamfordham in Northumberland, Doncaster in South Yorkshire, and Ripon in North Yorkshire, and in the following autumn at Filey Brigg in North Yorkshire, Hornsea in North Humberside and Swarland in Northumberland. Records in the following winters are from Ripon, Thirsk and Fairburn in North Yorkshire, Doncaster and Sheffield in South Yorkshire, Driffield and Spurn in Humberside, Edwinstone and Retford in Nottinghamshire, Hyde in Greater Manchester, Hatfield in Hertfordshire, Coldstream in Borders and Overijssel in the Netherlands, two winters later.

It would seem that Greenfinches move either north or south in times of migration and are not very faithful to particular wintering areas, even in the same winter, though hard weather may influence these movements.

Birds controlled or recovered in Cleveland in winter had been ringed in previous winters at: Knaresborough and Kirbymoorside, North Yorkshire; Lesbury, Northumberland; Luton, Bedfordshire; Weymouth, Dorset and Dundrum, Co. Down.

(EUROPEAN) GOLDFINCH *Carduelis carduelis*

In the 19th century, this finch was a favourite cage bird and in many parts of Britain it was quite scarce. Nelson (1907) stated that it used to be fairly common, but at the time of writing had been reduced to a winter visitor only. Legislation passed in 1881 to stop the catching and selling of wild Goldfinches began to have an effect in the early part of the 20th century with numbers slowly but steadily increasing throughout Britain, including what is now Cleveland.

A flock of about 20 in a Middlesbrough garden in November 1916 was then regarded as notable, but since at least the 1960s, flocks of up to 100 individuals have been found in places where weeds prevail, such as the edges of industrial areas, fields and parts of Teesmouth.

At present it breeds principally in suburban gardens and parks, with a small number in deciduous and coniferous woodland. The Cleveland breeding population is estimated to be about 1,000 pairs.

After the breeding season, flocks can be found in many areas, though some birds probably head south for the winter, perhaps being replaced by others from the north. The only ringing recovery concerns a pullus ringed in Stockton in August 1984 and found dead near Doncaster, South Yorkshire, in March 1985, indicating that some of the

Cleveland-bred birds do indeed winter further south. Over 600 Goldfinches have been ringed in Cleveland.

In some winters, quite sizable night-time roosts build up; one in trees along Central Avenue in Billingham has been in existence since at least the late 1960s. During the winter of 1972/73, many were regularly seen there, the maximum being about 360 on 31 December 1972, this being the highest count for Cleveland at the time and probably contained most of Cleveland's wintering Goldfinches. The next largest flock was about 250 on Seaton Common on 29 September 1985 and flocks of 100-200 have been seen at many places in subsequent years. Goldfinches have continued to increase in number, albeit quite slowly, with about 380 at Bowesfield on 13 October 2001 and 430 at Saltholme Pools on 6 September 2005 being the highest recent counts.

In spring, flocks are noted as late as the beginning of May, at a time when local birds are incubating eggs. These are probably birds from further north that will nest later in the year.

Spring passage is fairly noticeable along the coastline around Saltburn and Boulby from late April to early June with around 200 per day as a maximum. However, large numbers passed Boulby in the spring and autumn of 2003 with a maximum at least 650 on 29 April. Autumn passage is usually much less obvious, though a few birds have been seen apparently arriving from the sea on occasions.

A white juvenile with diffuse yellow wing-bars was at Lockwood Beck in early August 1991 and a finch in a Guisborough garden on 17 April 2002 was thought to be a Greenfinch - Goldfinch hybrid.

(EURASIAN) SISKIN *Carduelis spinus*

In Cleveland, this delightful little finch seems to be changing its habits. Up to the 1970s, it was classified as a spring and autumn passage migrant and winter visitor to larch and alder woodland close to water. Whilst it is still predominantly so, since 1980 it has been recorded feeding with increasing regularity on peanuts in gardens. As a result, relatively large numbers have being ringed in Cleveland and since 1983 singing males have been seen in suitable breeding habitat during the summer months.

As a passage migrant, more are generally observed along the coastline in autumn, usually between late September and late November, than are noted in spring. A few birds are regularly seen flying along the cliffs at Boulby in April, often in company with Linnets, pipits, Swallows and other migrants. A large fall of birds in autumn, especially of thrushes, tends to bring Siskins in as well, indicating a Scandinavian origin for passage birds. An influx of Crossbills in June 1985 included a few Siskin, the origin of which is open to debate.

Wintering flocks can be found at several favoured localities, in particular alder-fringed streams and ponds at Wolviston, Wynyard, Poole Hospital, Guisborough, Leven Valley and in coniferous woodland at Lockwood Beck, Grinkle Park and Guisborough Forest. Most flocks number 15-40, sometimes with a similar number of Redpolls, although about 100 Siskins were in Hutton Lowcross Woods on 27 January 1985 and Birk Brow in March-early April 1991, and about 300 were at Hutton Village on 31 January 1998. The habit of mixing with Redpolls in alder trees was noted as long ago as 1829 when small flocks were present "between Norton and Billingham".

The earliest report of a singing bird in potential breeding habitat was in late April 1963, but it was 1983 before singing birds were noted in May or June. Birds singing in April could easily be passage birds 'practising' before moving on to their breeding grounds further north. In most years since 1983, singing males have been seen at various sites, including Grinkle Park, Errington Woods, Saltburn Gill, Westworth Woods, Hutton Lowcross Woods and Lockwood Beck, while there are several other suitable sites where this bird could easily be overlooked. At one locality, a male and several recently fledged juveniles were present in late June 1985, at another locality a pair was seen nest-building and incubating in April 1991, but no young were recorded. Successful breeding was confirmed in the Guisborough area in 1998.

The occurrence of Siskins in gardens is a recent phenomenon, very nearly all records being between late February and mid-April, with peanuts generally being mentioned as the attraction. This has resulted in over 2,200 birds being ringed in Cleveland, almost all since 1984, providing an interesting set of results. One ringed at Guisborough on 25 March 1984 was at Sherringham, Norfolk, nine days later and another ringed at Guisborough on 13 February 1994 was at Ickburgh, Norfolk, four weeks later. Another bird, caught at Guisborough on 25 April 1986, had been ringed at Whickham, Tyne & Wear, 12 days earlier. Since 1986 there have been several other recoveries of birds ringed in Guisborough in the months February-April and found in Scotland in April-May. Also there are recoveries of birds ringed in Surrey, Kent, Hertfordshire and Hampshire in January-February occurring in Cleveland in April. Another ringed in Limerick, Eire, on 29 January 1989 was in Guisborough on 26 January 1992. One ringed at Hauxley, Northumberland, on 12 October 1988 was at Guisborough on 31 December 1988 and two ringed in Cleveland in February 1992 were still in Cleveland 17 days and two months later respectively, one being found dead at Norton and the other being re-trapped 9 km from where it was ringed. One ringed in Nunthorpe on 20 February 1994 was re-trapped at Malmohus, southern Sweden, on 9 October 1994 and another ringed at Hartlepool on 27 September 2000 was at Aust-Agder, Norway, on 28 April 2001.

(COMMON) LINNET *Carduelis cannabina*

This finch can be found in Cleveland throughout the year, but, as is the case with a fair percentage of small birds, it is a passage migrant in spring and autumn and a summer and winter visitor, rather than a resident. It breeds throughout Cleveland in many habitats where there are small bushes and trees; these range from bushes behind Seaton Dunes on the coast to the scattered trees and bushes on the moorland fringes. No particular habitat seems to be favoured over another, though parks and the larger gardens hold a good number of pairs.

The total population is estimated at 1,500 pairs; this is considered to be slightly less than it was in the 19th century when there was much more suitable habitat. However, the Linnet was trapped and kept as a cage bird in the past, though apparently not as intensively as the Goldfinch.

After the breeding season, small to medium-sized flocks gather in fields and around waste ground, but whether those seen in autumn and winter are made up of local breeding birds is open to debate. Ringing has shown that some full-grown birds caught in Cleveland (mostly in autumn) are wintering as far south as southern France and Spain, though one ringed at Graythorp on 2 October 1965 had got no further south than Patrington, Humberside, by 18 December 1965. Another ringed at Guisborough in May 1983 was in Madrid, Spain, in December 1983. Three others do not apparently fit into this pattern of spring-autumn movements: one ringed at Teesmouth on 26 August 1983 and found at Dunvagel, Strathclyde, on 15 September 1984; one ringed at Spurn on 2 February 1972 and found at Redcar on 25 November 1972; and one ringed at Saltholme on 19 August 1990 and found in Noord-Holland, the Netherlands, on 3 September 1991. In common with many other migrants it is presumably the relative severity of autumn and winter weather that influences the movements of this bird. Over 4,000 Linnets have been ringed in Cleveland, the vast majority since 1972.

Spring passage is fairly conspicuous along the coastline from Saltburn to Cowbar between mid-April and late May, thousands passing during this period, with occasionally several hundreds on single days. Autumn passage is less obvious or predictable; however, good numbers are sometimes seen during 'falls' in August or September, but equally there are occasions when very few are noted. There is little indication of Scandinavian or north European birds being involved in this passage, though it breeds only in south Scandinavia.

Flocks of 100-300 are quite regularly noted in some areas, in particular the undeveloped ground around Teesmouth and Teesport, where wild plants grow unchecked, the biggest gatherings being over 1,000 at Graythorp in September-October 1965, 800 on

Coatham Marsh on 20 August 1971, 800 at Graythorp in December 1993, 800 near Hart on 6 October 2001 and 700 at Wynyard Woodland Park on 12 September 2002.

Single pale buff individuals were seen at Hartlepool in August 1991, Saltburn in September 1991 and April-May 1993, and South Gare in August and September 1992. The same bird may have been involved at the three localities. An almost completely white Linnet was seen at Bowesfield from October 2006 to April 2007.

TWITE *Carduelis flavirostris*

It appears that this nondescript member of the finch family has declined during the 20th century from a breeding bird on the moorland in East Cleveland and a regular winter visitor to Teesmouth in good numbers, to a scarce passage migrant in spring and autumn, and a winter visitor in small numbers.

Nelson (1907) mentions breeding on moorland at Grinkle and Waupley, as well as other areas on the North York Moors, as being quite regular, yet the BTO Atlas of Breeding Birds conducted during 1968-1972 recorded no nesting Twite in North Yorkshire, which included the area that became part of Cleveland in 1974. The decline in the number of wintering birds is not well-documented, there being no mention of numbers in Nelson's writings and no records at all between 1907 and 1936. The highest numbers from 1936 are: up to 20 at South Gare in January and February 1936; up to 50 by Redcar Steel Works in February and March 1950; and 20 at Scaling Dam on 14 September 1959. From this date to 1975 there are records for almost every year, but mostly of singles and none of more than four birds.

Since 1976, numbers have been slightly higher, there being counts of: eight by Seal Sands in November 1976; nine in February 1977, 12 in February 1978; up to 25 in December 1980 and January 1981; 22 in January and February 1988; and up to 17 at South Gare in the winters 1985/86, 1986/87 and 1987/88. In the 1988/89 winter, up to 35 were at South Gare and 30-70 on Greenabella Marsh and in the following six winters gatherings of 30-45 was regular in the Long Drag - Seal Sands area. Since then, the highest counts have been 80 at Marske on 19 November 1995, 55 at South Gare in November 1996, 60 on Greenabella Marsh in November 1997, up to 80 on Greenabella Marsh in November and December 2000, 84 by Greatham Creek on 17 November 2001 and 90 in the same area on 18 January 2003.

Perhaps the 1960s and early 1970s, saw the lowest point in the number of wintering Twite, there now being a gradual increase, with a possibility of breeding on the moorland in the south of Cleveland in the future.

It should be remembered that this bird can be relatively difficult to identify and a percentage of the birds actually occurring may be missed. The increase in the number of

Birds of Cleveland

birdwatchers and the vast improvement in their field skills has probably affected the overall picture, so it remains to be seen whether this species continues to increase in the future.

The earliest and latest dates are 5 September (1964) and 13 May (1973) although most of the records are between late October and early April.

About 70% are recorded around Teesmouth, a few having been seen at Normanby, Portrack Marsh, Brotton, Liverton, Hartlepool, Seaton Tip, Redcar Stray and Boulby Cliffs.

LESSER REDPOLL *Carduelis cabaret*

Up to the year 2000, this and the Common Redpoll (*Carduelis flammea*) were regarded as the same species, but different subspecies. In Cleveland, the Lesser Redpoll breeds in a few areas of coniferous and mixed woodland, and on the moorland edges where birch and other trees grow. It is probably commonest in the area between Guisborough and Grinkle Park, although it has declined quite considerably in recent years. Redpolls were known to breed in hedgerows and the suburbs of several towns in the mid-1970s. Locke Park held a small population up to at least 1984 and the area between Nunthorpe and Lovell Hill, including Eston Moor, had at least 22 pairs in the summer of 1985. The breeding population is currently estimated at about 25 pairs.

There are regularly small flocks in the winter months in suitable habitat, generally alder and hazel scrub beside water, as well as in mixed conifer plantations. The recent regular wintering haunts are Poole Hospital, Charlton's Pond, Northburn Beck near Wolviston, Grinkle Park, Birk Brow, Guisborough and Wynyard. Recent flocks usually number about 20-60, but in the 1970s, flocks of over 100 were fairly regular, the highest count being of about 200 near Wolviston on 23 October 1971.

There is a small amount of passage through Cleveland in spring and autumn, usually in September and October, and April and early May. Rarely more than 20 birds per day are observed, although it is virtually impossible to separate fly-over Lesser Redpolls from Common Redpolls.

At least 600 Redpolls (mostly Lesser) have been ringed in the area, resulting in 10 recoveries, most being from parts of Britain to the south of Cleveland. However, a single juvenile ringed near Hartlepool in August 1971 was found in France in January 1973 and an adult ringed at Guisborough on 22 May 1977 was recorded in Belgium in October 1977. Birds ringed in the months May-September in Cleveland have been re-trapped in November - March at Fleet in Hampshire, Beachy Head in East Sussex, Chertsey and Virginia Water in Surrey. From these movements it is possible to deduce that some, if not all, of the breeding population move south for the winter and the birds seen in winter have moved into Cleveland from further north.

COMMON REDPOLL *Carduelis flammea*

Better known as the Mealy Redpoll, it is almost entirely a late autumn passage migrant and winter visitor to Cleveland. It is more inclined to feed on waste ground and open spaces than the previous species, consequently some of the records are from areas like Teesmouth, and the coastal watch-points such as Hartlepool and Redcar.

Birds have also been seen at Hunt Cliff, Boulby, Birk Brow, Guisborough, Flatts Lane, Poole Hospital, Scaling Dam, Cowpen Bewley Pond, Belasis Technology Park and Grinkle Park.

Rarely are more than 10 seen together, although at least 200 were observed along the coastline in November and December 1995, followed by 700-800 in the Eston Moor and Park Wood areas in March 1996.

ARCTIC REDPOLL *Carduelis hornemanni*

All the accepted records are of birds seen with Mealy (Common) Redpolls, and are of singles at Redcar from 9 to 28 February 1986 (caught and ringed on 11 February), in Hargreaves Quarry on 2 November 1995 (caught and ringed) and South Gare on 5 and 6 December 1995. Between four and seven birds were in Park Wood, Guisborough, on 31 March 1996 and three were at Birk Brow on 9 April 1996.

Both trapped birds were considered to be of the race *Carduelis hornemanni exilipes*.

(COMMON) CROSSBILL *Loxia curvirostra*

The number of Crossbills in Cleveland seems to fluctuate over a period of about 20 years, with known peaks in 1909-1910, 1927, the late 1950s, early 1960s and again in the early 1980s. This fluctuation is much greater than in almost all other species of finch, but the Crossbill is also different in other ways. Its specialised bill for feeding mainly on pine cones and its habit of nesting appreciably earlier than the vast majority of birds are well know, so that in years of a plentiful supply of cones, many Crossbills are reared, conversely, when poor cone crops result, birds move far and quickly. This was particularly noticeable in 1985, when the supply of cones failed in Scandinavia, forcing large numbers of Crossbills across the North Sea in early to mid-June. Many were seen on the east coast of Britain, and Grinkle Park held 200 on 18 June 1985 and probably a similar number were in suitable woodland over the rest of Cleveland.

Pairs have been known, or presumed to nest, by the Wynyard Woodland Park, Lockwood Beck, Eston Nab and Westworth Woods, and perhaps in other wooded areas, in the last 25 years. Breeding may have occurred in Cleveland every year from 1982 to

1988 (proved in 1986), 1991-1992, 1995, 1998, 2000 and 2003.

Favoured locations in recent times include Westworth Woods, Guisborough Forest, Errington Woods, Lockwood Beck, Stanghow, Upleatham, Skelton Castle, Park Wood, Eston Nab and Birk Brow. Unfortunately very few of the mature trees in Grinkle Park area remained after felling operations in the summer of 1988.

A few birds are occasionally seen away from the coniferous woodland, in woods with very small numbers of mature conifers, such as Poole Hospital, Stewart Park and Saltburn Woods. Additionally, one or two are occasionally noted and heard flying over virtually anywhere in the county and birds have been recorded at the coastal watch-points of Hartlepool and South Gare, generally between mid-June and mid-October. The biggest recent invasion on the coast occurred on 9 and 10 September 2002, when 200 were seen at both Hartlepool and South Gare.

PARROT CROSSBILL *Loxia pytyopsittacus*

A large-scale invasion of this bird into eastern Britain in late 1990 resulted in between six and 12 being present at Lockwood Beck from 11 November 1990 to late December 1990, with two or three still being there to 12 January 1991.

On 1 March 1991 about 30 were seen at Birk Brow, increasing to 47 or 48 on 3 March 1991, this being the largest number of Parrot Crossbills ever seen in Britain. Numbers then dropped to 28 on 5 March, 23 on 11 March, and four on 18 March 1991 were the last.

SCARLET ROSEFINCH *Carpodacus erythrinus*

There are 19 records of this finch for Cleveland, all but two being at coastal locations.

Date	Location	Notes - single immature/female birds unless stated
19 August 1977	Hartlepool	
23 to 30 May 1987	South Gare	
10 Oct 1990	Boulby	
31 May 1991	Lovell Hill	adult male caught and ringed
8-9 June 1992	Hartlepool	
21 May 1993	South Gare	
27 May 1993	South Gare	Pair
17 to 27 September 1994	South Gare	Up to three
8 September 1995	Hummersea	
23 September 1995	Redcar fox covert	caught
19 May 1996	Hartlepool	
19 May 1996	South Gare	
12-13 September 1996	Hartlepool	
25 September 1997	Billingham Pond	
29 May 1998	South Gare	
24 September 1999	Hartlepool	
22-23 September 2000	South Gare	
25 September 2001	South Gare	
5 October 2002	Hartlepool Golf Course	
Scarlet Rosefinch Records		

The earliest and latest spring dates are 19 May and 9 June, and the equivalent autumn dates are 19 August and 10 October; eight of the birds were seen in the second half of September.

(COMMON) BULLFINCH *Pyrrhula pyrrhula*

This rather secretive finch is widespread throughout Cleveland, though nowhere is it common. It breeds in areas of deciduous and mixed woodland and occasionally gardens in the well-wooded suburbs such as those in the Linthorpe area of Middlesbrough. However, it tends to be recorded in gardens and parks more often in the winter months.

The Bullfinch appears to have been commoner in the early years of the 20th century, and a combination of factors has been responsible for its decline. Destruction of habitat is probably the main cause, although at one time numbers were trapped, along with Goldfinches, by cage-bird fanciers and it has always been unpopular with some gardeners and persecuted throughout Britain because of its appetite for buds. Nelson (1907) records 300 Bullfinches being killed in one year around Grinkle.

The Teesmouth Bird Club conducted surveys of the species in 1982 and 1997, and it would appear that Bullfinch breeds in about 30-40 localities within the county and has a population of about 120-160 pairs.

The largest winter gatherings in recent years include 13 in Stewart Park on 22 February 1959, 25 at Graythorp on 11 December 1965, about 30 in Saltburn Woods on 1 February 1969, 18 at Wynyard Woodland Park on 9 January 1986 and 17 at Billingham on 6 January 1999. Such gatherings are probably quite normal, but the species secretiveness renders it rather difficult to count at times.

The larger Northern Bullfinch *Pyrrhula pyrrhula pyrrhula* is recorded in most years in Britain and birds showing the characteristics of this subspecies have been reported from Loftus, singles on 17 January 1948, 28 February 1951 and 1 March 1951 and two on 21 February 1950; Marske on 1 February 1959; Saltburn in December 1959; Hartlepool on 20 April 1962, 18 October 1990 and 26 April 1995; South Gare on 22 October 1974 and 23 to 30 April 1995; and Lockwood Beck on 23 October 1990. Also small influxes along the coastline occurred in mid-October 1994 (at least 15) and 2004 (at least 16).

Historically single Bullfinches were recorded as landing on the Tees Light Vessel anchored in the navigational channel just off the mouth of the river in March, April and November 1884, as well as October 1884 and 1887. These may have been birds of the northern race.

More than 2,000 Bullfinches have been ringed in Cleveland, yet there are no reports of significant movement, indicating a sedentary nature for this species.

HAWFINCH *Coccothraustes coccothraustes*

This large finch must rate as one of the most secretive of Cleveland's birds, but the persecution that the Hawfinch has suffered in the last 100 years or more renders this habit almost desirable, as well as understandable.

Nelson (1907) records a colony, since thought to be in the Ormesby area, in 1897 which held 20-30 pairs, but nearby pea-growers killed 35 birds in 1902 and at least 50 in 1916. Not surprisingly, this colony no longer exists, although habitat destruction will also have played a part in the local decline.

Apart from the colony previously mentioned, Nelson recorded the bird nesting sparsely "between Loftus and Yarm", and by 1917 breeding was also recorded at Yarm, Wolviston, Wynyard and Dalton Piercy. In the 1980s, breeding was confirmed or pairs seen in summer at Saltburn, Skelton, Guisborough, Marton and Wynyard as well as Ormesby-Normanby. During this period, birds were also noted at Grinkle Park, Moorsholm, Poole Hospital and Lovell Hill - Wilton. This gave a breeding population in Cleveland of about 10-15 pairs, but this bird has continued to decline through the 1990's and by 2003 Hawfinches were probably breeding only in the Hutton Gate - Hutton Village area.

Hawfinches are generally easier to observe during the winter months and the Guisborough area has provided many such records in recent years. Apart from the Hutton Gate area, the trees around the sewage farm, the Priory and the disused railway line have held a bird or two. Stewart Park and Saltburn Woods also had a few birds in the winter months, up to 5-6 being reported at least in the 1980's.

The maximum counts for Cleveland are 20 at Skelton Castle on 7 May 1991, and up to 18 in Guisborough - Hutton Village area in January 1992.

Very occasionally birds are recorded in coastal localities, perhaps indicating continental origin. There have been at least five single birds seen in Locke Park in the last 30 years or so, all in April, except for a single bird on 1 June 1983. One was caught and ringed on Hartlepool Headland on 19 April 1962, but was found dead next day, and one was seen in the same place on 20 October 2004.

LAPLAND BUNTING (LAPLAND LONGSPUR)
Calcarius lapponicus

As a winter visitor, this bird is noted every year, being seen in variable numbers between mid-October and mid-March, principally on Cowbar, Redcar - Marske fields, Seaton Common and the Cowpen Marsh - Brinefields area.

In most years one or two birds appear in September, usually at the coastal migration points, such as Hartlepool Headland and South Gare, and occasionally they are also seen there in April and May. The earliest date is 3 September (1965) and the latest 1 June (1983), both being at South Gare. The June bird was a male in resplendent breeding plumage. Occasionally, males in transitional plumage are heard giving a sub-song on sunny days in March, prior to their departure.

A visit to the coastal fields between Redcar and Marske in the months November-February used to yield Lapland Buntings in most winters, the maximum count for Cleveland being made at this locality, about 130 on 8 January 1980. Usually there were 10-20 birds on these fields, and 10-15 on Seaton Common, Cowpen Marsh, Saltholme Pools and Boulby - Cowbar Cliffs, and less frequently, the Long Drag area. Since 1994, numbers have declined quite dramatically, with eight being the maximum count and in some years only two to four birds are recorded.

There are several inland records: singles at Scaling Dam on 6 December 1959 and 28 February 1988, near Wilton on 29 October 1972 and 20 April 1991, Bowesfield on 9 December 1995, Skelton on 8 November 1996 and Longnewton Reservoir on 17 and 30 November 2002.

SNOW BUNTING *Plectrophenax nivalis*

This species is perhaps the most aesthetically pleasing of the regular winter visiting passerines to Cleveland, the sight and sound of a flock of Snow Buntings frequently being the highlight of a day's birdwatching.

Their regular winter haunt is the tide line of sandy beaches, especially around North and South Gares, and sometimes, when the weather is bad, in any of the nearby coastal fields. There are a few records of birds well inland in Cleveland, mostly singles or very small parties, although about 140 were at Stanghow on 9 November 1958, about 100 at Scaling Dam on 6 December 1959 and about 60 flew inland over Wynyard Woodland Park on 19 November 1987. Inland birds have also been recorded at places like Guisborough Moor, Sleddale, Roseberry Topping, Moorsholm Moor, Lovell Hill and Greatham.

The first autumn birds usually appear in early October, although they have been seen as early as 8 September (1968). Numbers build up over several weeks, the peak invariably being reached in the four months November-February. Up to 1996, the highest counts were generally between 150 and 350, but since then the peak has been around 80-130. The highest counts are approximately 1,000 near Graythorp on 25 November 1961, about 500 by Seal Sands on 16 December 1971 and about 550 at South Gare on 21 December 1984.

Numbers dwindle rapidly in March, sometimes there being no records after the end of the month. However, males have occasionally been heard singing in mid to late March, with the latest recorded date 8 May (1997).

Since 1976, about 1,900 Snow Buntings have been ringed at Teesmouth, resulting in at least 20 recoveries. All birds have been ringed in January or February, near North or South Gare, and controls have been made within two to three months at Cambois in Northumberland, Musselburgh in Lothian, Kirkcaldy in Fife and in several areas of Highland Region such as Cairngorm and Glen Shee. Single birds have been seen at Hunstanton in Norfolk and Glen Shee in Highland in the following winter. One caught at Seaton Carew in February had been ringed at Titchwell in Norfolk in the previous February and singles ringed at Salthouse, Norfolk, on 9 November 1993 and 22 January 1994 were both at Redcar on 7 February 1994. Another three Norfolk-ringed birds, from Heacham on 6 January 1998 and 13 December 1999 (two), were at South Gare on 21

February 1998, 26 February and 5 March 2000 respectively and a Suffolk-ringed bird, from Felixstowe Ferry on 30 January 1999 was also at South Gare, on 27 February 1999. This shows that Snow Buntings begin to move north well before winter is over. Also one ringed at South Gare on 3 March 1985 was found dead at Neuenkirchen, Rostock, on the north coast of Germany on 25 January 1986, and one ringed at South Gare on 26 December 1995 was controlled at Austur Skaftafells in Iceland on 16 March 1999. The vast majority of the wintering birds are immature females and it is very unusual for an individual to return in following winters. Birds ringed at Spurn, Humberside, have been found in Belgium, Norway, Iceland and Orkney in the following springs.

During the winter of 1972/73, a completely off-white bird was seen in the usual Teesmouth flock from mid-November to early February. A second, similar, bird was also noted, but only on one day in mid-November 1972.

YELLOWHAMMER *Emberiza citrinella*

A resident which can be found throughout Cleveland, this bunting is one of the commonest birds in the agricultural habitat, although it has declined nationally in recent years. Reasons for this include changes in agricultural practises and the destruction of hedgerows by some farmers and developers.

Historically Yellowhammer was probably a bird of scrubland and it can still be found in areas of hawthorn, bracken and gorse, such as on the Eston Hills and around Flatts Lane. It will also utilise young conifer plantations which generally have an assortment of other plants like gorse and bracken growing amongst them.

The area of farmland near Pinchinthorpe, on which the Common Bird Census was conducted from 1962 to 2000, showed a marked fluctuation from five pairs in 1962-63 to none to two pairs in the years 1964-80, then up to six to seven pairs in 1982-83 and 11-16 pairs in 1984-86. This appears to be a very localised fluctuation rather than a Cleveland-wide one, there being no noticeable increase in other areas of the county in the 1980s, but no other location was surveyed as accurately year by year.

From this study area, it would seem that the Cleveland population is approximately 600-800 pairs. The size of the winter flocks does not appear to have altered dramatically in recent years, up to 100 birds in a scattered flock being the normal winter maximum, although about 300 were noted around Upleatham on 15 March 1980 and on Hartlepool Golf Course on 15 December 1981. Winter flocks can be found almost anywhere around farmland, though stubble fields and haystacks are especially favoured. Severe winter weather sometimes pushes flocks close to the coastline, though in general Cleveland Yellowhammers do not appear to move much throughout their lives.

At least 1,000 have been ringed in Cleveland, but the only two interesting reports concern individuals ringed at Graythorp and Wilton in December 1960 and July 1964 respectively which were both found at their place of ringing, the first in July 1965 and the second in September 1969. The first bird indicates that the species may summer and winter in the same area; the second was over 5 years old when retrapped.

Very few birds are seen at the coastal migration points, generally only one or two birds per year, although occasionally north European birds have been found elsewhere in Britain.

CIRL BUNTING *Emberiza cirlus*

A male at Redcar on 17 September 1960 is the only record of this bunting. It appeared during a big fall of migrants.

ORTOLAN BUNTING *Emberiza hortulana*

Since the first 20th century record for this bird in Cleveland in 1968, this European bunting has averaged about one bird every two and a half years, all but one being during autumn passage and most being seen at Hartlepool. The majority of birds have been immatures.

The spring record concerned a beautiful male at Hartlepool on 7 May 1970, and the autumn records (for Hartlepool) are singles on 14 September 1968, 14-15 August 1969, 2 October 1976, 18 August 1979, 20-21 August 1983, 27 August 1986, 14 to 16 September 1993 and 9-10 September 1995.

The records away from Hartlepool are: three in spring, about 1865, near Guisborough; singles near Guisborough on 16 August 1863 and 2 October 1971; singles at South Gare on 25 September 1977, 9 to 16 September 1993 (two on 16 September 1993) and 8 September 1994; at Seaton Carew on 9 September 1995; at Hummersea on 10 September 1995; at Boulby on 4 September 1998 and at Zinc Works Road 10-11 September 2005.

Apart from the May 1970 bird, the earliest and latest dates are 14 August (1969) and 2 October (1971 and 1976), and only two out of the 17 birds since 1968 have stayed more than two days.

RUSTIC BUNTING *Emberiza rustica*

There are nine records of this European bunting for Cleveland, seven in autumn and two in spring, though spring records are relatively scarce in Britain as a whole.

The first was near North Gare on 7 September 1958, then one was in Locke Park on 9 and 10 May 1975; followed by one at Hartlepool on 17 and 18 September 1976; one at

South Gare on 29 and 30 September 1984, 22 April 1990 and 16 to 22 September 1993; Locke Park on 25 September 1994; Coatham Marsh on 6 October 1998 and Hartlepool again on 25 September 2000. Only the April 1990 bird was an adult male.

LITTLE BUNTING *Emberiza pusilla*

This small bunting has been recorded eleven times in Cleveland, all birds occurring in the autumn.

The first was shot at Seaton Snook on 11 October 1902 and was the second British record for this species (Milburn 1904). More recently, singles were: near New Marske Reservoir on 11 November 1967; at South Gare from 3 to 7 October 1972, 25 October 1988, 12 September 1989, 19 October 1990, 26 September 2000 and 27 October 2005; Hartlepool on 30 September and 1 October 1983 and 10-11 September 2005; and Locke Park from 11 to 14 September 1989.

REED BUNTING *Emberiza schoeniclus*

This bunting is predominantly a bird of marshland and water-side vegetation and thus it is most numerous around Teesmouth, with approximately 100 pairs spread around the North Tees Marshes and about 60 pairs in South Gare - Teesport - Coatham Marsh. In addition there are quite a few small marshy areas around Cleveland that hold a few pairs, such as Margrove Ponds, Lovell Hill, Scaling Dam, Billingham Bottoms and Portrack Marsh. Although predominantly a marsh bird, farmland also has a scattering of Reed Buntings, particularly if there are streams or pools close by. The overall Cleveland population is estimated at about 500-600 pairs.

After the breeding season, small flocks gather in the marshy areas, maximum counts generally being around 50-60, though 80 were present near Port Clarence in August 1974, 100 at South Gare on 6 October 1998, 90 by the Long Drag on 13 October 2002 and 140 on Cowpen Marsh on 17 January 2004.

A few birds are occasionally seen on the coast in autumn, but very few in spring. At least nine on Hartlepool Headland on 7 October 1977 is the biggest count of apparent migrants, these birds arriving with large numbers of thrushes and other migrants. Judging by the few ringing recoveries, it seems likely that the flocks, when present, are made up of mostly local birds, with a few from elsewhere in northern Britain and the occasional continental bird.

Ringing has shown that there is some movement of birds within Britain. One ringed at South Gare in October 1971 was at Wintersett Reservoir near Wakefield, West Yorkshire, in December 1972, one ringed in Hargreaves Quarry on 16 October 1977 was at Thurlestone, Devon, on 26 November 1977 and one ringed at Haverton Hole on 13

August 1983 was near Rotherham, South Yorkshire, on 26 January 1984. However, one ringed at Billingham in January 1985 was at Greatham in April 1985, indicating that at least some of the breeding birds winter locally. Perhaps the severity of the winter determines how far they move, as is probably the case with many so called 'resident' birds. Another ringed at Saltholme Pools on 23 July 1988 was at Walcot, Shropshire, on 1 December 1988, one ringed at Haverton Hole on 23 July 1994 was on Jersey on 22 February 1997, one ringed near Hexham, Northumberland, on 26 July 1997 was in Hargreaves Quarry on 18 October 1997, one ringed at Haverton Hole on 30 August 1997 was at Wing, Buckinghamshire, on 22 January 1998, one ringed at Pocklington, Humberside, on 29 December 2000 was at Billingham Bottoms on 9 June 2001 and one ringed by the Long Drag on 21 September 2002 was at West Felton, Shropshire, on 24 November 2002. Finally, one ringed in Vest-Agder, Norway, on 14 October 2001 was by the Long Drag on 13 October 2002, indicating that this species does cross the North Sea.

At least 5,500 Reed Buntings have been ringed in Cleveland and the very small number of significant movements indicates a rather sedentary nature.

CORN BUNTING *Miliaria calandra*

Chislett (1952) described this large, rather undistinguished bunting as "local but not rare" in Yorkshire, a status which was very similar in Cleveland until the 1990s. It is a bird of farmland, but has declined over the last 10 years to the extent that it is now only seen with any regularity in the Hart, Elwick and Dalton Piercy areas. It has disappeared from many other places in the 1990s, including Redmarshall, Cowpen Bewley, Boulby, Marske and Pinchinthorpe.

The Cleveland breeding population was estimated at about 500 pairs in 1985, but only about 25 pairs in 1995 and perhaps three pairs in 2007. Something over 1,000 Corn Buntings were estimated to be present in Cleveland throughout the winter months in the 1970s and early 1980s, but only about 80-100 in the winter months in 1995, and 16 in the winter of 2003/2004. The highest count was 180 between Hart and Hartlepool on 5 February 1970.

Small numbers occasionally visited other areas away from known breeding sites, including Coatham Marsh in May and South Gare at various times, but there are no recent records of birds near the coast.

About 150 birds have been ringed in Cleveland, and the only known control concerns one ringed at Newton Bewley on 14 February 1984 that was near Seal Sands on 18 January 1985.

PRESUMED ESCAPES

CHILEAN FLAMINGO *Phoenicopterus ruber chilensis*
Apart from one passing Redcar on 27 July 1994 and one at Scaling Dam on 28 March 1995, all records are from Teesmouth: singles in February 1953, November-December 1964, August 1967, September 1971-May 1980 and irregularly July 1982 to January 1998, two birds seen in October-November 1965, November 1975-February 1976 and throughout 1991 and 1992 to May 1993. A bird constructed a mud nest at Wilton in 1980s.

STRAW-NECKED IBIS *Threskiornis spinicollis*
One was at Saltburn on 16 June 1992.

FULVOUS WHISTLING DUCK *Dendrocygna bicolor*
Single birds were by the Redcar Ore Terminal on 24 May 1998, Albert Park, Middlesbrough on 11 October 2000, Belasis Technology Park on 16 October 2000 and 1-2 at Scaling Dam on 12-13 June 2007.

WHITE-FACED WHISTLING DUCK *Dendrocygna viduata*
One was at Scaling Dam on 31 May 2007.

BLACK SWAN *Cygnus atratus*
Singles were on Saltholme Pools in June 1979, on Coatham Marsh in May 1980, June 1987 and May 1998, and single pairs were around the North Tees Marshes from 30 April to 2 May 1980 and June to October 1998. Two pinioned pairs were at Stewart Park in the 1990s and an unpinioned pair was introduced to a pond by the Tall Trees Hotel, Yarm, in 1986. Cygnets have been recorded at Stewart Park in some years between 1990 and 2000, one juvenile being seen in Ropner Park and at Teesmouth early in 1992. Also one was on Scaling Dam on 20 November 2004. Recent sightings are one at Dormans Pool, Saltholme Pools and the River Tees, Stockton between 9 June 2006 and 12 October 2006, a second bird was also seen from 9 September 2006.

LESSER WHITE-FRONTED GOOSE *Anser erythropus*
An adult was on Saltholme Pools on 15 June 2006.

BAR-HEADED GOOSE *Anser indicus*
Most records refer to birds on Scaling Dam; two were present on 7 June 1983 and 9 June 1998, plus singles from September 1997 to January 1998 and June to August 2004. Others include singles on Seaton Common on 10 March 1984, Seal Sands on 23 April 1988, two passed Saltburn on 19 June 1993, six flew from Reclamation Pond on 22 June 1993, one was on Saltholme Pools on 9 and 10 June 2002, three being there for the next week, one was in Wynyard in November 2003 and February 2004, two were on Seaton Common on 31 May and 1 June 2005.

EMPEROR GOOSE *Anser canagicus*
One was seen at North Gare and South Gare on 26 May 1995, but found dead next day.

ROSS'S GOOSE *Anser rossi*
One was on Saltholme Pools on 5 October 2007.

RUDDY SHELDUCK *Tadorna ferruginea*
This species is occurring in ever-increasing numbers in Britain, so one day may be regarded as a countable species, as opposed to an escaped bird.
Singles were at Teesmouth 19 May-21 June 1988, 23 March-18 June 1989, 23 August 1989, 10 February-8 July 1990, 6 September 1990, 31 December 1990-20 January 1991, 22 June-3 July 1991 and 18 June 2005, and Scaling Dam on 20 August 1989. Also, four were at Lovell Hill for a week from 2 August 1994, two were on Saltholme Pools on 28 June 2004 and three at Bowesfield from 1 to 7 August 2004, two still being there on 8 August 2004.

CAPE SHELDUCK *Tadorna cana*
Singles seen on Seal Sands 1 September-1 November 1967 and 23 October-12 November 1977.

WOOD DUCK *Aix sponsa*
A duck was in Ward Jackson Park, Hartlepool from at least 16 March to 3 April 1993, two drakes were at Saltburn from 28 May to 27 June 1996, one remaining to 7 July 1996, a drake was at Belasis Technology Park from 27 August to 6 September 1999, and a tame duck was in Locke Park from March to May 2004, perhaps the same bird being on the River Tees at Stockton from December 2004, to May 2005.

AUSTRALIAN WOOD DUCK *Chenonetta jubata*
One seen by the Long Drag and on Dormans Pool in early August 1987.

CHILOE WIGEON *Anas sibilatrix*
One was around Teesmouth during 24 September-30 October 1976, 22 September 1995 and 26 November 1999.

PUNA TEAL *Anas puna*
One present around the North Tees Marshes during 17 July-6 September 1979, on Coatham Marsh on 29 September 1979 and in Locke Park on 6 October 1979.

SILVER TEAL *Anas versicolor*
One seen around North Tees Marshes from 10 July to 2 September 1991.

SPECKLED TEAL *Anas flavirostvis*
One at Scaling Dam from 26 October to 2 November 2006.

CAPE TEAL *Anas capensis*
A pair seen on Coatham Marsh on 18 May 1986 and one at the same place on 11 February 1987.

WHITE-CHEEKED PINTAIL *Anas bahamensis*
One at Saltholme Pools on 10 September 1995 and Greatham Creek on 4 October 1995.
CINNAMON TEAL *Anas cyanoptera*
A male at Saltholme Pools on 8 May 1994 carried a pale blue colour ring, and a different male was on Cowpen Marsh on 22 April 2003.
RINGED TEAL *Callonetta leucophrys*
A duck was near Teesmouth Field Centre on 9 October 1977, a drake was on Crookfoot Reservoir 20-21 October 1993, a duck was at Billingham Beck Valley in February and March 1996, three drakes were on the Brinefields on 14 July 2003 and a duck was at Ward Jackson Park from 15 May 2006 to 19 March 2007.
WHITE-HEADED DUCK *Oxyura leucocephala*
A drake was present on Saltholme Pools, Dormans Pool and the Reclamation Pond from 29 March to 24 October 2004 and 29 March - 7 April 2005. This species may be added to the official British List in the future.
WHITE PELICAN *Pelecanus onocrotalus*
One was on Saltholme Pools on 26 August 2006.
REEVE'S PHEASANT *Syrmaticus reevesii*
One seen by Scaling Dam on 15 December 1983, one was at Skelton Castle on 8 April 1999 and one was found dead at Billingham in September 2002.
HARRIS' HAWK *Parabuteo unicinctus*
Singles or the same bird were seen at Seaton Common on 31 October 2001, Cowpen Bewley Pond on 13 January 2002 and Greatham Creek on 27 January 2002.
RUPPELL'S GRIFFON VULTURE *Gyps rueppellii*
One was in Sleddale on 8 and 9 March 2007, then at Skelton Castle to 21 March 2007.
DEMOISELLE CRANE *Anthropoides virgo*
Four were near Cowpen Bewley during 6-12 July 1967, two remaining to 17 September 1967.
MOUNTAIN QUAIL *Oreortyx pictus*
One was in a Nunthorpe garden from 13 to 15 April 1993.
PALM DOVE *Streptopelia senegalensis*
One was found dead at Kirkleatham in early February 1994.
BARBARY DOVE *Streptopelia risoria*
One was at Hutton Gate, Guisborough in December 1968 and January 1969, and one was in Locke Park on 6 and 7 April 1989.
DIAMOND DOVE *Geopelia cuneata*
One was in Billingham on 16 September 2003.

CROAKING GROUND-DOVE *Columbina cruziana*
One was in a garden at Carlton, near Stockton, from mid-September 1992 to 27 April 1993.

COCKATIEL *Nymphicus hollandicus*
Several seen in recent years, including birds at Hartlepool and South Gare.

SUPERB PARROT *Polytelis swainsonii*
One flew over Cowpen Marsh on 20 April 1997.

CRIMSON ROSELLA *Platycercus elegans*
One was at Hartlepool on 27 June 1998.

EASTERN ROSELLA *Platycercus eximius*
One was at Lockwood Beck in November and December 1995, and one was in Billingham on 25 July 1997.

RED-RUMPED PARROT *Psephotus haematonotus*
One near Guisborough from May 1994 into 1995.

AFRICAN GREY PARROT *Psittacus erithacus*
One flew south-west over Middlesbrough on 23 June 1994.

BUDGERIGAR *Melopsittacus undulatus*
Single birds quite frequently seen around Cleveland, including Teesmouth and the coast-line.

FISCHER'S LOVEBIRD *Agapornis fischeri*
One seen in Seaton Cemetery and over North Gare bushes on 9 August 1975.

ALEXANDRINE PARAKEET *Psittacula eupatria*
One was present in Middlesbrough from 1997 to 2005.

BLUE-CROWNED PARAKEET *Aratinga acuticordata*
One was in Marton on 28 August 2003 and 6 November 2003.

BLACK-HOODED PARAKEET *Nandayus nenday*
One was in Billingham on 4 December 2007.

PATAGONIAN CONURE *Cyanoliseus patagonus*
One was near Thornaby on 7 November 1997 and 22-23 December 1997.

EAGLE OWL *Bubo bubo*
Singles at Hummersea on 5 November 1875 and Redcar in October 1915 might have been wild birds, but the species has been commonly kept in captivity since the 19th Century, so all birds seen in this area are of doubtful origin. An individual with jesses was in Guisborough on 19 October 2004. One made the news when it moved from Stewart Park to Middlesbrough during November 2006, staying to April 2007.

RED-HEADED BUNTING *Emberiza bruniceps*
Single males were seen at Hartlepool on 11 September 1965 and 3-4 June 1971, in Hargreaves Quarry on 5 June 1976, and at Haverton Hole on 2 September 1989. A total of seven birds in Yorkshire between 1956 and 1976 all occurred in the months May, June and September.

POPE CARDINAL *Paroaria dominicana*
One seen in Locke Park in mid-August 1960 and one at Cargo Fleet in about 1964.

CANARY *Serinus canaria*
One-two birds quite frequently seen around habitation and at places like Saltholme Pools and South Gare.

YELLOW-FRONTED CANARY *Serinus mozambicus*
Singles were at Nunthorpe 3-6 July 1994 and Guisborough August-October 1994 and September 1999.

ZEBRA FINCH *Poephila guttata*
One was in Locke Park on 18 October 1994, a white bird was at Skelton Castle on 7 August 1997, a normal-coloured bird was dead at Skelton Castle on 6 November 2003, one was at Marton on 20 June 2004, at Redcar on 19 May 2005 and Skelton Castle on 31 October 2005.

JAVA SPARROW *Pada oryzivora*
One was in Middlesbrough in 1934 and one at Hartlepool Headland in about 1969.

RED-BILLED QUELEA *Quelea quelea*
One seen in a cemetery in central Hartlepool in about 1968.

BLACK-WINGED RED BISHOP *Euplectes hordeacea*
A male was in Nunthorpe in the summer of 2002.

RED-BILLED BLUE MAGPIE *Urocissa erythrorhyncha*
One in central Hartlepool on 16 September 1993.

GLOSSARY

Beached Birds Survey
Once a year count in February of dead birds found along the shore line. Organised by the Royal Society for the Protection of Birds.

Colour-ringing
The marking of birds by placing a coloured plastic ring or combination of coloured rings on their legs so that they can be individually recognized in the field without the need to recatch them, as is required with birds with numbered metal rings.

Common Birds Census (CBC)
A mapping technique covering the UK used by the British Trust for Ornithology from 1962-1996 to count birds in open country. Observers made 10 visits to a designated site during the breeding season and plotted on a map all birds recorded, together with an indication of their activity (singing, nest-building, etc.). The results from all the species maps were then analysed to provide an estimate of the abundance of the species in the UK for the habitat covered. The CBC was replaced by the Breeding Bird Survey (BBS) in 1994. The BBS is a much simpler technique based on two 1,000 metre transect counts within a 1-km National Grid square.

Control
A term to indicate a bird marked with a metal numbered ring has been recaptured alive and then released, rather than one found dead.

Fall
A mass arrival of migrant birds grounded by inclement weather conditions, particularly noticeable on the coast.

First-summer
A bird that has hatched the previous year, normally recognized by plumage differences from an older or full adult bird. The term first-year is sometimes used to cover first-winter and first-summer birds.

Hirundines
Birds such as swallows and martins, which have streamlined bodies and catch their insect prey on the wing.

Hybrid

A cross between different, but usually closely related, species. The offspring are viable, but not necessarily fertile. Many hybrids birds seen in the wild are the result of cross-mating by aviculturists, but a few also occur naturally in the wild. Hybrid birds usually show intermediate characters of the parent species.

Irruption

An irregular mass arrival (migration) of certain species, usually associated with high population and/or food shortage in their native region.

Leucism

Partial loss of pigments affecting all the colours present and reducing them in intensity, resulting in unusually pale birds, often referred to as 'dilute'. Unlike albino birds, in which all pigmentation is absent, it is possible to detect the plumage pattern in leucistic birds.

Melanism

Darkening of the plumage caused by an increase of the black/brown melanin pigments and by its spread to other parts of the plumage that normally lack melanins. Less common than leucism and albinism.

Moult

The full or partial replacement of feathers. All species have an annual moult, typically after completion of the breeding cycle, but some (e.g. waders and the males of ducks) replace their bright plumage after the breeding season by a dull one and have a second moult prior to breeding when the more conspicuous breeding plumage is restored. Others (e.g. sparrows) have a post-juvenile moult when the adult plumage is adopted.

National Significance Threshold

A wetland in Britain is considered nationally important if it regularly holds 1% or more of the estimated British numbers of one species or subspecies of water bird.

Population estimates are revised every three years in keeping with internationally agreed timetables. The National Threshold is used as a generic term to imply the 1% British threshold for sites in Great Britain. The term "National Importance" implies sites that meet this threshold.

Passage migrant

A species that neither breeds nor winters in the area, but passes through between breeding and wintering grounds.

Pelagic species

A species that spends most of the year over deep oceanic waters, coming ashore only for breeding.

Phase

Different form of the same species, better referred to as a morph of a polymorphic species; i.e. a species that occurs in one or more forms.

Pinioned

A bird that has one wing removed at the carpal joint so that it is incapable of flight and used particularly to contain collections of wildfowl and large ground birds.

Pullus

A nestling prior to fledging.

Race

A geographical population of species, which is slightly different from other populations of that species; also called a sub species.

Ringtail

The female or juvenile of Harriers (Circus spp.) showing a characteristic white patch at the base of the tail.

Roding

The flight of a Woodcock over or around its territory at dusk.

Species

This is a disputed concept. In 1895, Darwin posed the question "What is a species?" in his Origin of Species. The answer he gave was "No one definition has yet satisfied every naturalist." This answer still holds good today. There are currently two widely used concepts. The Biological Species Concept (BSC) defines a species as a group of organisms that breed freely in the wild producing fertile young; the problem with the BSC is how to deal with groups that do not naturally come into contact. The Phenological Species Concept (PSC) defines the species as the smallest group for which there is a parental pattern of ancestry and descent; the problem with the PSC is what characteristic, or combination of characteristics, should be used to determine common ancestry. It should be noted that subspecies (q.v.) are not recognized by the PSC and, increasingly, particularly through the use of DNA analysis, there has been a splitting of previously recognized species into two or even more 'full' species, some of which are not even distinguishable in the field! The result is that the definition of a 'full species' is currently in a fluid state and it has to be appreciated that even separation on the basis of DNA analysis still depends on subjective criteria. Decisions on the status of birds on the British List are published from time to time by the Taxonomic Sub-Committee of The British Ornithologists' Union Records Committee.

Speculum

A distinctively coloured area on the wing of a bird, especially the metallic coloured patch on ducks.

Sub species

See Race

Summer visitor

A migrant present only during the breeding season, though in some species a few individuals may overwinter (e.g. Blackcap).

Vagrant species

A rare accidental visitor hundreds of miles off course, usually seen at migration times, frequently during a 'fall' (q.v.). Conventionally applied in Cleveland to species with less than 10 records.

Wetland Bird Survey (WeBS)

A monitoring scheme in the UK for non-breeding waterbirds on all wetlands, including coasts, estuaries and inland waters. Organised by a partnership between BTO, WWT (Wildfowl & Wetlands Trust), RSPB and JNCC (Joint Nature Conservation Committee).

Winter visitor

A migrant species that normally occurs only in the winter months.

REFERENCES

Almond, W. E. et. al.	1939	Birds of the Tees Valley. *Trans. North. Nat. Union.* 1:229
Beck, B.	1999	Hume's Yellow-browed Warbler – New to Cleveland. In : G. Iceton ed. *Cleveland Bird Report.* Teesmouth Bird Club.
Beck, B.	2000	Short-billed Dowitcher – New to Cleveland. In: G. Iceton ed. *Cleveland Bird Report.* Teesmouth Bird Club.
Bell, T.	1999	Red-breasted Goose – New to Cleveland. In: G. Iceton ed. *Cleveland Bird Report.* Teesmouth Bird Club.
Blick, M. A.	1978	*The Birds of Tees-side.* 1968-1973. Teesmouth Bird Club.
Blick, M. A.	1999	King Eider – New to Cleveland. In: G. Iceton ed. *Cleveland Bird Report.* Teesmouth Bird Club.
Blick, M. A.	2000	Pallid Swift – New to Cleveland. In: G. Iceton ed. *Cleveland Bird Report.* Teesmouth Bird Club.
Blick, M. A.	1995	Citrine Wagtail – New to Cleveland. In: D. G. Bell ed. *Cleveland Bird Report.* Teesmouth Bird Club
Blick, M. A.	2006	Cetti's Warbler – New to Cleveland. In: G. Joynt ed. *Cleveland Bird Report.* Teesmouth Bird Club
Blick, M. A	1999	Little Swift – New to Cleveland. In: G. Iceton ed. *Cleveland Bird Report.* Teesmouth Bird Club.
Booth, M.	1845	Occurrence of Bearded Titmouse in Cleveland, and Notes on the Osprey. *Zoologist.* 3:1135
Brown, A.& Price, P.	2005	*Birds in England.* T & A. D. Poyser. London.
Chislett, R.	1952	*Yorkshire Birds.* Brown & Sons. Hull.
Coates, B. J.	1960	Dusky Thrush in County Durham. *British Birds.* 53:275
Combridge, P.& Parr, C.	1992	Influx of Little Egrets in Britain and Ireland in 1989. *British Birds* 85:16-21
Cowton, D.	1996	Spotted Sandpiper – New to Cleveland. In: D. G. Bell ed. *Cleveland Bird Report.* Teesmouth Bird Club

Dunnett, J.	1992	Long-toed Stint: New to Britain and Ireland. *British Birds.* 85: 431-436
Dunnett, J.	2005	Long-toed Stint in Cleveland. In: A. Pitches, & T. Cleeves. *Birds New to Britain 1986-2004.* T & A. D. Poyser. London.
Evans, P.	1953	Terek Sandpiper in County Durham. *British Birds.* 46: 188
Foster, I.	1996	Great Spotted Cuckoo - New to Cleveland. In: D. G. Bell ed. Cleveland Bird Report. Teesmouth Bird Club.
Galloway, B. & Meek, E. R.	1978/ 83	Northumberland's Birds. *Trans. Nat. Hist. Soc. Northumbria.* Vol. 44.
Gantlett, S. & Millington, R.	2000	Honey Buzzards in September 2000. *Birding World* 13:363-365
Gee, M.	1997	Great Knot - New to Cleveland. In: D. G. Bell ed. *Cleveland Bird Report.* Teesmouth Bird Club.
Hogg, J.	1845	A Catalogue of the Birds Observed in South-eastern Durham and North-western Cleveland. *Zoologist.* 3:1049, 1106, 1169
Joynt, G., Parker, E.C. & Fairbrother, J.V.	2008.	*The Breeding Birds of Cleveland.* Teesmouth Bird Club
Joynt, G.	1999	Snow Goose - An Addition to the Cleveland List. In: G. Iceton ed. *Cleveland Bird Report.* Teesmouth Bird Club.
Joynt, G.,	1998	Balearic Shearwaters in Cleveland. In: M. Blick et. al. eds. *Cleveland Bird Report.* Teesmouth Bird Club.
Joynt, G.	1996	Pacific Golden Plover - New to Cleveland. In: D. G. Bell ed. *Cleveland Bird Report.* Teesmouth Bird Club.
Joynt, G.	1995	Pied Wheatear - New to Cleveland. In: D. G. Bell ed. *Cleveland Bird Report.* Teesmouth Bird Club
Lawson, I.	1997	A Wintering Woodlark in Cleveland. In: D. G. Bell ed. *Cleveland Bird Report.* Teesmouth Bird Club.
Ledley, R. C. B. & Pedler, E. G.	1938	Nesting of the Little Ringed Plover in Hertfordshire. *British Birds* 32:90-102
Little, R.	1996	Red-rumped Swallow - New to Cleveland. In: D. G. Bell ed. *Cleveland Bird Report.* Teesmouth Bird Club.
Mather, J. R.	1986	*The Birds of Yorkshire.* Croom Helm. London.

Milburn, C. E.	1904	The Occurrence of the Little Bunting (*Emberiza pusilla*) at Teesmouth (County Durham). Proc. *Cleveland Naturalist's Field Club*. 1:258
Mitchell, H.	2001	Desert Wheatear – New to Cleveland. In: G. Iceton ed. *Cleveland Bird Report*. Teesmouth Bird Club.
Money, D.	2002	Red-flanked Bluetail – New to Cleveland. In: R. Little ed. *Cleveland Bird Report*. Teesmouth Bird Club.
Money, D.	2001	Desert Lesser Whitethroat – New to Cleveland. In: G. Iceton ed. *Cleveland Bird Report*. Teesmouth Bird Club.
Nelson, T. H.	1907	*The Birds of Yorkshire*. Brown & Sons. London.
Prest, I.	1965	An Enquiry into the Recent Breeding Status of some Smaller Birds of prey and Crows in Britain. *Bird Study*. 12:196-221
Sharp, C.	1816	*The History of Hartlepool*. Durham.
Sharp, J. L.	1995	Bufflehead – New to Cleveland. In: D. G. Bell ed. *Cleveland Bird Report*. Teesmouth Bird Club
Stead, P. J.	1964	The Birds of Tees-side. *Trans. Nat. Hist. Soc. Northumberland*. 15 (1):1-59.
Stead, P. J.	1969	*The Birds of Tees-side 1962-1967*. Teesmouth Bird Club.
Strickland, A.	1832	*Proc. Zoo. Soc.* (ii) 129
Summers-Smith, J. D.	1963	*The House Sparrow*. Collins. London.
Taverner, J. H.	1959	The Spread of the Eider in Great Britain. *British Birds*. 52:245-258
Taylor, R.	2000	Lesser Scaup – New to Cleveland. In: G. Iceton ed. *Cleveland Bird Report*. Teesmouth Bird Club.
Temperley, G. W.	1951	A History of the Birds of Durham. *Trans. Nat. Hist. Soc. Northumberland, Durham and Newcastle-upon-Tyne*. 9:1-296
Tristram, H. B.	1905	Birds. In: *Victoria County History of Durham*. 1:175-191
Williams, T. J.	1996	Double-crested Cormorant in Cleveland: New to the Western Palearctic. *British Birds*. 89:162-170
Williams, T. J.	2005	Double-crested Cormorant In: A. Pitches & T.Cleeves. *Birds New to Britain 1986-2004*. T & A. D. Poyser. London.

INDEX